The Fight Against Hunger

Books by Charles Morrow Wilson

NONFICTION:

Backwoods America, 1934
Roots of America, 1936
Country Living, 1938
Aroostook, 1938
Cornbread and Creekwater: A Study of Rural Poverty, 1940
Central America, 1941
Ambassadors in White, 1942
Oil across the World, 1943
Middle America, 1944
Trees and Test Tubes, 1944
New Crops for the New World, 1945
Empire in Green and Gold, 1947
Liberia, 1947
Tropics: World of Tomorrow, 1950
The Bodacious Ozarks, 1956
Let's Try Barter, 1960
Grass and People, 1961
The Magnificent Scufflers, 1962
Roots: Miracles Below, 1968

FICTION:

Acres of Sky, 1930
Rabble Rouser, 1936
A Man's Reach, 1944

The Fight
AGAINST
HUNGER

Charles Morrow Wilson

Funk & Wagnalls   NEW YORK

To two good and cogent friends—
Arthur Krock of *The New York Times,* and
George David Aiken, United States Senator
from Vermont

INTRODUCTION

Many commentators have believed and still believe that hunger, famine, and mass starvation continue to be inevitable for much of planet Earth. This writer and this book take issue with that grim and loose-lugged premise.

The fight against hunger began when living protoplasm began. Apparently, as higher life forms materialized, the fight gained in reach and versatility, and clearly the coming of man—the most ingenious and combat-prone of the animal species—brought a turning point in the global and perennial fight against hunger.

There is good reason to believe early man was chronically hungry. Hunger was not only his prime fear; one deduces it was also his most important motive for working and fighting. To obtain a sustaining diet, early man usually was obliged to pick or browse and frequently to battle his way over several thousand acres. Even in more favorable environments three square miles were required as the minimal subsistence range for each individual.

A long-term historian may reflect by relaxed approximation that man has already effected upward of a thousand-fold increase in food production from a given unit of land. Even so, man has not yet conquered hunger. We remain of a hungry world, in which malnutrition persists as commonplace and starvation persists as a terrible but no longer silent death. There are better-fed nations, including our own, but there appears to be no sufficiently well-fed nation. In the United States an estimated 10 to 12 million of our 202-plus million people are still acutely hungry. At least 30 million are chronically impoverished, and over 100 million are continuously malnourished, particularly in proteins and amino acids.

But competent agricultural food-production is only in its borning, and the productiveness of that direly abused but life-crowded film called soil is as yet not even competently explored.

Moreover, forty-four years of farm reporting and country corresponding around the world have convinced me that agriculture, which continues to provide 99 percent of man's food, is a profoundly human phenomenon. It is much more than the scientific institution of agronomics; it is a human institution of many different kinds of people—plus sunlight, air, moisture, temperatures, land, and rooted soils—all living, working, and begetting lives together. Herein is a special promise for victory in the fight against hunger.

This book is the journal and, in greater part, the glad tidings of people on the land—the developers, planters, and reapers of food supplies. It is the story, as I have seen it, of these extraordinary advocates of a more provident, peaceful, and tolerant world.

Charles Morrow Wilson
Cedar Key, Florida
March 1969

CONTENTS

Going Global   165

Homeland
Is the
First World

PANTRY MOUSE EMERGES

FROM AMONG the woodland shadows four shapes made down on Lyin' Johnny Wells's store at the backhill crossroads then known as Weddington Gap (Arkansas). They were migrant apple pickers; all were lean young men considerably lost in faded blue and multiply-patched blue jeans. Three of the apple pickers—the Ozarkian pronunciation was "peckers"—were fuzzy-faced; the bearded elder, who may have been as old as thirty, exhibited a somewhat startling lack of teeth along with a deep, self-assured, and somewhat mushily articulated speaking voice.

After scanning the two store shelves of canned goods and peering intently into the cookie barrel, he smiled self-appreciatively and began speaking fundamental philosophy of the timeless interrelations of hunger, food supply, and basic economy: "A man has got to eat so as to peck apples so as to make money so as to buy food stuffs for to feed hisself so as he can peck mo' apples."

With that off his narrow chest, the head pecker lifted down an obese tabby cat that was asleep on the cover of the cheese bin, removed the rounded wooden cap and, borrowing a gently rusting butcher knife, extended the gap in the roughly shorn cheese round by somewhere near two pounds. Having twice bisected the purchase, he deposited the cheese cut on the already littered counter, then reached deep into the cracker barrel to probe out about a dozen big and soggy soda crackers. Meanwhile, another pecker had reverently lifted down a tall can of salmon—called "saul-mon"—and began using his heavy jackknife to cut open the top of the can. While the youngest and most fuzzy-faced pecker was negotiating with the storekeeper for a gallon of skimmed milk and the loan of four tin cups, the fourth member was clearing off a square yard or so of the "sellin' " counter.

That accomplished, the apple peckers assembled their purchases, paid for them in dimes, nickels, and pennies (the total came to about sixty cents), and began their improvised luncheon by apportioning the cheese on four oversized soda crackers and emptying the salmon out onto four others. The fuzzy-faced one then filled the borrowed tin cups with milk while a companion solicited the "loan" of a jar of mustard and a dip of salt from the open salt barrel.

As an interested onlooker I scented the mingled aromas, which were surely revealing and not unpleasant, and reflected that the "counter snatch" provided a commendable nutrition balance. After the edibles were reduced to a few licking points for the thoughtfully observant cat, and after the storekeeper had duly recovered his tin cups and the mustard jar and delivered several lusty slaps at invading bottle flies, the apple peckers began a group exodus toward the rusty screened entranceway.

Once more the bearded elder was in a mood for philosophizing; by then his audience had grown by three. A farm wife with a toddler at her apron strings had brought a dozen eggs to swap for three boxes of torch matches. The other onlooker was a hard-hobbling countryside paralytic, who had come to rest directly beside the patent medicine shelf. At the doorway the eldest apple pecker paused to deliver a brief postlude:

"All of us peoples do a mighty sight of talkin' and stewin' about a mighty lot of things but what we all really think the mostest about is eatin', on account of eatin' is the most fun they is and the most needful of acts."

As a third-generation and farm-raised Ozarker, I regarded the statement as exceptionally pertinent. At the time (early autumn 1923), the Ozarks of upper Arkansas and lower Missouri were in principal part a lingering, poor-land, rather centrally located American frontier spread over about thirty thousand square miles. The human census remained sparse: the count per square mile was about half the national average, and by individual counties the population averages were from near 65 percent to almost 90 percent rural.

Among the general truths I was on the verge of learning was the prime item that in many vital ways the Ozarks of the 1920s were rather profoundly delineative of what are now termed the "developing countries," the so-called "newer hundred"—a majority of which, back in the 1920s, were colonies.

According to 1920 census about 72 percent of all residents of the entire Ozarks "uplift" were farmers—supposedly food producers. Yet in 1923 the preponderantly rural region, like approximately 75 more rural than urban nations in the present-day world, was less than dependably self-sufficient in terms of food production. In definable terms of home-grown food supplies easily half of the Ozarkian country people were what sociologists were beginning to list as "marginal ruralists"; they dabbled at farming but even during the more favorable farming years they just barely scrimped or eked out their basic fare. When recurrent droughts or occasional floods or other weather mishaps occurred, their vehicle of subsistence food production usually floundered or wavered or broke down completely. As in some five-eighths of the world today, including most of Asia and Africa, much of the Middle East and Latin America, and many populous islands of the Pacific, Caribbean, and Indian Oceans, the shadow of hunger, or what the United Nations' Food and Agriculture Organization now designates as the nutritional danger line, was insistently discernible.

The Ozarks had remained a sparsely settled frontier. There was plenty of land—about twenty-five acres per capita, more than twice the then world average, about three times the present world average. But for various socio-economic reasons, in the main still prevailing in decisive areas of the present-day world, the land was not being used effectively for food production. By averages about two-thirds of the settled lands of the Ozarks was not actively in cultivation; by prevailing practice most of the uncultivated land was precondemned as "poor" and accorded no productive use. This phenomenon was, and remains, a more or less global *non sequitur*. Then, as now, such outrageously broad designations as "rich land" and "poor land" were traditionally misleading, usually based on rather haphazard guesses about the existent ratios of organic materials present in the living films called soil. The still fairly typical range of "organic contents" of soil is between .5 and 2.5 percent of the total volume. With suitable rainfall an organic ratio of 1 percent or more usually designates "good" food-producing land. But certainly the act or habit of listing all other lands as unsuitable for food production is much like listing all babies as paupers: the mere fact that they are born without money or immediate earning power does not establish that they will remain so. Similarly, as I had already learned in growing up on a more than averagely poor hillside farm, so-called

"poor land" simply is not predestined to remain incapable
of valid food production. Year after year I had helped in
growing an abundance of passably good food on sloping acres
that ever vocal neighbors continued to brand as "too pore to
sprout corn."

At the time of listening to the apple-pecking philosopher
at Weddington Gap, I was baffled by the persisting truth
that this far-flung up-and-down Ozarks frontier seemed ever-
lastingly on the ragged edge of distressing hunger.

By 1923 I had struggled through a typically poor and
ragged public high school and a first ragamuffin year at the
then painfully impoverished University of Arkansas. I had
also collided with the need for making a choice of employment: to continue as a helpful boy without wages on my father's largely diagonal, erosion-plagued farm, or to take to
one or both of the areas of wage-earning employment then
available locally—late-summer and early-autumn scullery in
the local canning factories or fair weather ditch-digging for
the local water works. The more esoteric and less remu-
nerative alternative was seeking answers and molding words
for printing in a local newspaper.

My quest of employment had veered toward the last. During my second college year I had taken the querulous post
of Fayetteville (Arkansas) correspondent for the Little
Rock *Arkansas Gazette,* by its own admission the oldest
newspaper west of the Mississippi and by my readily arrived
estimate quite probably the stingiest. During the previous
nine months, at the *Gazette*'s then prevailing rate of $2 a
column, exclusive of captions and photographs, I had earned
a gross of $48.32 as Fayetteville correspondent. Of that
munificence, $19.81 had gone for postage and pictures and
$13.07 for out-of-pocket travel expenses; the more significant
news seemed to keep happening in the country—farther and
farther beyond town limits.

When my notebook ledger showed net earnings of slightly

less than four cents an hour, I began probing for another "outlet" for my product. During the previous spring college vacation I had ventured forth afoot to report the recurrent backwoods invasion by transient throngs of strawberry pickers. Never before had I seen and mingled with so many hungry people of such divergent ages and ethnic backgrounds. During the week I devised a series of articles about the wet and bothered berry tramps who hungered so despairingly and worked so benumbingly in order that the less hungry might be the better fed. Then, boldly, I mailed the product to the one competent newspaper of the region, the *St. Louis Post-Dispatch*.

By return mail I received a sky-blue check in the amount of $36.85—clipped to a blearily penciled invitation to call on the Complete Edition Editor when next in St. Louis. At the time I had never been in St. Louis; I had, however, been charged with indulging in the traditional Ozarker's daydream of stopping by St. Louis en route to Heaven.

The following weekend bargain excursion found me aboard a Frisco day coach, bound for St. Louis. A fellow student had agreed to take over my *Gazette* correspondence during my bold and impetuous sally; by then my grade averages at college were high enough so that I felt fairly secure in risking a week of class-cutting.

Early the following morning I picked my way through the slums that engulfed St. Louis Union Station and made for the grayed and mausoleumlike *Post-Dispatch* building at nearby Twelfth and Olive. On the editorial floor I located the wildly littered desk of the Complete Edition Editor. In time an engaging plump face appeared above a disorderly mound of back copies. Paul Greer, formerly the eminent news talent of the Omaha, Nebraska, *Bee*, began massaging his windblown mop of curly graying hair with great violence.

"So how's our Hungry Joe correspondent from Greezy

Creek, Arkansas?" he shouted, quickly adding, "Don't answer that, boy, anything you say or misspell could be held
against you."

His huge smile gave way to a forehead-crinkling scowl as
he assured me that he had no regular job to offer; that he
was acutely aware that most Ozarkers can't read and most of
those who can don't. He added that his paper's circulation
in the lower Ozarks was so malnourished that if somebody
forced it to swallow a very small olive it would look positively pregnant. "However, we need some color pieces now
and then," he conceded, "and I wrote that stupid note because your stuff about the stump-hopping berry tramps got
to me. I won't say just where, but I'm stupid enough to let
you try out as a stringer, beginning as soon as you care to."

He continued less impulsively. "God forbid, I've seen
your by-line in that moldy *Arkansas Gazette*, which I detest
without trying, and maybe for that reason nothing of yours
in that sheet has ever impressed me as being worth a hill of
beans. Speaking of which, I would add that one particular
itch your copy gives me relates to wondering why the hell
there should be hungry people down where you come from.
I know damn well there are too many hungry people there
—also everywhere else I've been to date, which takes in quite
a lot of this hard little planet called Earth."

Greer shouted loudly for a copy boy. "Your pitch is that
food supply or the lack of it comes of people working or
not working together on the land. That's a damn long ways
from being *new*, but in places and on occasion it gets close
to being *news*. Sure, there's God's own plenty of usable
land that's not being used. And still more that's being used
very stupidly or otherwise badly. That's your angle and,
like I say, it impresses me as being valid not only for these
ever-loving, vine-swinging Ozarks, but for pretty much everywhere else. So I wouldn't too much mind seeing you try

your underprivileged hands at digging a bit deeper and a lot more humanly, or do you follow me? If so, you'll have a chance to prove out. And where *is* that damn copy boy?"

On my way back to Union Station, where the Frisco Meteor was steaming fiercely for take-off, I shaped a plan of action. I would strike out for a full week's try at backhill reporting, seeking advantage of knowing counsel. As I settled into the smoky purgatory of a day coach, I made a choice of counselors. I recalled that my father's most intelligent and least conforming brother, George, then 68, was or had been an ambulatory encyclopedia of the Ozark backhills. He had intermittently tramped, farmed, moonshined, counterfeited, and hell-raised pretty much all over the realm; by misturns he had been a shooting deputy sheriff, a dealer in ginseng roots, a muskrat trapper, a wild-honey hunter, and above all a people-knowing, people-liking country man. Now in his latening sixties, Uncle George was divorced again and once more hermiting in the flinty backlands along the Missouri-Arkansas boundary, within a half day's tramp of a crossroads called Garfield. As a first move I resolved to locate Uncle George and hear what he had to suggest.

At daybreak and the Garfield watering stop, I took leave of the day coach and overtook the local storekeeper in the act of opening another day of the R-Can-Saw store; its trade sign was a homemade letter R, followed by recognizable sketches of an oil can and a crosscut saw. The storekeeper knew Uncle George and his whereabouts, and graciously spilled the directions. After following a flinty backtrail for about half the morning, I found my most cogent uncle full to overflow with the spirit of hospitality, homemade persimmon beer, and lucid advice.

"I don't surely know what you seek, but I do know what most of the yahoos hereabout seek, some being a full belly." He repeated that in his own threescore years of moving hither and yon, he had learned that in most of the back-woods hunger had remained the unyielding haunter. In his own lifetime he, too, had put in a mighty sight of combat against the grim gray wolf. He repeated that he knew no better way to know the story than to go foot-padding out to its true and living sources. But he agreed with that upstart newspaper yahoo in St. Louis that going hungry isn't "double obliged" to happen. Uncle George reflected that the best hunger avoider he knew in person—as he put it, the feedingest man ever loosed in hungry country—was a former hired man for a former damnyankee general and President, U. S. Grant. This Abel Clark had lately passed his eighty-fifth birthday. Close to half a century earlier this same Abe Clark had settled way and long gone out in War Eagle Valley, two days of tramping from where I now stood and fourteen miles from the nearest village. There Grant's man had endured as the hunger-whuppin'est Ozarker ever laid eyes on.

Next morning I struck out for War Eagle country. Only a few miles on the way I tarried to view the grounds of the biggest Civil War battle west of the Mississippi: Peavine Ridge, later shortened to Pea Ridge, in the Ozarks of North-west Arkansas.

As I walked the fringelands of impoverished farms, I pondered how two then mighty armies, in all more than 65,000 combat troops, many days from established supply bases, had managed to forage their ways through a country-side which in the 1860s, as now, was sparsely settled, church-mouse poor, and barely able to feed itself.

By 1923, sixty years had come and gone since these Americans fought the Battle of Pea Ridge, and quite obviously the hungry country of the 1860s remained the hungry country of the 1920s. I paused before the crudely hacked battle monument. The square-headed granite angel had no answer to my queries. Neither did a staggery old man who deposited an immense shotgun on the monument base and explained sadly that he was out doing a turn of squirrel hunting but his rifle gun was too danged big for the game; every time he fetched down a squirrel, the crittur appeared to get pulverized to bloody slop.

The patriarch confided that back in his boyhood he, too, had given considerable time to pondering the question of how so many fighting men had managed to fight off mass starvation. "They must of hungered like pizen," he reflected, adding, "I was goin' on fourteen when that battle was fit. I recollect the cannon jolts like they was only yisterday. And I recollect how a pack of us young 'uns went searchin' the Yankee dead to seek for eatables in their knapsacks or their shot-up supply wagons. Funny thing was, we ended up hongrier than when we begun."

His statement was supported if not explained by another passer-by, an old woman in billowy calico who hobbled along the road plucking wild-growing greens. "Hit'll be yet some while before my garden sass is readied," she told me. "Till that comes along, I be obliged to rustle and bustle whatever I eats."

I walked across a succession of failing fields, heading southeast toward War Eagle country. After I had located another dimly meandering road, I was no longer alone. Directly ahead was an oddly contoured figure wearing ragged overalls and a mustard-yellow shirt. When I saluted him with a somewhat belated "how-de-do," the little one lifted off a floppy straw hat to reveal a great mop of frosty white hair.

With a magnificent disregard of continuity the dwarf told me that he, Sammy Blankhall, was then crowding eighty; he farmed a six-acre valley plot on the far side of Tater Knob; and he grew or plucked all he ate, or else went hungry.

This had come about because Sammy was "pecking my way out of debt"—a wickedly aggravating indebtedness that dated back some twenty years, to a time when he tried a turn at keeping a country store. He did passably well until there came a night when his store ketched afire and burnt to the ground. Sammy didn't have insurance, plague take it, and the ruinous fire left him moneyless, goodsless, and up past his eyeballs in debt.

Since that unhappy morn, Sammy had been "scratchin' out my victuals" from his patch of land, and paying his debts by collecting native treasuries of black walnuts. He steamed and "pecked out" the kernels and sold them to stores and soda fountains in near-about towns. In another twenty years or so he expected to have all his indebtedness squared away. Meanwhile, as he explained meaningfully, he was managing to feed himself in order to live proper and squaring his debts in order to die proper. "My helpers is the same as always—growin' land, warmin' weather, rain and sun and Godamighty."

The honest one next confided that he believed his experiences as a storekeeper would have made him a "purty fair" peddler, but insofar as he had lived through a lot of lean moons and hungry weeks in a lot of hungry places, he had decided to put in the rest of his working days at producing what could help feed the hungry.

By midafternoon, the rough and dimming road widened abruptly to make room for another crossroads village. One of its four visible buildings was marked with a home-lettered sign: GOLLEHAR'S GEN. STORE & P.O. The storehouse was a small, sagging wooden building with a once impressively large front porch that was gently rotting away. Even so, the porch was being pleasantly occupied by somewhere near a dozen countrymen, who were seated on the markedly decrepit board benches. While joining the group of loungers, so impressively free of productive intentions, I heard another arrival inquiring what they were setting to gab about.

The answer was temporarily deferred by many inarticulate sounds, including yawns, finger drumming and foot patting, and self-comforting grunts related to stretching in the general shapes of X's and Y's. But the prevailing topic of conversation presently emerged; it was a jolly potpourri related to foods and eating.

As an opener there was the simple saga of Parson Milsap, the roving evangelist, who stayed and et a stewkettle of summering weasels, having mistakened them for gray squirrels; of how Aunt Martha Peppitts set twenty-six hens that in due course hatched out three pullets and two hundred and ninety-four roosters; of young Leander Leathers, who gained acquaintance with that mysterious fruit the banana—after he had pulled off the peel and thrown the cob away, there wasn't hardly a danged thing left of it for to eat. And there was the no less wistful recounting of how Grandpappy Hatfield, the shy old loner, finally broke down and attended the moonlight picnic at Brushy Ford School House. Inadvertently Grandpappy cooled his mug of coffee from the buttermilk pitcher instead of the cream pitcher. When one of the kind ladies moved to bring him another mug, the old-timer merely said, "Hell, Miz Heffelflinger, I allers takes buttermilk in my coffee."

GRANT'S AIDE

NEXT DAY I tramped on to Abel Clark's. It was a day of tumbling clouds and intermittent showers that put the upland rivers very near to flood level. There were no bridges then; both the fords on upper War Eagle

River were muddied and deceptively deep. Night was settling when I arrived at the Clark cabin, wringing wet and
chilled.

At eighty-five, Abel Clark remained a beautiful man. He
and his wife, Hester, hardly less beautiful at eighty-one,
welcomed me to share what they termed their fireplace supper. Abel recalled that back at Galena, Illinois, when he was
twenty-three and newly married, he had bought a wagonload
of stovewood from and otherwise befriended a glum, horse-
fancying farmer known locally as Sam Grant. A year or so
thereafter the Great Unpleasantness, known to some as the
Civil War, began. Following the siege of Vicksburg, Corporal A. Clark found himself chosen as a general's aide; the
general was the same shabby little Sam Grant who had delivered the newly wedded Clarks a reasonably honest
wagonload of firewood. Corporal Clark stayed with the improbable and soft-voiced general, and in the surprising ripe-
ness of time found himself named personal secretary to the
fifteenth President of the United States.

After five detested years in and around the White House,
Abel decided he had had enough of politicians' "antics"
and resolved, as he told me, to quest for a free man's life and
"reach out for the dignity of honorable self-support." After
a great deal of pondering over the remaining frontiers (such
as they were in 1877), the former General's Aide chose the
traditionally hungry Ozarks as a preferred combat zone in
his very personal war against empty bellies.

From Springfield, Missouri, where his wife was obliged to
spend several months convalescing from malaria, the former Union Army corporal set forth on a tramping tour to
locate what he termed a "lasty" homestead site—"lasty"
dependent on food production. "I reckoned all along that
good eating is ever the prime need," he explained, "and I'd
already learned that good eating calls for more than land.

Food comes of people working the land and planning and trafficking with other people."

In his teens Abel Clark had spent several years among some of the straggling clans, or bands, of Indians who then lived in lower Illinois. He remembered them as capable gardeners who rarely succeeded as farmers, in greatest part because they had no "feeling" for draft animals, farm implements, or meat or milk animals. "They were still open-foragers, and there was no longer enough land for them to forage on," he recalled.

The Clarks homesteaded half a square mile (320 acres) that they had chosen painstakingly, making sure they had both fertile valley soil and hillside "patches" that were not vulnerable to the recurring springtime or early summer floods. That done, they continued to plan their battle lines against the common enemy, hunger, with a well-studied, Grant-style defense in depth. Having cleared and planted to grains a first fertile field beside the river, they next established a midland vegetable patch. On a moderately fertile hilltop they cleared a six-acre plot for use as a permanent pasture. After they had limed the hilltop and planted it to bluegrass, the pasture plot endured as a sustenance base for their two cows, one a "milker," the other a "cheeser," and their span of long-used Army mules.

The defensive foreplanning proved to be their special salvation when the early 1880s brought a ruining and almost continuous succession of droughts. Before the next cycle of rainy years materialized, hunger spread through the hills and lurked disturbingly close to the Clarks. When the dry cycle finally ended, the two homesteaders used most of their remnant of savings for buying fruit trees to establish a "family mix" orchard, including apples, peaches, cherries, and pears, and a miniature vineyard. They planted their fruit trees in a sheltered and well-drained "draw" partways up a hillside. Though Ozarks orchard crops are notoriously vulnerable to frosts and freezing, within another seven years the plantings were producing an abundance of fruit for the Clarks' needs, with plenty for canning or drying, and presently a still larger "overage" for giving to the needy backcountry neighbors, who grew more and more numerous. Within another decade the Clarks were selling more of their homegrown foodstuff than they ate, and giving away several times as much as they sold. The lesson was as self-evident as a country washday: the old couple, working and planning together, had managed to use their backwoods land competently.

LI'L SQUIRREL-HEADED NUBBINS

THE ABLY planned hunger-fighting of Abel and Hester Clark seemed to bloom with significance and encouragement. Following my first somewhat impulsive sashay into backwoods reporting, "encouragement" stories began to grow tryingly scarce. Late in June 1923 a cruel, searing drought began to move in from the Great Plains. By the end of July, field crops and the remainder of garden crops were twisted and withered. Mercury columns kept reaching above 100 degrees Fahrenheit. Wells and creeks were fading away. Customary hard times began turning bitter hard.

At Hiwasse settlement, in the bushy hills of Benton County, Arkansas, a roving evangelist and hymn singer was settled to leading a preachin' and rain-prayin' service. After Parson Horatious Grammer had paced through "Abiding Grace, How Sweet Thy Name" and offered opening bene-

diction, he began the service by calling on likely-looking individuals to "testify." The first volunteer closed his
supplication with a deeply felt climax: "Let hit rain, Lord,
suffer us a steady downpour. 'Cause effen You don't, we
won't get raised no corn crop. We won't make nothin' but a
hatful of li'l' squirrel-headed nubbins that all hell can't
shuck!"

After the passing of several sultry minutes another peti-
tioner arose to testify, a gaunt, nervous man with a fiercely
black beard and a penchant for violent twitchings and specific enumerations. "Lord, in Heaven, us folks down
hereabouts is runnin' out of victuals. Even should we get a
foot of rain tomorry, hit won't stay us through no long
winter. So I humble ask you give each household a barrel
of flour, a barrel of pork jowls, a barrel of sugar, a barrel of
potatoes, a barrel of salt, a barrel of pepper . . ." Apologetic
pause. "Hell, that's too damn much pepper."

I left the meeting with lasting recollections of the wor-
ried and hungry faces of the participants and a share of their
distressed bewilderment. This, after all, was merely one dry
spell. In the Ozarks and for vaster temperate-zone areas a
severe drought must be expected every third or fourth year.
Why were these long-settled agrarian people now without
bolster or cushion from this substantially normal weather
phenomenon? The answer could only be that these rather
typical lands and their not too exceptional tenants were
simply not meshing. For here, not far from the literal geo-
graphic center of the greatest food-producing nation on
earth, long-settled yeomen were profoundly fearful of hunger. How could what they termed "pizen bad times"
materialize so quickly and irrevocably? Hiwasse, granted,
was but one isolated poor-land community. But I was roaming through scores of comparable communities in which
malnutrition was already as obvious as an old-fashioned

country washday. In county after county the poorhouses, then the only charity centers available, were full to overflow.

No less significantly the same held for the court dockets, which were confirming that hard, hungry times and virulent outbreaks of crime, in great part violent crime, seemed to be inalienable companions.

I was gaining firsthand acquaintance with several back-woods communities that were rife with crimes clearly associated with hunger. For example, the millrun of court records showed that most of the breaking-and-enterings were directly in quest of food. The prevailing shape and tenor of the multiplying larcenies had been well delineated down in Van Buren County some fifteen years earlier, when Arkansas's then most illustrious rabblerouser, Ole Jeff Davis, at the time a United States Senator, volunteered to serve *gratis* as defense attorney for a ragged and cringing old countryman who was on the verge of being convicted for horse stealing. (As it was a small horse, the indictment read "pony stealing.")

The only defense witness was the defendant's wife, an aged and obviously malnourished cripple, who waited abjectly beside her lean and despairing "husband man." The prosecutor had entered a relentlessly convincing case. The crippled wife contended tearfully that her man had "borrowed the li'l critter so that he could haul deadwood he had pecked up along roadsides to a storekeeper willin' to pay in flour and salt and liver meat"; otherwise the defendant and his "wife woman" would surely starve.

Ole Jeff Davis of Arkansas blew his long and ruddy nose very loudly, blinked at the bench, then strode to the jury box. "Friends and neighbors, country neighbors, that is . . ." he began shrilly. "I tell you square and candid there ain't no real doubt that my dee-fendants took that pony. These here old folks was only striving for to fill their bellies that's been empty for God alone knows how long. But these old folks I speak for here don't need punishin'; they require feedin'. What theirs is, is dang sure a world story. So, therefore, I am asking you, gem'men of the jury, also I'm askin' this honorable court, and the honorable prosecutor, to help make these old folks free for to go back to their shack with their ole bashed-up wagon cart packed full of eatables. Right here and now I'm openin' with this here twenty-spotter."

Grandly Ole Jeff handed the jury foreman a twenty-dollar bill. In appreciative silence the jury retired to the woodshed, and returned with the verdict—Not Guilty, along with an additional collection of about four dollars. The judge put in another five and the sheriff threw in the purloined pony, which had belonged to an out-of-state sawmill firm.

"Sheriff," the prosecutor remonstrated, "you can't do that lawful and proper. What in tarnation has got into you?"

"It has to be this ga-damn drinkin' water," the lawman murmured dejectedly. "I don't ordinarily use the stuff."

THE HONEST BEAD

PRODUCING FOOD requires money incentive. The Ozarks were grievously, chronically lacking in farm-sustaining markets and harvests capable of winning dependable acceptance in more opulent regions. This condition, too, was and remains what good Ole Jeff Davis had noted as "dang sure a world story." And the sheriff's dour revelation about his water-drinking misgivings held a rather profound applicability to the more effective of prevailing quests for a money-earning market.

The infamous folly called National Prohibition had motivated the most solvent cash crop of the time and place. This was corn duly and illegally converted to whiskey. Moonshining was fast burgeoning as the most profitable as well as the most folkish of Ozark trades, and a pillarstone for enduring remnants of backwoods solvency. With varying degrees of directness many thousands of the country people were participating. Countryside grain mills were being restored for grinding the coarse corn meal best suited for liquor making, and, as I soon noted, dozens of otherwise failing crossroad stores were being revived (or resurrected) by demands for requisite merchandise such as containers (principally glass fruit jars), sugars and malts, copper tubing and still-making materials, and related merchandise. While the court dockets were formally recording that hungry people cannot be restrained by laws or the paraphernalia of law enforcement, the catapulting increase of illicit liquor-making was openly proving that ill conceived and corruptly administered laws can directly beget or resurrect a predominant source of farm income and, less directly, of food grower's survival.

My most lucid informant was Dick Saullee, an oldline "shiner" of Madison County, Arkansas. Saullee took very real pride in the fact that he had at that point 'stilled and sold some 20,000 gallons of what he described as "tolerable drinkin' likker."

Not incidentally, the veteran success story had bought and equipped two good farms; one for himself, the other for his son and partner, Alfred. While I interviewed "Uncle" Dick (the title was one of local esteem rather than kinship), Alfred came up from the creek bottom and joined us. The youngster explained that he was just back from a convention. "A distillers' convention?" I inquired. "Nope, Sunday School convention." With that Alfred took from his jacket pocket a bottleful of light amber nectar that he explained was a sampler from the latest run. The senior partner took a swig, spat it out as became a lifelong teetotaler, then delivered his expert verdict: "Not too nasty bad."

Uncle Dick asked me into his home. The settin' room was newly painted, high-ceilinged, beautifully clean, and furnished with very old beds and highboys and straight chairs, all built of walnut or wild cherry, evidently by long gone generations of cabinet makers. My host ran a hand through his graying hair: "Here's our way of figurin'. Me and Alfred plants the corn, raises it, shucks it, and takes it to mill. Now if my woman goes and makes a pone of cornbread, we ain't violatin' no law. Then why shouldn't we put part of our crop to likker? We do the work; we take the risk. And with likker as our sellable crop we can keep goin' two good farms and grow a sight more than drinkin' likker. I learnt long back that unless you got one good money crop, no farmin' ever wins out."

The working arithmetic of moonshining was convincingly simple. Dick Saullee estimated the actual cost of distilling corn whiskey as around $2 a gallon, including about half-a-bushel of corn, six pounds of corn sugar, a quarter-pound of mixed yeast and malt, the required firewood, and about two hours of competent labor. By averages then prevailing, the "shiners" were getting about $5 a gallon from the interstate liquor runners, or wholesale bootleggers.

THE DISTURBING DISTRIBUTION

OPTIMIST THAT he was, Dick Saullee admitted openly that the Ozarks could not expect to stay fed and monied on moonshine alone. There had to be other money crops to "underwrite" the general farming. That was the big, hard rub. In earlier times hardwoods, particularly white oak for railroad crossties and beer barrels and red oak for plowhandles, wagon wheels, and liquor curing barrels, had helped sustain the backwoods food harvests. But Prohibition had largely erased the demands for kegs and barrels; the era of railroad building was grinding to an end; in the more gifted farm realms the tractor was beginning to erase demands for hand plows.

The unrestrainable advent of the automobile age was intermittently helping and hurting food production. In the backhills, where hand-pumped gasoline tanks were appearing in front of country stores and customers were beginning to call out: "Or-vul, gas up my tank and are my tars!" the epoch of the internal-combustion engine was proving more hurtful than helpful.

There were other significant retarders of food growing; several of these were mirroring more or less worldwide developments. Autos bestirred demands for roads. Prior to the 1920s all of the Arkansas and most of the Missouri Ozarks were lacking in travelable highways and even dependable through roads. The railroad had carried almost everything not left behind. Now, for the first time, "improved" highways began to reach in. They promptly lured automotive traffic, which dealt extensive mayhem to the open-range livestock, maimed and mashed all too many backhill people, and dealt irreparable injury to two of the better proved money crops—apples and strawberries. Granted their excellent flavor qualities, both crops had gained commercial success mostly by way of rail shipments to major markets from Boston to San Francisco. The prerequisites for this success had been exacting sorting and grading and painstaking packing in crates or baskets, plus competent icing of the cars. All these factors had joined in gaining and holding responsible city markets—and when one city could not accommodate, the produce could be rolled along to another, or to several more.

When the highways materialized, throngs of independent buyers came spluttering in—driving their own or rented trucks and their own ensnaring bargains. The produce recruiters promptly instated farmside buying as a routine procedure, then at even lower prices began buying the apples and berries as they grew in the orchards and beds.

Quality standards and dependable markets vanished together. The markets within trucking range were quickly glutted; expert grading and packing standards faded. Within a very few seasons the reputable markets for Ozarks fruits were substantially erased; the "quality rail hauls" were never effectively restored. Ozark fruit growers were heard to agree that apples and strawberries had gone plum to hell on them newfangled highways.

It was irony-weighted proof that expanded transportation facilities per se cannot assure improvements of food production; they can, indeed, injure it.

TOWN AND SHROUD

THERE WERE many other food-related befuddlers. Late in 1923 a mustering of distinguished British commentators, including H. G. Wells, Thomas Hardy, and Bernard Shaw, joined in decrying the failure of England's towns and farming communities and villages to dovetail or congeal in "restorative union." In my own stumbling words and ways I had been seeking to describe the same punisher of larder and spirits in my own homeland.

My native town served as a point in proof. Fayetteville,

Arkansas, founded in 1828, had survived and grown ever slowly as a countryside trading center. Togetherness with its countryside seemed its most rational cause for being. Its building lots continued to merge with planted fields; cows and pigs still occupied backyard pens and from time to time roamed at large; early-rising roosters continued to serve as neighborhood alarm clocks. Country ways prevailed but, ever so bafflingly, country people did not. The divergence could not be accounted for in routine economic terms. By averages and by totals the country people and town folks were on or near a common footing of poverty. The town shops were tawdry and impoverished; the habituated posture of the local merchants was that of waiting dourly at customarily vacant doorways with arms folded and spirits sagging. With a census of slightly fewer than five thousand, Fayetteville was a kind of happenstance union of slums. It needed trade in the worst way, and thin-pursed as most of them were, its country neighbors were its principal trade bringers. But the town disdained them.

When I returned to Fayetteville for my final year of intermingled college and news correspondence, I grew increasingly aware of the apartness of the town and its even longer-settled countrysides. Similar cleavages were prevailing in other towns of the region.

The chronic lapse was of awareness that the town was inevitably dependent on its countryside for the prime ingredients of productivity as well as cultural integrity. The town's business community had long since congealed as a conspiracy of greed; it would buy as it saw fit and sell by duress. As in most poor communities, the preponderance of trade, such as it was, related quite directly to foods. Approximately two-thirds of all business establishments in Fayetteville were food shops. At least 40 percent of their total sales were to rural customers.

Yet the grocers insistently purchased from wholesalers and jobbers out of the immediate area. They minimized or shunned completely any substantial purchases from nearby farmers—to the end of bigger profits and greater convenience. In collusion with local politicians and the burgeoning and conspicuously nitwitted chamber of commerce, the local merchants conspired to keep farmers from peddling or otherwise making direct sales of their home-grown produces and fruits and surpluses of meats or dairy products to townspeople. The inevitable interdependence of food production and sale was perennially evaded and squelched. Productive incentives were being poisoned at root levels.

The dire *non sequitur* was grievously aggravated by long chronic racial injustice. The Indian by then had been pretty well erased there and throughout the Ozarks. Thanks to a somewhat less than benevolent federal government, tribal remnants had been herded to the so-called, but never actual, "reservations" of nearby Oklahoma, which had been granted statehood about two decades earlier. But Negroes remained—direly beneaped in the swill and muck of lazy farming and oppressive poverty.

With appallingly few exceptions the local Negroes went hungry most or all the time. Such was part and parcel of the racial intolerance that had long been notorious and was now intensified, like a particularly ugly disease. "I know everybody in Fayetteville," the home-town mayor confided. "And I know damn good and well the nicest people in town are niggers. But creeping Jesus, man, just go and look at them! And take along a bag of groceries!"

Since Civil War times Fayetteville, Arkansas, had kept its Negro town, called Tin Cup, austerely segregated in the big gulch beyond the courthouse. Though the population of Tin Cup was barely 300, it was the largest Negro community between Springfield and Fort Smith. Other Ozarks towns

(Rogers, Arkansas, was one of the more notorious) openly boasted that they would never permit a nigger to be caught by sunset within their corporate limits.

Fayetteville, though permitting Negroes to live within its limits, determinedly kept them in their "place"—within ready reach of outright starvation. A few of the Negro girls and women were able to "get theirselfs hired" (in the prevailing language of the Little Athens of the Ozarks) as cooks and maids in some of the less poor white homes at prevailing wages of from 50 cents to $2 a week. There was no "boarding in" for Negroes.

For the Negro males the only available regular employment was shining shoes or bellhopping at the local hotel, or serving as manservants for the college-connected clubs and rooming houses. Intermittent employment was limited to the most menial of unskilled labor, from ditch digging to privy cleaning. Not one Negro was locally employed as a carpenter, mason, plumber, or other artisan, or as a store clerk, a postal or bank worker, or even as a taxi driver or delivery man. Tin Cup had one wretched little school with six grades, and there was no chance for attending high school or any accredited college. There were no Negro doctors, dentists, or pharmacists. The two Negro preachers were quietly hungering at $30 a month. No hotel or lodging house in the town would even consider registering a Negro guest. In cases of extreme illness or imminent death the local hospital occasionally assigned Negroes to basement cots. The county poorhouse had never been known to admit a Negro. Their dogging poverty and telltale symptoms of malnutrition, particularly evident among the children, were a persisting reminder that racial injustice and competent food supply simply do not go together.

Beyond town limits I visited and "wrote up" several Negro farmers who were among the most competent small-tract farmers I had yet encountered. But their numbers were regrettably few; most members of their race, lacking land or any reasonable hope of buying it, endured the life in town. Among them was my special friend Abe "Briss" Bell. Then past seventy, and duly designated as "Uncle," Abe was partly paralyzed and barely able to stand. He earned his food and lodging, such as they were, by doing odd jobs, including sweeping and mopping the local bakery, one of the restaurants, and Drake's Grocery.

One night, after finishing his cleanup of the latter, Briss Bell found himself being berated by the local police chief, who demanded to see what he was "sneakin' away with." The proprietor's son called out, "It's all right." (Later the police chief represented that he did not hear. The Drake boy vowed he had called out clearly.)

For reasons never explained, Briss tried to hobble around the corner. The police chief ran after him, shouting "Halt!" When the old Negro turned about, the out-of-uniform lawman fired twice. Abe fell. He died while a local hackman was seeking to haul him to the hospital. No charges were filed against the police chief, whom the local paper praised for his "vigilance." My paper, the St. Louis Post-Dispatch, did not echo. I invited the vigilant defender of law and order to pursue the libel suit he threatened; he did not accept the invitation.

I resumed my attempts to decipher the repeated overlaps of hunger and racial violence. The Negro was being held in place as the hungriest component of a malnourished society that maintained an almost unbelievable abundance of unused land. What exactly was holding him in the vise? One outcome of my quest for answers was an onlooker's association with the somewhat belated local revival of the Ku Klux Klan.

During April 1924, the local chapter of Ku Kluxers announced plans for holding what they termed an "open muster," during which the brethren would parade "bare-faced," i.e., wearing their robes but not their hoods. For several months I had been hearing of the Klan's "recruit-ment," which included boy Kluxers and female or "lady" Kluxers. All of this added to my anticipation of reporting the barefaced parade and all its trimmings, including the visiting "orators." The first of these, a Kleagle from Joplin, turned out to be a dismal little man with a big voice and a seemingly incurable flux of words that seemed to pour forth wholly without physical or mental effort. His topic was the Anglo-Saxon's responsibility to join in "keeping Neegrows in their places," which, one gathered, did not include tenure as sharecroppers on the fringes of poor cotton farms to the immediate south but did include refrainin' from insultin' our Southern white womanhood. Bill Rose, the other local reporter, who presently graduated to the status of advance man for the Coles Brothers Circus, poked my shoulder: "Doesn't that old buzzard make you want to puke?"

My affirmative answer held for the ensuing barefaced parade, which began at Boggs' chicken-pickin' plant down near the depot ice plant. There was no band or marshal; the besheeted brethren shambled along to the eerie cadence of a metal triangle beaten with a length of iron pipe. There was no evidence of marchers' pride; the ranks wavered like winter-whitened sedge grass in a strong wind. In the fore-ranks I recognized the garrulous, overage "grocery boy," a notoriously drunken stone mason, a coal shoveler who was locally renowned for never paying his debts, an elderly bar-ber equally renowned for his habit of carrying home his cash register every night, and the local chief of police, who had slain Briss Bell. Also readily recognizable were the sanitary policeman (understandably without his Negro assistant), the dour little interim secretary of the local chamber of commerce (earlier known as the Binness Man's club). Then I beheld, directly beside the stubby little Chamber man, my very own Uncle Sam, the plumber. Slow-motioned and perceptibly confused, my mother's next younger brother was conspicuously out of line and out of step. But he was a Kluxer, and he was right in there, upholding the Honor of the Anglo-Saxon Race.

I continued to recognize others of the marchers. I identified former schoolmates, and remembered how they had looked and consorted a dozen years earlier; their lethargy and unhappy boredom; their spiky arms and legs, how they had slouched, how badly some of them had smelled. Most of those whom I clearly remembered had been among the poorer and hungrier pupils. As the wavering tinkle of the iron triangle led on I continued to ponder motivation. Was theirs a hunger for legitimacy or self-respect? Or more basically, was it hunger for adequate food?

The dismal and floppy parade weaved along to a hillside pasture, where, beyond a rusty barbed wire fence, wisps of smoke were rising from a succession of newly dug pits. In the larger pit a side of beef writhed and spluttered on a bed of whitening hickory coals. A local restaurant cook was sweating and grumbling while knifing into char-blackened but drippy red beef. The other beef side and apparently all of the bread-and-butter sandwiches already had been consumed by nonparaders. Two partially disrobed Klansmen were knifing open a boxful of baker's rolls, but those, too, were fast disappearing. Reserves of food appeared to be far less than adequate. A fat member who was shirtless as well as disrobed was emptying two oversize frying pans filled with frankfurters. The contents seemed to vanish before they could be inserted into buns.

Beyond the pits was a hastily raised board stand backed by a rusty and extremely smoky kerosene stove with several burners, each topped with a frying pan filled with spluttering and extremely greasy hamburgers. The two disrobed Klansmen who attended the stand were unashamedly dumping loaves of dry bread into a tubful of water. When the cast-off bread became suitably soggy they used potato mashers to mix it with pink and tallowy ground beef. A frowning on-looker remarked, "Hell, I feed my dawgs better grub than that!" Another concurred by spitting out his first mouthful of what he termed the skunkburger and noting, "Many a damn fool would of swallered a hot mess like that jest to be polite!"

But there were multitudinous exceptions. I had never seen more ravenous freeloaders. Before most of the brethren could get within smelling distance all the free barbecue was gone, and panful after panful of the bread-diluted hamburgers were disappearing into the crowd, along with the remainder of the frankfurters. Another tubful of adulterated hamburgers was served up, but the lines of hungry grew longer and, from all indications, ever hungrier. Even when the last edible scrap was gone and the last buckets of coffee had been emptied, the Klansmen appeared to be fully as hungry as when the gut stuff began.

At about that point I began to realize that the slobbish robe wearers, or most of them, were hungry mavericks seeking to fabricate strength and self-importance, and, more impressively, seeking to fill up their bellies. The majority wolfed and gulped like starvelings. I found myself forecasting that when the Klan "barbecues" were discontinued, as they presently were, the membership would plummet—as it presently did.

Yet I felt quite certain that so long as cruel and commanding poverty persisted, so long as many Americans were achingly hungry or certainly malnourished, all, much, or some of their time, there would be Ku Klux Klans or comparable bullies' clubs. As long as race was set against race, and quite regardless of place, there would be hunger. At a ripening twenty years, I had by then grown convinced that food supply is the premier decider of American behavior.

Good old Art Lewis, the home-town bank president and probably the most intelligent citizen of the town, thoughtfully listened to my recitation, then slowly nodded: "I kind of go along with that. Only I don't believe what you say holds jest for us squirrel chasers here in Arkansas. I believe it holds for about everywhere. Way I see it, people is people, wherever you find 'em. What all people truly want most to be sure of is somethin' to eat. And around here, like in God knows how many places, too many people ain't gettin' that sureness. What's more it could worsen before it betters."

The Broadening
View

THE FAT LANDS

TOWARD MIDYEAR 1928, I moved less than cautiously on St. Louis. As usual, the *Post-Dispatch* was busy, thriving, and budgeting; as usual, too, St. Louis was murky, hot, grumpy, and beerily provincial. My newspapering labors seemed to fall soddenly into the environmental mold. After two furiously hot days of indecision, the Complete Edition Editor put me to work at copy editing the farm pages and, as time permitted, "wading the slush"—newspaper jargon for reading and occasionally recovering printable material from the dribbles or gushes of free-lance submissions.

As the summer bored on I was permitted brief flings at local reporting. For one, it came to pass on a cruelly sultry late August morning, while I was dawdling in the sweltering interior of Union Station, that a special Pullman car carrying the then President of the United States pulled in without forewarning. Calvin Coolidge (back in Plymouth Notch, Vermont, christened John Calvin Coolidge) had, in his own words, "snuck into St. Louis without any hullabaloo." By sheerest happenstance I overheard an off-duty trainman ask another if the President's car was still on the siding. The answer was a small but visible nod. Quite directly I learned that the Vermont-born Silent Cal (in living person he could be appallingly loquacious) had been responsible for giving the working press the slip when the train that carried (his own word was "drew") his private car had been abruptly rerouted, presumably by an unrestrainable seizure of Vermont mischievousness, by way of St. Louis instead of Chicago, as earlier announced. Tom Pegler, a veteran reporter for the Chicago *Herald-Examiner*, had got wind of the changeabout and hitched a ride to St. Louis aboard one of the very early mail planes.

Pegler had earlier prepared a very able interview covering the President's recently completed tour of Montana and the Dakotas. As the other newsman, I merely trailed the white-haired old-timer into the President's "special coach," and laboriously transcribed the Coolidge answers to the Hearst man's excellent questions. By outrageously good luck (for me) I was with an afternoon paper with time for ingesting the story, whereas "Pappy" Pegler, despite his most commendable enterprise, was too late to "make" his morning paper in Chicago. I will ever remember how the President of the United States, still belching softly from a whopping big trout breakfast, had delivered himself on the subject of U.S. farming. "There will mostly always be plenty to eat, at least here in America, and plenty of farmers to grow it and fetch it to market. Our farmers never will make any money to speak of, but that's their own business."

My accidental and outrageously cribbed Presidential interview story apparently precipitated my boss's decision to free me from the desk and permit my return to open reporting in what he termed the "St. Louis Corn and Hog Belt."

As several months of first-hand looking and listening

lengthily confirmed, great numbers of Midwestern farmers were sustaining the Coolidge clairvoyance. Indeed, my ensuing stint as a farm reporter, principally in the Missouri Corn Belt, lower Illinois, Indiana, and from time to time, lower Iowa and eastern Kansas, presently burgeoned with confirmations.

At the time these regions were the confident strongholds of No Scrub Bulls, Younger and Fatter Hogs, New and Oncoming Hybrid Corn (interspersed or interplanted with a then novelty legume called soy bean or "saw-ya"); of super state fairs with their usually overweight judges of practically everything from Berkshire boars to home-canned peaches, and of "supercolossal" auction sales of purebreds. (Good old Joe Gossard was vehemently auctioning registered Shorthorn bulls for $50,000 apiece, payable with two milking strain cows worth $10,000 apiece and a $30,000 Jersey bull.)

These and related antics presently shaped a pattern of proof that what some continued to list as the "Original Corn Belt," beginning with "Little Egypt," the underhorn of Illinois, had ceased being young country. The same held for the generally adjacent "Abe Lincoln country," centering about Springfield, Illinois. The realm at large had remained corn-hog country, including its blocky little towns where the local W.C.T.U.'s continued to keep close lookout on the private lives of the local schoolteachers. But the more definitive fact was that the area as a whole was showing bald patches, missing teeth, expanding middles, and other telltale hallmarks of middle age. Little "new ground" was being planted. There were substantial numbers of untilled farms, even greater numbers of vacated country schools and preacherless churches. Here and there one came upon backwoods and untenable rough lands, complete with unpainted shacks, hip-deep gullies, and ragged tenant farmers with self-evident disposition to vary the monotony of sitting down with the more satisfying procedures of "layin' down."

I was doubly reminded of this when the *Atlantic Monthly* of the Ellery Sedgwick vintage published belatedly one of my early essays about the rural Ozarks, somewhat figuratively entitled "Elizabethan America." It turned out to be one of those occasional magazine pieces that unexplainably attract reader mail. To my surprise most of the letters came from this same Midwest. The prevailing tenor was: "So why attach this 'Elizabethan America' title to the Ozarks? I can drive fifty miles in practically any direction and find a similarly 'Elizabethan' America right here in Indiana (or Illinois, Ohio, Iowa, etc.)." One cogent reader protested only my adjective and inquired, "Why not just label it 'Hungry America,' or 'Unhungry America'? That covers the actual range and choice."

This seemed almost squelchingly correct. Most of the Midwest, by vivid contrast to most of the Ozarks, was unhungry America. The proofs piled in the fields, pastures and gardens, and stock pens, and protruded from midriffs of all ages and both sexes of residents. There were, of course, occasional thin people, particularly skinny children, but the preponderance were living proofs and aftermaths of momentously plentiful meals, including fat pork, red-eye ham gravy, stuffed fowl, and ever multitudinous pies.

In the main Corn Belt farmers were not subsistence food growers in the manner or with the primitive directness of the Ozarks yeomen. Yet, as anyone could see, they heartily fitted their prevailing food intake to their living crop routines. For the most part they ate more, and more fatteningly, than the Ozarkers; by obvious averages they were inevitably bigger and fatter people. As I soon discovered (again speaking broadly), the Corn Belters were more hospitable and neighborly than the Ozarkers, and far more charitable.

As I gained acquaintance with greater numbers of the Corn Belt farmers I began to sense (perhaps deduce is the better word) that, more markedly than the Ozarks people, they were, to state it tritely, "typical farmers." The Corn Belt practices of practical growing were not only more devoted and aggressive than those I had known before, but they were more convincingly of the people.

This precept encouraged thought and reweighing of the various background factors and values. Even in the Corn Belt the country schools and most of the smaller town schools were very far from commendable or adequate. Even so, they were markedly better than those of the Ozarks; the apparent levels of conventional "education" were about six school grades higher; the prevailing proportion of college or junior college graduates was at least ten times that current in the Ozarks.

The functional practices in crop growing were comparably superior to those of the poor-land frontier on which I had grown up; this fact held most impressively for the livestock, which had acquired a commanding preeminence in the Midwest's agronomy. Livestock continued to replace grain as the decisive cash crop. In particular, corn, the predominant field crop, was being marketed as fat beef animals or fattened hogs. "Market" meant commercial meat packers, either local or interstate firms, while "fat" meant excessive fat: animals encased in, or wobbling under, the weight of thick layers of sheer blubber.

As a newcomer I found the position or commercial attitude of the meat packers and their local buyers completely baffling. They were urging or even demanding that the farmers produce fat-meat animals. Yet the processors complained most dourly of the hurtful results thereof. They pointed out that the superfattened hogs yielded a most uneconomical amount (up to 40 percent of dressed weight) of lard, which was difficult to market and predestined to comparatively niggardly prices. The hyper-fat beef animals in turn were yielding veritable mountains of tallow and miscellaneous fat that packers could dispose of only as soap material and a few other minor and not very profitable uses.

But the meat packers kept on with their oddly fatalistic reasoning. Yes, the prevailing fat ratios were damagingly high; from the raiser's standpoint as well as the packer's, they injured, at times irreparably destroyed, the markets. But lean-meat animals were virtually unsalable except as "canner's junk." The concept of progress in livestock husbandry had become predicated on growing and fattening to maximum size the beef- or pork-bearers in the minimal time. As an inevitable result beef was being replaced by fat veal, pork by even fatter pig meat. Breeding practices sustained the perennial obesity binge. For better or worse, meat animals were being sold by live weight. Traditionally-meat animals were being used as living machines for converting the principal grains to more highly nourishing and more readily marketable foodstuffs.

Back of this use was the insistent fact that grains were ceasing to be readily marketable as such. Corn was the dominating instance. "Maya maize" was durably established as the crucial field crop. Yet the absolute maximum of developed or exploited demands for corn as human food, i.e., as meal, hominy, margarines, salad oils, cereals, etc., could no longer even begin to dispose of the ever increasing harvests. The conversion of corn to meat and animal products was being further multiplied by the expanding advent of the "feeder pens"; by rapidly increasing numbers, grain growers were importing lean young cattle from grass ranges to the west and fattening—"feeding out"—with home-grown grains, in greatest part corn.

Understandably, the meat packers did not choose to upset or discourage the feeder trade, but their best merchandising efforts could not make it validly dependable. As packers' profits dwindled, farmers' profits were dwindling even more markedly. There were no readily attainable replacements; the wool trade was sloughing away; horses and mules were being replaced by tractors, autos, and trucks, for a double farm loss of outlets for feeds and erasure of the once immensely profitable breeding and selling of draft animals. For the most part, poultry growing was less than adequately profitable. Milk farming was already seriously ensnarled by soaring distribution costs and related impediments. It followed that the red meats, particularly beef and pork, were by now the commanding products of the so-called "fat land" agriculture. But "meat" meant extravagantly fat meat; fat was the prime qualifier for marketing, yet the ever pernicious destroyer of profitable markets.

Stockyards foremen agreed, buyers agreed, the meat-packing industry at large agreed. But the grease-dipping fantasia lingered and kept on intensifying.

As a roving reporter I watched the livestock-raising farmers, both individuals and determined groups, attempting to "get the jump" on the markets by hurrying their fat pigs or calves or steers to local stockyards in frantic and usually futile attempts to "catch" short markets or others possessing, for the moment, a "sharp bite." The odds against success were literally hundreds to one. Again and again I noted the nighttime loadouts (usually on trucks) of live animals for quick and addled dashes to the nearest stockyards in response to a hard to explain telepathy of Now's-the-right-time-to-sell. The ever mysterious rumors would often reach several, sometimes several dozen, of the livestock farmers almost simultaneously. The buyers would be literally deluged with meat animals, and the customarily "soft" markets would sink even lower.

Yet, in the main, the losses of the livestock raisers rarely translated into profits for the meat packers. The latter's sustaining profits, such as they were, were almost invariably dribbles from the recovery of lesser animal by-products, such as insulin and other pharmaceutical bases, fertilizer ingredients, and inedible body parts such as blood, hair, hoofs, horns, viscera, and layer fat, for assorted uses in making soaps, glues, weather coatings, and sundry other nonfoods. By long-established tradition, profits on marketable meats were infinitesimal; Armour, Swift, and Wilson spokesmen repeatedly assured one that their companies felt fortunate to net 10 cents per hundred pounds of "market standard" meats.

In all, Corn Belt reporting persisted in implanting the general conviction that obese meat animals were helping build an obese nation and literally millions of poor fat farmers.

Yet one could not fail to sense the absolutely momentous potentials for producing foods; nor could one indefinitely evade the very real and seemingly gargantuan factors of extravagance that seemed implicit to this now aging Middle West. The already traditional farming practices were almost fantastically laborious and wasteful of energy and materials. This extravagance began and, one suspected, ended with the excessively deep and frequent plowing. The cultivation of corn typified the dire punishment of harvest-giving roots. A minimum of seven fiercely thorough plowings was then standard practice. One, sometimes two, initial deep plowings were followed by a heavy disking prior to planting;

then followed at least five successive row plowings or "cultivator work-overs."

One wondered and wondered how any of the root structures could survive the unmerciful upsettings. The advent of the tractor added to the mayhem of excessive cultivation and the overall violence of the tillage. The tractors were formidably overweight and every phase of the plowing seemed outrageously deep. "There's a lot you can say in favor of Corn Belt corn growin', and a lot you can say against it," a glum county agricultural agent assured me, "but nobody can deny that our corn gets the livin' thunderation plowed out of it." Similarly, nobody could deny the formidable extravagance in terms of tractor fuels and lubricants.

The machine era of U.S. agriculture had begun expensively and in a mood of functional violence. There were impressive advances in the mechanical harvesting of grains, particularly of corn, and harvesting machinery for soy beans, hay crops, and ensilage was being improved. But at or near that point the gains seemed to fade away. For the harvest procedures for fruits, berries, potatoes, vegetables, and other minor crops were almost shockingly inadequate and primitively extravagant. Practically all the lesser crops were being harvested by hand, and stored by makeshift, and marketed with appalling sloppiness. In particular, tomatoes, green peas, and snap beans, then the three principal cannery crops of the region, were being picked and processed with incompetence and wastefulness. In Indiana a local manager for Heinz, certainly one of the more competent processors of perishables, assured me matter-of-factly that he felt "darned lucky" if his factory could recover half of the matured tonnage of the local tomato crop, and that the processable recovery of green peas and snap beans averaged little or no more than 40 percent of the measurable harvests.

There seemed to be no convincing explanation for this inefficiency or for the prevailing lapses in storage of other "homegrown edibles." The so-called "storing experiments," such as barreling sweet potatoes in dry sand and white potatoes in wet sawdust, were staple enterprises of experiment stations, including college and research centers throughout the area. But in the main the procedures and techniques for efficient storage of perishable harvests were getting nowhere at all. This failure appeared to be the superfluous Achilles heel of subsistence farming and family gardening.

In due course I was befriended by a most likable Illinois farm family of nine, who happily boasted, "We raise and put by more eatables every year than all of us and the visitin' kin can even begin to eat through." In a quantitative sense those were words of pristine truth. By or before October, the family's root cellar, potato "holes," and drying attic were invariably crammed with homegrown produces. Yet, except for the home canning and related enterprises, little of the homegrown bounties was edibly stored. It followed that beginning around Thanksgiving the oversize family settled to a winter's fare of partly rotten apples, "et along" in order to keep ahead of the rots and scabs, gently decaying potatoes, moldering squashes, and so on. The crocks filled with home-made "waxed-over" sausages or isinglassed eggs rarely endured past the Christmas holidays. Repeatedly, wintertime thaws or warm spells necessitated the dumpage of home-cured pork. The real competition was between commend-ably diligent people and the enduring forces of decay.

County agricultural agents, newspaper people, and working farmers alike discussed, pondered, and argued ways and means of remedy or improvement. The county agricultural agents and other professional students of farming almost unanimously recommended a studied revision of food crops, both major and minor. Improved hybrid strains of corn were already proving their possibilities for producing more bushels and tons of grain on fewer acres. Engineers and practical mechanics tended to agree that the prevailing generation of tractors should be junked and replaced with much lighter and less expensive machinery. Livestock experts were beginning to urge that meat animals be crossed or hybridized toward the end of reshaping them as leaner and no less fast-growing grazing animals; the purebred enthusiasts and commercial breed registry associations were opposing the heresy with more emotion than logic. Other agronomic scholars were beginning to advocate the reestablishment of orchard crops, particularly apples, with varieties of better flavor and market appeal. Others advocated a new concept of canneries, readily portable plants suitable for moving from farm to farm. There were convincing appeals for the restoration of commercial vegetable growing.

As an interested onlooker I found the controversies meaningful as well as entertaining. I sensed in them not only increasing awareness that a primary agriculture of grain and meat could not suffice for what was already the Number One farming nation, but common acceptance of fast-expanding significance of the region as a whole. Even if foggily, I sensed that far-reaching spread of above average fertile soil film could be a verdant symbol of favored spheres or pockets of fertility on which the survival of nations can and in time almost certainly will depend. It was a big and squashy thought; at the time I was reeking with big and squashy thoughts.

THE STUDENT

MY LABORS at farm reporting in the lower Midwest began to proliferate into longer pieces that I began submitting to various magazines. For several months the rejections were unanimous as well as remorseless. Then, begrudgingly, usually with requests to rewrite and reduce to a few hundred words, acceptances began to materialize. My partly wishful deduction that farming and rural living have much in common in most regions of the country were confirmed by cautious acceptances from both the *Christian Science Monitor* and *The New York Times*.

As more of the usually groping efforts were published, letters began drifting in from miscellanies of readers or glimpsers. Among the more gracious writers were Howard Odum, then at the University of North Carolina and one of the most widely revered rural sociologists of the period, and Addison Hibbard, then dean of liberal arts at the University of North Carolina and shortly thereafter at Northwestern University. Toward the end of 1928 Dr. Odum invited me to a "rural life panel" that he was promoting for Vanderbilt University. There the distinguished sociologist suggested that I make a try at extending the reach and depth of what he termed my "experiments in rural appraisal." He explained that the University of North Carolina had been seeking to maneuver some exchange fellowships in rural sociology and that if I were interested, he and Dean Hibbard would have a try at finding a spot for me.

Several weeks later I received a terse, England-postmarked letter advising rather vaguely that I was being considered for admission as a special student at one of the colleges of Oxford—"specifics pending arrangement." I was requested to favor with a detailed letter of "proposal." After I had sought to accommodate, Howard Odum wrote a terse suggestion that I might begin packing bags and booking passage to England.

In an enchanted daze I applied unsuccessfully for a year's leave from the *Post-Dispatch*, and painstakingly recounted my customarily feeble financial resources. I had managed to bank most of my magazine earnings, which ranged from $12.16 paid on publication by *The Nation*, $84 paid eventually by *The American Mercury*, an "honorarium" of $100 from the *Atlantic*, and a fee of $250 paid punctually by the *American Magazine*. The total could not possibly suffice, but another gracious client, Parkhurst Whitney of *The Outlook*, had promised that he would try to find room for two or three "pieces" from England. So bolstered, I traveled to New York by day coach and boarded a decrepit and badly listing Cunard liner bound for Plymouth. I arrived at Oxford ten days later with a painful attack of appendicitis and the rather austere pedagogical counsel to find myself an inexpensive hotel room and await "acceptance."

That involved more than a month of waiting. Most of the colleges were not viewing American candidates as bargains. Rhodes scholars were still lolling and pubbing around, awaiting bids even from the poorer and more feeble colleges; I took due consolation from the fact that at least I was awaiting the convenience of one of the better colleges.

From my attic room at the King's Hotel I stumbled upon two veritable fountains of knowledge of land use and development. One was John Ramsey, a temporarily shelved divinity student; the other, Harris Poole, a sharp-visaged, London-raised territorial recently arrived from Melbourne. Ramsey, then newly returned from an assignment as student assistant to a country vicar in Exmoor, had spent his childhood and youth as a mission brat in various bizarre places, from interior India to coastal Malaya. He was deeply interested in farming and farmers; while a "sub-vicar" in a troubled rural England, he had organized a milk farmers' cooperative and developed what he termed an exhibition truck farm, from which all harvests went to local charities. During his adolescent years in India, Ramsey had witnessed a succession of famines and had worked to relieve them. His exceptional talents for verbal exposition made his recountings of these experiences both vivid and enlightening. Since I had never experienced a mass famine, or even glimpsed hungry Asia, John's detailed recountings of his adventures among the hungry multitudes and their faminous background greatly impressed me.

The erstwise cockney was the son of a Londoner who had earlier won fame, fortune, and some infamy by his international enterprises in restoring so-called "dead lands." The senior Poole had first journeyed to South Africa as a very young soldier in the Boer War. There he had won a combat medal and displayed exceptional talent as a trouping gambler; he invested part of his sizable military dice-winnings in a "block" of Transvaal real estate, on which he planted an orange grove. The trees prospered for about three years, then promptly and almost unanimously died as their taproots simultaneously struck a deep and impenetrable hardpan. Joey Poole acquired another tract in British South Africa, again at a laughably low price, planted it to citrus, and while the second grove was thriving sold it to a regimental officer whom he had served as orderly and for that and other good reasons loathed. During the ensuing year the young orange trees struck hardpan and punctually died. The former officer filed suit against his onetime striker and "warranted" his arrest for fraud. Brought to trial, Joey Poole admitted his first calamitous experience, but persuaded the court and jury that he had reason to believe the hard underlayer of his newer acquisition of frontier land would presently be penetrated by the citrus-tree roots, and that he had sold the property in good faith.

Joey Poole next moved on to Australia, where he acquired a strip of almost sterile shore land that he presently converted to one of the first successful banana plantings in New South Wales. The roving cockney did not immediately reveal his secret of success; he had discovered that the sterility of the land was caused not by inadequate rainfall, as some asserted, but by the lack of minor or trace minerals such as zinc and molybdenum, which most vegetation requires. Eventually the elder Poole's finding and his subsequent development of application techniques for zinc and molybdenum led to the effective use of several million acres of former wastelands in Australia as effective sheep and cattle ranges, and in some areas for field crops.

Poole's cogent and worldly son was dynamically interested in devising ways and means of reviving dead or sickly soils, and understandably eager to observe experiments in "revitalizing" moss banks, sand dunes, and comparable waste areas in the homeland. His enthusiasm was strongly contagious; his insistent thesis was that the ill-used planet Earth has multitudes of what he called "poxes of bad lands" that definitely can be restored to food-bearing capabilities.

Ramsey's no less volatile interests were centered in people rather than lands, and the capabilities of people for getting good from otherwise wasted lands. He saw adequate food production as a climaxing crusade, a spirit-provoked mission to survive and attain abundance.

Both my companions in waiting were what I termed *a priori* internationalists; neither had ever felt himself to be tethered to or permanently associated with any particular country, island, continent, or for that matter, hemisphere. Both regarded my attempted classification as rather silly;

they believed that what I had termed international-mind-edness was the normal status and station of any reasonably intelligent man. Both derided the American foible of sub-stantially fictitious nationalism, pointing out that the United States is at least a half dozen recognizable nations "potted" together in one. And they were quite confident that particular regions of the United States typified all the really noteworthy farming environments existing on earth. Poole pointed out that my particular and somewhat addled home-land, the Ozarks, delineated nothing special except mortal slothfulness. He took for granted that at least most of the land was validly "developable," adding that history keeps proving that mere worthless people presently erase themselves by natural aftermaths of their own worthlessness.

From Oxford, Ramsey, Poole, and I set out for an im-provised bicycle tour of English farms. Within two weeks we had visited or viewed in passing some of the best and some of the worst food-producing establishments I had yet seen or vividly imagined. They ranged from "moss vales" too poor to support any higher plant-life through poxed and desolate hillside "rabbitries," where even the hardiest of hares could not survive without artificial feeding, to su-perbly productive and splendidly managed thousand-acre live-stock and grain farms. Even in the brief tour I became aware that the large-acreage, mixed-crop English farm had endured as a world-revered model for diversified farm operation, one that was being more and more effectively imitated by the more successful American farms.

The coordination of meadows and ranges with livestock holdings, particularly beef and milk cattle and sheep, seemed to me especially enlightened. While pedaling through Yorkshire, we visited a renowned dairy and vegeta-ble farm that was generously dotted with the so-called "Roman ruins," revealing vestiges of ancient farming estates duly earned by centurions of the Caesars' Sixth Legion, which was stationed at York for more than five centuries. The remnants of these land plots, earned by lifetime-service in the legions of "Roma Altera," still had bits and corners of the stone buildings, including granaries, wool sheds, milking parlors and butteries, cheese works, flax-curing and -spinning shops, metal smithies, and other significant remnants of the first enduring roots of what is now labeled Western agriculture.

The surface archeology was no doubt alluring to archeologists and miscellaneous antiquarians, but the message that most affected me was the evidence of productive continuity. Eighteen to twenty centuries ago these lands of England were feeding and supporting people, as they still are.

The manager—he disdained the title of governor—of the largest of the Gloucester "general farms" was a retired Colonial Office man who had spent his best years viewing and, from time to time, seeking to improve farm practices in various of His Majesty's colonies and dominions from the Camerouns to the Caribbean Crown Colonies. These and supplementary experiences had made him a devoted convert to organic gardening. He was convinced that duly rotted manures and composts of vegetable wastes are the best and surest restorers of plant nutrients; he limited the use of commercial fertilizers to nitrates and phosphates, and he had these applied not directly to the soil but rather to the well-tended compost heap. The farm plant included about 900 acres of highly productive cultivations and meadows. Food harvests ranged from dairy cattle to apples and "produces," including potatoes, rhubarb, and green vegetables.

Harvests had been gaining about 5 percent annually during the previous eight years; profits had grown almost proportionately. The manager granted that England could never hope to regain self-sufficiency in food production, but he insisted that on many of the ancient cultivations food yields could be maintained at averages well above those that obtained during the long-gone centuries when England was the Roman Empire's "granary to the north." He insisted that England's importance as a way-shower to food production should never diminish. On the strength of his foreign travels he listed Italy, Denmark, Poland, New Zealand, and the United States as revealing road signs to what he termed globally capable food production.

The manager's side theories included the hypothesis that world food production falls into two less than inevitable classifications, the grain-diet category and the "omnivorous" category, which includes substantial quantities of meats, dairy products, fruits, and vegetables. Holding that in time the prevalence of grain diets will diminish, he believed that the primary lesson of Western agriculture is support and sustainment of meats, milk, fruit, and vegetables, and that the ratio of these foods will increase throughout most of the populated earth as more people are motivated to qualify as better farmers. He insisted that the squandering and miscellaneous depreciation of soils are implicitly avoidable and unnatural, the more so because nature is forever striving to replenish the soil, from both above and below the surface.

The thesis provided the most enlightened item of study I encountered during my solitary school year in England. Back at Oxford, Ramsey and I made plans for spending the oncoming term vacation at a continued study tour of farming throughout the United Kingdom. But directly before our take-off from Wincombe, then an oldline farming village in Gloucestershire (it is now a rather dismal suburb of Cheltingham), I was again stricken with appendicitis. Following surgery, I contracted peritonitis, and spent the ensuing summer intermittently rotting in a shire hospital and seeking to convalesce in an inexpensive farm home on nearby Cleave Hill. With noble consistency, Ramsey kept calling back for brief visits and detailed reports of his exceptionally capable studies of English and Irish farming as he saw and interpreted them. He also favored me with a veritable volume of painstaking journal notes. These turned out to be at least as revealing and far more pertinent than any of my reading at Oxford.

I kept at reading until my money melted down to minimum steerage fare to New York. Howard Odum wrote that he was struggling to obtain a teaching fellowship for me and to "pry open" an eventual teaching job at North Carolina. My appreciation could not repress the fact that by then I was back in New York, unemployed and almost penniless. At *The Outlook,* then my most tolerant client, a new editor, Carl Dickey, explained sadly that he would be obliged to "rob the mail" in order to pay me for my work already published; the magazine was at the precarious edge of bankruptcy and could make no "immediate commitments."

When I explained that I hoped to once more work my way through college, probably in Tennessee, he fidgeted thoughtfully. "I know a Tennessee newspaperman named Arthur Krock who's just moved up from the dying *World* to the living *Times.* Why not go and let him tell you about newspapering down in Nashville?"

I took the suggestion. Before nightfall, I found myself a distinctly probationary editorial hireling of *The New York Times.* It was wanderer's luck; the depression-racked city was spilling over with jobless newspaper men. However, in the course of digging in as a national newspaper, the *Times* was determinedly expanding its coverage of regional and national news and viewpoints. Certainly there was no shortage of competent reporters and desk men in New York. But the changing editorial leadership was seeking to coordinate and complement the work of out-of-town correspondents with in-town reporters who, as Krock put it, "had a feeling for the sticks."

CITY MOUSE

MY WORKADAY adventures as a fledgling and somewhat superfluous *Times* reporter kept leading to an astonishing variety of farming enterprises in New York City: an alligator farm, a mink farm, a breeding farm for chimpanzees, a duck farm, numerous chicken and egg farms, and a still greater number of miniature truck gardens. In the upper Bronx I met an engaging old lady who had converted her back yard to a pheasant farm. A top-story factory loft in the garment district had been effectively refurbished as a vegetable-growing hothouse. In the Canal Street area I located a factory loft that was used for growing and sprouting various green and white vegetables used by Chinese restaurants. At the time most "Chinese" vegetables used in the metropolitan area were being grown in suburban sites, including parts of Long Island and the Princeton area of New Jersey.

I met a stock brokerage employee who kept a lobster "farm," actually an ocean-water pond where he stored and fed, and at a healthy profit bought and sold, live lobsters. A Hungarian physician had very effectively surrounded his penthouse sun deck with soil boxes in which he grew superb tomatoes, cresses, and other flavor vegetables. I met a department store worker with a profitable hobby of growing fine everbearing strawberries in soil-filled holed barrels discreetly placed on the roof of the store building; also, a laundry proprietor in Harlem who had a superbly productive broiler farm in an otherwise vacant tenement loft. Though the Sanitation Department had not given official blessings, the "chicken battery" was notably cleaner and certainly less odorous than some of the adjacent apartments. Further, the chickens appeared to be much better fed than most of their human neighbors.

As a working reporter, I also had occasion to learn that New York had a great many backyard gardens, which suggested, even if somewhat feebly, that the biggest and one of the worst befouled of American cities had capabilities for producing at least some part of its food requirements within its crowded boroughs and nearer suburbs. In the latter connection a persuasive economics professor at Columbia showed me a chart that he had compiled to prove, or suggest, that New York City could be fed completely by foods produced within an inland radius of no more than two hundred miles. The then prevailing radius was about six times that long.

The thought for mulling deals with the potentialities, conceivably of life-or-death importance, for a much greater degree of attainable self-subsistence for city dwellers. In nuclear times in a world without peace, the idea here may be worthy of weighing.

In the past, American and other history has confirmed the local attainability of urban food supplies. Particularly in New England and parts of the Middle Atlantic, many of what are now cities or principal towns grew directly from communities of farms. Particularly during Revolutionary times and the strife-ridden early nineteenth century, there were repeated instances of towns that survived either wholly or in principal part because they were able to produce all or substantial portions of their food supplies within corporate boundaries. I kept toying with the possibility that self-subsistence in terms of food supply may well be a decisive shape of the predictable future, and a primary reason why, in due course, the United States and other countries may grow to be confederations of city-states.

A primary motivation, obviously, would be the burdening expense of transportation. Here, in the deepest trough of an appallingly deep and dark depression, the travails of distributing food had already taken over as a principal cause for weeping, and this was especially evident in New York. Throughout that era of farm-pauperizing prices, the predominant rail and highway truck haulage of foods remained cruelly and most uneconomically expensive. In New York of 1930–31 a "gross average" of about 38 cents of the consumer's food dollar went for transportation.

As Al Smith pointed out, "that hoit." I interviewed beef dealers who vowed that rail freight alone was taking as much as 60 percent of the market value of run-of-the-yard beef cattle. A responsible commission broker recounted that a superior client had rail-shipped 600 bushels of early East Shore Maryland potatoes to sheds in New York. Rail costs came to 58 percent of the gross receipts, and when all other overhead items, including broker's commission, were paid, the grower netted one cent a bushel.

The head of a Maryland market gardeners' cooperative showed me the audited records of how his association was making a net profit of 30 cents a freight carload on fresh spinach (after paying $109.30 for freight charges) and losing an average net of 60 cents a carload for quality snap beans (after paying 93 percent of the total "get" for transportation).

By then such recountings had little news value. Consumers, as usual, were paying the transportation tabs. Farmers were losing their shirts, while uncensused millions of city dwellers went hungry. Unfortunately, it happened here and it could happen again.

MORE MOBILE MOUSE

MY ADVENTURES in pantry mousing were in for dispersion. The estimable city editor seemed able and willing to restrain his enthusiasm for my "box features," about such intriguing subjects as window-box radishes. Again Arthur Krock was understanding. He appreciated that whimsical little accounts of tomato tubs in penthouses can in time become monotonous. He reflected that what he termed the economic crucifixion of the food industries was losing news value and gaining only in monotony. He agreed that the feat of feeding any nation competently required an uplift of industrial earnings and urban living standards. And he also doubted that U.S. agriculture could affect convalescence unless or until more of its producers could fulfill more and greater nonfood uses. With those prophetic sparklers ably spoken, the newspapering Nero from Nashville replaced his chewing cigar with a lighted one. "I think maybe you'd better get out of town."

With great effort he began hoisting a tousled mass of papers from his jacket pocket. "It says here that out in a town called Dearborn, Michigan, lives a man named Henry Ford. His publicity drum pounders are making ado's about the imminent birth of his twenty-five-millionth auto. This handout of hogwash mentions that H. Ford is the world's biggest owner of farm lands. That's only one more Fordly superlative. But here is some boiler plate about his use of farm crops in making autos. It relates to the going guk called 'chemurgy.' Why not go out to Dearborn, do a square dance with the old coot, and try a definitive story about proved and possible industrial uses for farm crops?"

I went for a briefing by an old-time copy reader who had served time as city editor for one of the sizable Detroit papers and more or less inevitably had learned "considerable" about Henry Ford, now the billionaire squire of nearby and synthetically quaint Dearborn. My first question dealt with Ford's interest in farming. Did the erstwhile Detroit editor believe Mr. Ford had any real desire to help American farming?

"I honestly doubt that Ford has any real desire to help anything except Henry Ford. He knows, of course, that Ford autos and Ferguson tractors will never roll without farmers to buy them, and be two-bitted to death by same. However, this idea of stimulating food production by developing money values of crops as industrial material is a damn important idea, or seems so to me."

I arrived at Dearborn on a blowy March day and took quarters at the Ford-owned Dearborn Inn, which I found almost painfully homelike. When I telephoned Mr. Ford to ask for an appointment, a secretary told me that Mr. Ford would return the call at the Inn, when, as, and if he saw fit. Next morning when I returned from a stroll through the duly restored countryside, the room clerk beckoned excitedly. "The Boss just now telephoned you. I suggest you hurry up to your room and return the call."

A scared-sounding voice told me that Mr. Ford would see me at ten the following morning at the laboratory.

"Which office?" I asked.

"Mr. Ford doesn't keep an office!"

At the appointed time I reported to a male receptionist at the "Old Lab" building. The receptionist viewed me resignedly, suggested that Mr. Cameron would see me, then led me into an office occupied by a fat scowling man, who was swallowing aspirin and repeatedly drinking glasses of water. Without speaking, Mr. Cameron managed to stand upright. That accomplished, he again scowled darkly and peered down the hallway, then disappeared into the heavy shadows.

After five or ten minutes he returned, followed by a tall and slender elderly man, whitish-gray of hair, handsomely tailored, slightly stooped, and from appearances almost fiercely alert. Mr. Ford stared at me without speaking, then bared his lips as if to smile, but all that happened was a brief display of upper dentures. He eventually said, "Good morning!" and motioned me to be seated. Bill Cameron scowled again and disappeared. Mr. Ford approached me. I noted the razor-sharp creases of his trouser legs and the almost startling length of his shoes. "What do you know about technocracy?" he began.

"Not much, and I care even less. I believe it's merely a shabby revival of some sloppy thinking of about a hundred years ago."

He peered at me even more closely. "Funny thing, I agree with you. So let me ask you something else! Do you happen to know anything about square dancing in the Ozarks?"

"Pitifully little. My father was the dancing member of my family. I didn't inherit any of his talents."

"Come and show me that 'pitifully little,' " the great man commanded. He led the way down an aisle between glass-enclosed office rooms, clipped along through another lobby and passageway that led to a kind of auditorium equipped with spangled ceiling lights and a polished hardwood floor. "Put on that 'Skip to My Lou' record." The command was obeyed by a handsome young Negro who stood by as if built ingeniously into the furniture.

"Show me how you remember dancing it Ozark style!"

Mr. Ford directed, meanwhile readjusting his upper plate. "Folk dancing's my special hobby. We all do it here. Come now, Twinkle Toes, make like I'm the girl!"

Feeling infinitely silly, I struggled to recall a square dance sashay. "You are light on your feet and your jig turn is amusing." Mr. Ford pranced to the side like an aging horse stricken with a mood of playfulness. His large feet continued to scoop along the polished floor like unanchored chair rockers. "I've heard lots about Ozarks square dancing."

"I've seen it done, but I'm sorry I can't demonstrate."

"Don't apologize," Mr. Ford commanded sharply. "With time and practice you could be a good dancer, as good as I am."

I was recalling blurredly how Peter, the mad Czar of the Russias, reputedly commanded his palace guard to dance in the snow like the oversize puppets they reputedly were. As I followed Henry Ford back to Cameron's office I reflected that American plutocracy, with its tremendous political and publicity support, was and is by odds the most secure royalty remaining. Since 1914, in some instances earlier, the more orthodox king business had been on the skids. But the American of great wealth still reigned without real challenge or protest. Money talks and multiplies. Mr. Ford's was no doubt multiplying and Mr. Ford talked, when in the mood, almost incessantly.

I spent the noon hour deciphering my scribbled notes, and later that afternoon, when the interview resumed, I read back the transcript to the billionaire auto king. Mr. Ford said he approved of the way I had put my "thoughts" on paper. I reminded him that all I had put down were his thoughts, substantially as he had spoken them.

He peered at me warily. "That's what I mean and what I like. You put down on paper quite exactly what I say in my own words. Too many of my ideas have been written around and bounced around by smart alecks. I don't like smart alecks. I like journalists who can recognize good ideas,"—he raised a long thin arm in a spontaneous gesture —"and print them precisely the way I speak them. That makes for good reading." The Great Man paused to readjust his uppers and began pacing the floor with purposeless energy. "Later on, I may want you to write some magazine articles for my signature. The magazines will pay you for them; in case they don't, I will. I want you to put down what I have to say . . . the way *I* say and think it." The king looked down at me. "Right now I feel in the mood to think and to talk some more. You can ask questions that you think are worth asking, but mostly I want you to listen. . . ."

Back in the hotel room that night I began deciphering the gospel revelations of Henry Ford as spoken at what may have been his zenith of absolute assurance as the world's biggest auto maker, land owner, antiquarian, and quite possibly the world's richest man. What I had transcribed had somehow taken on a most astonishing cogency:

We have several names for the type of mind and the kind of people who want to run everything, particularly other people's business. "Communist" is the name for those people.

Anyone who tries to grab power, prestige and property which other people have earned, without paying for it, is anything unfavorable you wish to call him; a public enemy, a parasite or a Communist. He has just one use: his greed and audacity can serve to wake us up. And we can always benefit from alarm clocks. Waking people up is the surest safeguard for democracy. If a dictatorship comes here (and Communism or Fascism means dictatorship) it is because the people have been asleep on the job, and, therefore, deserve what they get.

You came to ask me about food production and farming. Well, let me begin by saying that no nation can prosper unless and until its farms prosper too. Farming remains the really basic trade. It is our first source of materials and by that I mean industrial as well as eating. Progress on the farm means progress off the farm. City streets lead to growing fields and vice versa. I was raised on a farm here in Michigan. My father was a career farmer. I've been farming in one way or another most of my life and I've never lost one whit of my enthusiasm for it. Farmers as a rule have an extremely broad range of interests. This ability to get interested in a great variety of subjects is the real American culture. Incidentally, I can't get alarmed by all these reports that our young people are going to leave the land. Some boys are born to be farmers just as surely as others are born to be sailors or mechanics or baseball players. I'm a born mechanic. My father was a born farmer. He made about fifty crops, and he made each one a little bit better than the one before. . . .

"While the earth remaineth" . . . Lots of this talk about soil's wearing out is sheer poppycock. Land can usually grow what it needs to restore itself. There's a great deal of waste and misrepresentation of values in commercial fertilizers. My experience is that lime and wood ashes are probably the best and safest chemicals to put on soil, and that commercial fertilizers, in general, are a cheat.

The Old Testament gives some mighty fine farming advice when it urges farmers to let the land lie fallow now and then. The olden prophets knew that land has an almost magical power to restore itself. A fallow field does some extremely interesting things. In one corner one type of weed begins to grow, in another a crop of some other type of weeds, and so on. Study the weed growth and you will find that the land is actually growing the kind of vegetation which the soil needs for restoring itself. People don't do as well for the land as the land does for itself. One proof is in the machinery. Most of it is unreasonably bad.

During my lifetime I have watched the beginnings of most of our present-day farm machinery. When I was a boy, farming was a trade of the scythe and cradle and bull-tongue plow. There was entirely too much drudgery about it, and too many farms were put side by side without any towns in between them. Now the pendulum has swung to a place where there are entirely too many towns that are way too big. The concentration of industries in a few huge cities is bad. American industry will have to decentralize—break itself up into smaller plants which can be scattered here and there, through the country. This distributes wages and buying power. But let me get on with what I started to say.

American farm machinery is still a mess. I will go so far as to say a damnable mess. It needs to be much more specialized, better fitted to particular soils and climates and crops. Most farm machinery is too cumbersome and too heavy; it drags around entirely too much unnecessary weight and fuel and oil-wise it's too expensive to operate. You ask, "Are Ford's farm machinery and tractors any better than the rest?" Well, yes! But still not nearly good enough! It's still too much concerned with tearing around in the fields. We need to use farm machinery to process crops still farther so they'll be worth more to the buyers. As for my farm machinery, I'm sure it's the best on the market so far, but nowhere near good enough.

Before I answer your question about more nonfood uses for farm crops, let me say this: We've been hearing a great deal about the dangers of surpluses. That's non-

sense. It's only when you have a surplus that you can succeed in finding new uses for a material. So-called surpluses
grow into new industries, new products, new jobs. When
you hear people fearing and bemoaning surpluses, it's
time to tell them to go have their heads examined. We
and every other country need—must have—farm surpluses before farming can prosper as it must if anything
else is to prosper.

As long as this country is running at half or third capacity there won't and can't be good times. "What's the
cure?" The cure is to just plant more acres and work the
land right up to the fence rows. Get more products on
the market. Cut prices. Get better machinery and cut
down production wastes. Forget all this bunk and hokum
about machines robbing men of their jobs. The right kind
of machinery makes more jobs. The duty of American
industry, and this goes for farming, is to pay the highest
wages possible, and sell the product for the lowest possible price to the consumer. That makes for opportunity.
Tomorrow is going to prove a big improvement over today . . . it has to be. Experience has already taught us
that. Experience is the best teacher and the best property. Once you've got it, nobody can steal it from you.

Following publication of the *Times* stories, I returned to
Dearborn to complete a series of Henry Ford Thinks pieces.
The longer and harder I worked on them, the more questions sprang up. Anyone could sense Mr. Ford's love of
property, but his professed love of farming seemed to me
considerably less than convincing. He reiterated that he
owned "close on a million acres of farm lands in nineteen
countries all the way from Iceland to Brazil." But he was
extremely vague about specifics of how he was using or
planned to use his vast land holdings. He answered direct
questions with vehement generalities.

"Young man, I say to you that before the American people or any other people can eat really well, they must have a great deal over and above the mere access to farming lands. They must have the money for buying good food; and by 'good' food I mean mostly vegetables, fruits and meats. . . . As of today I'd say that half the American people are not eating well simply because they don't have or don't believe they have the money for buying good food. This isn't necessarily an outgrowth of depression. It's been going on as long as I can remember. Yes, sir, I'd say about half the United States public rates among the world's best-fed people; the other half comes closer to being among the world's worst-fed people."

At about that point Bill Cameron's head protruded through the doorway. Mr. Ford became abruptly silent. The public-relations man entered briefly and touched my shoulder; he was still frowning. "Burny, burny," he said. "Burn fingers."

Mr. Ford waited in silence until Cameron had left, then walked briskly to the door as if to make certain the redface was not eavesdropping. His voice grew more subdued. "I was speaking of well-fed and badly-fed Americans. I'm told that practically every big town or city in the country by now has some sort of a station for feeding hungry men. I keep wondering about all the hungry women and children. If there are hundreds of thousands of hungry men, there must be millions of hungry women and children." He crossed his long, thin legs. "I'm facing the same thing here. For example, in most of my company's schools we are handing out free lunches because many of the children and some of the shop trainees show up as hungry as starved stray cats. I get the idea that at least some of my own employees aren't eating anywhere near well enough, not because of niggardly pay —they're the best paid in this industry—but because so many are trying to share their earnings with so many jobless and otherwise down-and-out relatives and friends. That's all by way of an aside. No one employer can even hope to wipe away the depression and feed all the hungry all by himself.

"But let's get back to farming and food producing. The last-named is only one function and output of the first-named. The only way ahead is to plant more and grow more on our farms—not merely of foods but all kinds of materials for manufacturing and construction and human services."

Mr. Ford's eyes brightened and his lean face showed un-usual animation: "The biggest trouble with American farm-ing is industry's failure to buy enough of its materials directly from farmers. Every industry worth its belting ought to be buying from many farmers all the time. This is horse sense, also tit for tat. Blamed few industries can survive long without selling to farmers. You take when I ran a bi-cycle factory: I catered to the town trade, but what kept me out of bankruptcy was country trade. When I was a power plant engineer for Edison we stayed in business mostly be-cause some bigtime farmers were buying electricity—no other reason. Without farm customers the Ford Motor Company wouldn't have pulled through its first year.

"Well, my company is trying to return some of the favors to farmers. We are putting about a hundred and fifty pounds of vegetable harvests into every auto, including plastics made of shelled beans and soy flour, varnish coatings made of corn oils, various fibers for stuffing and insulating. I know this isn't enough—isn't half enough. Soy-bean or other vegetable oil goes into our paints and weather coatings, and we use a lot of vegetable waxes and dyes and woods. Here again we're dragging our feet—not using anywhere near enough. By all that's right and proper at least a third part of the gross weight of every auto should be built directly from farm harvests. So I admit I've been at fault. It's no easy job doing as well by farmers as I'm already doing. Mechanical and design people are mostly routinists. They balk like badly trained horses when it comes to using new materials. They know more about iron than soy beans so they want to use iron; more about copper than corn, so they yell to use copper. When I tell 'em to make vegetable paints and coatings they think I'm silly. It's themselves that are silly." He reiterated that farming can never prosper adequately until more of its harvest totals can find nonfood uses as manufacturing materials. "But the whole thing," the King of Auto Makers concluded, "must fit into a system of ideas and by that I mean a *free* system of *newer* ideas."

He restated his belief that farming is quite essentially the same, wherever practiced. "I say that again. Good farming, like good manufacturing, is actually the same anywhere regardless of boundaries or languages. We are too much inclined to say, 'But it's different here from what it is there.' That is hog slop, absolute hog slop. Our crops and livestock come from all over the world. We should be sending them back to all over the world, mostly as needed manufactured goods. We'll never eat better 'til we trade better, and we'll never trade better until we get the real worth and good of what grows all around us."

TREES: COURTESY OF GOD AND F.D.R.

ARTHUR KROCK was in a forgiving mood. "That guk you turned in about Ford wasn't as bad as I expected." I tried to explain that Henry Ford, however smug or fruity his exact words, was one of the few men who was offering at least a glimmer of interest in remedying the food growers' maladies.

Krock opened another box of White Owls, handed one to me and took two for himself. "I'm following you. I'm also following a currently refurbished name in American politics —Franklin Delano Roosevelt. He's a pretty slaphappy Governor, but he is getting the buildup to the point where he is the hottest thing out of Albany since his cousin T.R. came screeching out of the governorship and Albany to infiltrate the White House. The F.D.R. boilerplate we've had so far is pretty bad, but even so, the eminent Mr. Two Autos Hoover is damn sure getting boiled along with the two chickens in his every pot. It's even rumored that the *Herald-Trib* is on the verge of not being entirely sure the Republicans will win again next year; that's reportedly Mrs. Reid's hot tip from off the Philadelphia packetboat. Along with the rest of his routine, our Governor is representing himself as a land conserver and tree-lover. By the way, do you happen to know *anything* about forestry?"

"No sir."

"That's fine; it gives you something in common with Franklin Delano R."

As I rose to leave, Krock waved his cigar. "Up around Columbia College there are a couple of human shapes posing as professors who are already beating the Rooseveltian presidential drum and throwing cookies to the fishes. The names are Moley and Tugwell. I suggest you go up Morningside and talk with Rexford Tugwell. It's a lot sweeter for a fish to have a cookie in its mouth than a nasty old hook, now isn't it, dear boy? Furthermore, it's all in the Columbia day's work—politics and culture, I mean."

Later that day Rexford Tugwell tossed me the warming assurance that, true enough, Franklin Delano Roosevelt, Governor of New York, did indeed love trees, people, farmers, open lands, forests, woods, and trees. And, more pertinently, Franklin D. Roosevelt could be counted on to give me twenty minutes at Albany. "He is a philosopher!" explained the young Tugwell. "Get it? Governor Roosevelt is a philosopher."

I packed my hard-used suitcase and walked across town to Grand Central. On a Sixth Avenue corner I watched again the marrow-chilling emergence of a soup line. At the head of an alley three shabby men pulled three twenty-gallon galvanized cans from the back of a truck, set them on a platform, and began prying off the lids. The cans were filled with an odorous conglomerate of stew and soup. A shambling, ragged man hopped down from the truck cab and staggered forward, bearing an immense pile of porcelain bowls. As if by magic, dozens and scores of ragged and mostly unshaven men began spilling out of alleys, building entrances, and nearby side streets. The bowl carrier and the ladle man joined in bellowing profane instructions to form lines. Almost within seconds the soup line was nearly three blocks long. Ah, the best-fed America!

By around four that afternoon I was in Albany and seated uncomfortably in a crowded waiting room next to the Governor's office. A slender middle-aged man, with eyes that twinkled impishly, introduced himself as Louis Howe and ushered me into the inner office. Governor Roosevelt pushed back his rather ponderous wheel chair, smiled broadly, and motioned me to a chair. I noted his beautifully molded, graying head, his exceptionally long face, his restless grayish eyes that were set rather disturbingly close together. I liked his warmly resonant voice, and noted that he was a chain smoker of cigarettes. "Trees," he murmured thoughtfully. "What is *your* angle on trees?"

I explained that I had no angle, that my primary interest was in land use and food crops, but that I knew trees were rather vitally related to the American farm scene.

The Governor gazed reflectively at the ceiling. "How do you react to Christmas trees?"

The only answer I could think of was "Cordially."

The Governor inquired rather severely, "But don't you agree that trees are a key crop?"

Trees, I knew, when defined collectively as the timber crop, lead all others in value, but according to the prevailing records timber harvests were faltering regrettably. I heard myself murmuring that if trees are a key crop they weren't opening sufficiently.

The Governor next inquired my estimate of what he termed the political implications of forestry. My befuddled silence seemed to amuse him. He repeated his question, then shifted to more answerable ones. He asked the how-abouts of horse racing and open gambling in Hot Springs, Arkansas. When I was obliged to confess ignorance, he shifted to a topic with which I was better acquainted, Huey Long of Louisiana. He probed for the facts regarding Huey's pending invasion of Arkansas to attain the re-election of Hattie Caraway, then the only woman Senator and quite possibly the most inept individual in all the Congress. He next asked how the senior Arkansas Senator, "Old" Joe T. Robinson, kept gaining re-election. When I solemnly explained that Ole Joe accomplished it by arranging the appointment of all likely competitors to lush federal jobs, leaving only drips and droops as opponents, he smiled again, and continued smiling while I tried to restore the direction of the interview. What did Governor Roosevelt see as the "political significance" of forestry?

"Reporters frequently wish to do the talking and I rather enjoy listening to them interviewing themselves. . . . Very frankly, I don't know a great deal about forestry. It's just that I like trees and I have thought a lot about what might be done to get more good out of them. . . . Bring us all the stuff you have about forestry!" he called. Almost instantly a gaunt female secretary entered, bearing an immense wire tray filled with pamphlets and bulletins; obviously the formidable handout had been prepared in advance.

"That's all I know about forestry; actually it's a lot more than I know," my host explained. "I'm sure you'll find reading through that tripe quite salubrious. Or don't you want to be educated?"

I managed to reply that I wished an interview. What were the Governor's views on reforestation, land use, farm credit? What . . .

He raised his arms self-protectingly, then with somewhat patronizing charm began recounting what he termed his "philosophy" of trees and land. He showed a smattering of knowledge about forest resources of the lower Hudson River valley, but he seemed unaware that the ecology of much of the nation is of grass rather than trees. He did not conceive of trees as harvestable crops but rather as a means for keeping lands attractive; his phrase was "inviting for leisure use." He favored a combination of tree loving and the then lingering German concept of tree conservation by public ownership of forests and dating, ciphering, trimming, and policing each individual tree. (As I presently discovered, the armload of brochures that the secretary had dropped into my lap consisted mostly of shavings and augurings from neo-classic German forestry, which may have been just fine for Germany, on the narrowing principle that twin beds are just fine for twins.) The trees-are-keys philosophy seemed to advocate holding most potentially arable lands in trees until needed for food production; until that time, the "reserve lands" would make for engaging hobbies, both public and private. The concept was quite idyllic and beautifully worded. I listened and enjoyed, seeking to brush away images of the multitudes of increasingly needy Americans who owned no country estates, could not reasonably expect to own estates, and meanwhile were getting damn' hungry as well as extremely damn' broke.

The fact soon became apparent that F.D.R. deplored crop surpluses of any kind; he did not share or comprehend

Ford's proselytizing for more industrial or nonfood uses for food crops; he seemed to take for granted that food, like air and water, just comes free with the sunlight; the problem is to guard against too much of "any good thing." The farmers would "somehow" pull through; if they needed "relief" from government, they should receive it from government; trees, meanwhile, would safeguard future farming lands. Mr. Roosevelt apparently did not take seriously any possibilities of foreign export of American foodstuffs otherwise in surplus. By way of support he misquoted William Jennings Bryan, whom he seemed especially to revere. His reference here was to Bryan's first speech as a Nebraska congressman, in which the Boy Orator of the River Platte deplored the "dumpage" of surplus wheat into famine-stricken Russia of circa 1893.

On checking the records I found that Congressman Bryan had done or said no such thing. Actually, he had strongly advocated increased efforts to sell more of the Great Plains grain crops abroad; he objected to free gifts of western wheat to the "Czar's slaves" in lieu of legitimate sale of grains in what Bryan hopefully termed free-world markets. The Nebraskan believed and said that "dumpage without payment," along with the arbitrary, or politically expedient choice of recipients, was "wronging" the Great Plains grain farmer.

Governor Roosevelt was taking for granted that most foreign nations are capable of feeding themselves within home boundaries. He noted in passing that he regarded the long chronic grain shortages and persisting food imports by Asian, Middle Eastern, Latin American, and several European countries as only "temporary" expediences. The United States, he insisted, was obliged to protect itself from food surpluses; more trees and better forestry were the most feasible means for attaining this.

"If you were President of the United States——"

Louis Howe re-entered and stood by apologetically. "I'm really sorry to have to break up this nice party," he began, "the Governor has a commission hearing which simply cannot wait any longer."

"I'm sorry, too," F.D.R. noted somewhat fretfully. "I'm darned sick of hearings, not to mention interruptions." He gripped the forearms of his wheel chair resignedly. "Mr. Howe, I'll try my own luck at getting into that atrocious elevator, thanks just the same." The Governor turned toward me. " 'Bye, Mr. Arkansas! Come back and see us!" His pallid hands lifted in a kind of salute, which terminated abruptly when Howe began pushing the wheel chair.

His chore completed, Louis Howe rejoined me. "I am sorry the time ran out. The Governor was enjoying himself; I think he was about to tell you about the time he visited Puerto Rico when he was Assistant Secretary of the Navy." Howe paused thoughtfully. "You might care to listen in on a lecture the Governor's lady is giving in New York tomorrow night. It's to one of those beauty-parlored hen clubs known as the Junior League. If you are anything like me, that kind of business gives you the pip. However, Mrs. Roosevelt is a thinker. She reeks with bright ideas and may be able to take you on from where the boss left off."

I attended the Junior League "citizenship forum," which at first glance seemed to justify designation of an It's-Smart-To-Be-a-Thrifty-Lower-Park-Avenue-Hen Party. Eleanor, whom I had not previously seen or heard, arrived late and, it seemed to me, outrageously overdressed in a long formal white ermine cloak that grossly accentuated her bodily oversize. I liked her smile and sensed in her posture and expression an almost Lincolnlike stateliness. In the beginning her shrill, squeaky voice, much more piercing then than during her later years, was quite trying. Even so, as

Eleanor Roosevelt pressed into her discourse, her words began to shape a strange rare poetry of integrity. I jotted down her two closing sentences:

"Few revolutions have come about except as agrarian revolutions, the result of the desperation of the people on the land. Either we are going to do something about the deplorable rural poverty that prevails in most parts of this country, or else I should not be surprised to see this country in a very different situation from what we now have."

I walked out into the Manhattan night, which was steely blue and for the moment, at least to me, peculiarly revealing. Eleanor Roosevelt had spoken in her own unique voice. But her words had carried an awareness, a startling awareness, of the changing position of a materialistic, self-pampering, arbitrarily isolated nation that now would pause at least momentarily to seek self-appraisal. As an obviously pampered and wealthy matron, ensconced with inherited wealth and pre-established social prestige further amplified by shrewd, driving ambition, this figurative princess of privilege chose to address others of her kind with almost breathtaking sincerity. One could reasonably suspect that her actual acquaintance with what she termed "deplorable rural poverty" was relatively slight. She did not elaborate on the "very different situation from what we now have." Yet she showed vigorous awareness that inherited wealth and social advantage cannot endure in a resigned and enduring agrarian hellhole of poverty and despair. She was saying in her own métier that nations can survive only as people and land grow and gain in unison.

THE ROUGHHOUSE MOUSE

WHILE DRAFTING a would-be profile of a would-be President, I continued to ponder Eleanor Roosevelt's blow-hot–blow-cold lecture to the Junior League. I could not agree with her assertion that few revolutions have come about except as agrarian revolutions. Any amateur historian knows that many revolutions have been wholly or virtually entirely urban in origin; Latin America, for instances at wholesale, had scores of so-called cobblestone revolutions that began and ended quite definitively within capitals or principal cities, without any particular heed of "the people on the land." Karl Marx, the great encourager of proletariat revolutions, was restrictively a city man speaking to and seeking to influence urban industrial workers. But certainly the American Revolution was predominantly rural, at least in terms of participating personae, since perhaps 85 percent of the prevailing population was rural. But would "the deplorable rural poverty" that American government had done so appallingly little to remedy now crop into revolutionary violence? The Governor's Lady had a case here. Rural poverty in much of the nation was indeed "deplorable." Quite possibly as many country people as city people were that very night either hungry or on the verge of hunger. Farm earnings were deteriorating even faster than town incomes. On every side agricultural food production was being pauperized. American farmers had fought before and they might very well fight again.

Momentarily the best evidence in specific news was then the first impressive outcrop of "milk wars" in Wisconsin. These outbreaks were already examples of violent strife and civil insurrections. Were they real revolutions? I asked Krock to let me have a try at making a newsworthy answer. He agreed. Once more I headed west, several days late and several dollars short.

At Appleton, Wisconsin, as in nearby towns, the previously reported milk wars had subsided into grumblings, dour laments, lingering epithets, and a great deal of pathos. Occasional bands of belligerent milk farmers continued to halt trucks and dump out the cargoes of "under-priced" milk, a procedure that seemed gruesomely silly. The human casualties in the area had ceased with one man killed and four, or possibly five, seriously wounded. By way of post mortem several road crossings were being patrolled by rather seedy-looking, shabbily uniformed infantrymen of the Wisconsin Militia, who seemed to symbolize a merging of total confusion and cranial blackout. I went among the civilian soldiers, who reminded me of what I had read about Kerensky's confused followers during the incubation of the U.S.S.R., or perhaps of U.S. troops in the Boxer Rebellion in an earlier China.

One snag-toothed trooper with a lisp told me he would ga-damn sure shoot to kill "to dee-fend the flag of Wuscaunsun." But his patrolling companion at the same road crossing confided that he wasn't "out to hurt nobody a-tall." A militia officer waved aside the likelihood of bloodshed: "This is just a police detail; we have no intention of opening fire on fellow citizens." Drivers of the victim milk trucks seemed irreparably confused as to what course to take. One told me plaintively, "I got four kids and two women to feed. I only flip up the milk cans and drive the truck. If a cop says 'stop,' I stop. If a guardsman says 'stop,' I stop. If a gang of mad farmers want to dump out my milk load, like they done last Friday, they can dump ahead. I only drive a truck. . . ."

The local sheriff openly admitted that he and his four deputies were expecting more trouble with the "goosed up" milk farmers. When I inquired, "What kind of trouble?" he suggested that I might look for myself by joining him on patrol next day, beginning at 6 A.M. The night was Wiscon-

sin-cold. When the hotel switchboard operator called me at
5 A.M., I listened to a somewhat shivery female voice:
"Five o'clock and thirty-two degrees *below* zero!" Even so,
the sheriff called for me exactly as promised, but paused to
suggest that I relay his invitation to any other reporters who
were at the hotel. I knew one, Frazier "Spike" Hunt, who
was covering for Hearst magazines. When I phoned his room
the engaging Hearst man rasped, "Creeping Jesus, no! I don't
want to go out with the loony sheriff. You go right ahead
out and freeze your *tokus* off and see if I care!"

"I thought you wanted to grow up to be a reporter."

Spike's answer was tingling with profanity. "I *am* a reporter, Buster Boy, and a better one than you'll ever begin to
be. What's more, I'm a Hearst reporter, which means I can
snooze in a nice warm hotel room and imagine more than
you stupid *Times* bastards can track down in a month of
Sundays."

During the ensuing patrol I did not succeed in tracking
down any particularly notable news. The sheriff spent most
of the day paying brief pacificatory calls on milk farmers,
some of whom had participated in dumping their neighbors'
milk and practically all of whom were refusing to sell their
own "takes" to "them ga-damned distributors," thereby
leaving themselves the alternatives of spilling the milk beside the barn, feeding it to the pigs, chickens, or other livestock, or selling it to the cheese factories for even less than
the wholesalers were paying.

Their statements of grievances were touching but wholly
lacking in revolutionary intentions. They were dogged by
poverty and self-deprivations, but they did not wish to
change the "existing order," they merely wanted to "clean
up the nasty manure." They blamed politicians and
"crooked, greedy dealers" for their adversities and cruel poverty. "My wife ain't had a new hat for eight years. Last
April, when Myrtie, our frail daughter, passed on I didn't

have the cash money to buy her a decent casket. Also, I was obliged to sell off, next to give away, two good cows for to pay for the funeral, and now I got nothin' to ree-place them two cows with."

As the sheriff resumed his "patrol" I found myself deeply bewildered as well as saddened. The milk dumpage seemed totally futile. Local city markets were simply not "absorbing" and there appeared to be no competent marketing efforts. The milk dumping was bankrupting the two local wholesalers, but the farmers whose milk was being "spilt" were also being bankrupted, and certainly they had done nothing to deserve such punishment.

I reflected, too, on the American urge to respond to strife and upset by putting on uniforms and taking up firearms. What good could that do? Were the lean, grim shadows of the police state really that near at hand? The sheriff frowned his impatience at my queries. "Keep asking them fool questions and you'll have me as mixed up as you are. All I can say is, it'll eventually blow over, only don't ask me how soon or even how, on account of I don't know." After a thoughtful pause he added, "Could be us Americans just naturally enjoy a spin of hell-raising every now and then."

From the scene of one dourly confused effort to treat a food distributive malady with violence, I moved along to a stand of nonviolence. In Des Moines, Iowa, I found the way to a shakily lettered entrance sign:

NATIONAL HEADQUARTERS:
FARM HOLIDAY ASSOCIATION:
M. RENO, PRES.

The walls of the waiting room showed severe roof leakage and a series of charts indicating a rapidly growing membership in seventeen states. At a water-stained reception desk a somewhat overweight living replica of Whistler's Mother advised me that President Reno would see me "d'rectly." That noted, the receptionist returned to gulping a large chocolate-dipped doughnut. When my turn came, the receptionist took another doughnut and directed me to pass through the blue door with no knob and keep going until I found a room with no door at all. In that room I found the president of the National Farm Holiday Association, who was also munching a large chocolate-dipped doughnut.

Milo Reno was a rather handsome, middle-aged man, with hair that gave indications of having recently endured an extremely violent hurricane. He had a noble brow, deep-set blue eyes, and several extra doughnuts, which he insisted on sharing with me. Yes, indeed, he was *the* Milo Reno, the only Milo Reno he personally knew of; he was indeed the veteran organizer of farmers' parties, including the Farmers' Union, and he was currently head man of the Farmers' Holiday Association, which advocated and organized farmers' strikes or "set downs." The sense of this was "*not* to grow skin merely to get it skinned off," i.e., not to grow valid crops merely to have them dumped or burned after harvest, or leave them unharvested.

"We aren't radicals and we aren't Bolshevists," Mr. Reno further explained. "We are dirt farmers and we're asking that the people who actually grow most of the nation's food be assured of getting back at very least production costs properly computed." He raised his right hand. "We believe in the right to strike!" He got to his feet. "A strike at least gets the farmer's case and cause into headlines and to public attention. That signalizes the problem." He lowered the pitch of oratory. "There's got to be a solution by government . . . an ever-normal granary . . . a workable allotment plan . . ."

"Possibly another Sub-Treasury Plan, like the one the Populist Party advocated back in the 1890s," I suggested.

He smiled encouragingly. "Quite right, friend. But we will be coming up with our own plan, granting, of course, that whatever our plan is, there will be relentless opposition."

Reno revealed that a first condition of the oncoming plan would pay to producing farmers an "operational bonus" averaging one-third of the "base price" computed on 1914 farmside prices for valid food crops duly harvested; among these would be corn, wheat, oats, rye, soy beans, kaffirs, potatoes, and apples. Until these reasonable terms were reasonably met, participating farmers would not plant any crops or harvest those already planted.

Milo reached for another doughnut. "This is simple as spit and right as rain. Maybe not simple enough to percolate to the politicians, nor to that beetle-brained Hoover Farm Board that's too dismal stupid to see that it's people, good, able, hardworking farmers, that feed all people." Mr. Reno banged his desk with his right fist, barely missing the remaining doughnuts. "It's farmers—not land, not bank notes nor mortage papers; not politicians, not perfessors nor Presidents—that conjure food nurture for the human race."

I asked how the millrun consumers, great numbers of them already ill fed, could endure a food growers' strike of unpredictable duration. How could food processors, the prevailing majority of comparatively small packers, canners, millers, and the like, for the most part already staggering from hard times, survive a farmer's strike, and if they should survive, how would they regain their relinquished markets? "Not incidentally, since when can food production be cut off and turned on like a well-behaved water faucet? And speaking of farm holidays, down in the Arkansas Ozarks we've been having a farm holiday—at least in terms of at-

tainable production—for generations. It hasn't helped anybody to date; our region is rife with hungry people in towns
and country alike. How——"

Milo Reno smiled wearily, "Take another doughnut,
friend. Take dang near all the doughnuts. It helps to eat
away the dadgummed surpluses."

THE BELLY BARD

NEXT MORNING at the Morning Glory Tourist
Motel I stopped by the Coffee Shoppe for the
Twenty-three-Cent Bre'kfuss Special, which ended with an
amiable chat with a lank, toothpick-munching individual
who seemed to have been riveted behind the cash register.
When I handed him a quarter he viewed it dejectedly:
"Looks like you got the axe. Them that takes the Special
are generally out of work."

Farther south, at a cemetery corner near the Missouri
boundary, I stopped to pick up a gently gesticulating hitch-
hiker. When I inquired where he was going, the slender,
staring man said he was going whichever way I was going. "I
am a poet," he explained, "I am Vachel Lindsay, Poet of
America."

As he climbed into the seat beside me I inquired, "How
do you find the food these days?"

"I ask for it." The Poet of America gestured with his
graceful hands. "But I *never* ask at restaurants. Even when
I can afford them I can't *bear* the commercial eating
places. In traveling I keep away from the cities and the railroads. I carry no baggage and no money. At about eleven in
the morning I ask for lunch or dinner. At around five in the

afternoon I ask for supper, night's lodging, and breakfast. I travel alone. I keep civil and neat and preach the gospel of beauty."

"How do you find the picking up during these Depression times?"

"Generally ruinous, like in non-Depression times, but with some noble exceptions," he responded. "Let me begin with a noble exception or two. Logging camps frequently serve good food. Fishing schooners and riverboats sometimes serve good food. Threshing crews sometimes get good food. But cafes and tea rooms . . . God forbid! American eating has been barbarianed by tabs and bills and checks and salesmanship. Its only hope is in the freely given.

"I have eaten with prospectors," continued the poet from Springfield, Ohio. "Prospectors' biscuits! Curled-top, quartz-like, monstrous things. With them go salt pork, strong-flavored and nipping, coffee black and steaming with fierceness, and beans hard and crackling from high-altitude boiling. Our fruits and melons taste best when filched; the fruits I most favor are apples and peaches from irrigated orchards. They are sweet with penetrating, wonderful juices. Western cooking is harlotry in a frying pan."

"What do you think about Southern cooking?"

I watched the poet's features stiffen with horror. "God forbid!" he choked, then repeated more clearly, "God forbid and save us from such a horrible fate!" He next spoke of restaurant fare in the Border South: the greasy soups, the lard-coated sweet potatoes, the soggy cornbread, the sow's belly, the undercooked beans and the overcooked greens. His distress deepened; he repeated that the preponderance of Americans have been horribly badly fed all along. "Don't you like the fried catfish—first dipped in corn meal?" I asked. "And the roasted 'possum with sweet potatoes? Or the big white-and-yellow chunks of peach cobbler?"

I felt an abrupt tug at my sleeve. "You are making me

distinctly ill!" The Poet of America tugged at my sleeve again. "When you get to St. Louis, kindly let me go free. I have a friend there who keeps a restaurant but cooks for himself at home. He calls me his belly bard. I call him my belly savior. Both of us have found that the dinner plate is our world; on the dinner plate are our special hosts of jubilation."

I watched the amazing man stroll down a rain-misted alleyway, then spent the next two hours with another lonely poet, the city editor of the *St. Louis Post-Dispatch*. He had told me how his work-littered desk had grown to be his own very special St. Louis. On that desk top the entire city lived, loved, worked, and died, sometimes violently. Every auto wreck or truck collision or holdup or purse snatch, every parade or convention, every brawl or celebration or wake, every homicide or fist fight, every fire or riot—he had learned to see them all on that desk, within arm's reach.

"Your cue is to make the whole of the United States your desk top," he told me. "When you've attained that, the world will be your desk top. These United States, for better or worse, are really the world of our century—like Rome was in the first century before Christ; like the British Empire was during the nineteenth century; like Russia may be by the end of the twentieth; or as now-colonial Africa may be in the next century. Like Ford said, farming is farming the world over, like food is food, and hunger is hunger. Newswise, it's all for the same copy desk."

From among the tumblings of empty bellies and frustrated food production, I resolved to have a firsthand look at what remained a comparative horn of plenty: the unrelenting cornucopia of Kansas wheat. In quest of expert counsel I headed first for Emporia and the editor-publisher of one of the more competent western newspapers.

There was no problem about finding one's way to the

Emporia Gazette; it was just one block off Main Street, practically within spitting distance of the boxlike Broadview Hotel. In the entranceway of the Gazette building a pink lithograph of the Grand Canyon of the Colorado pointed the way to the editor's office.

A plump, white-haired, sunburned man with doll-blue eyes peered up at me through small, frameless spectacles and followed along to another pinkish lithograph, of a prairie schooner that seemed to be on the verge of tumbling into a broom closet.

"So you've come to see William Allen White and Kansas. Well, I'm Bill White and you're more than welcome to see me, though, speaking for Kansas, you've picked a hell of a time to look her over. You now behold my beloved Kansas mortified by running out of water and pregnant with still another hundred-million-bushel wheat crop. However, if you happen to be looking for a place that will never abide any form of agricultural birth control, you've damn sure found it."

The speaker's revolving chair squeaked loudly and the jacket of his white suit appeared to be at the verge of snapping buttons from being so very full of William Allen White. "Eighteen sizable towns already fresh out of water," he resumed. "Drought's beginning to give away to dust storms. Still and even so, there's enough wheat 'ready yellowing to founder grain markets, if there should be any left, from Wichita to Hong Kong. But such is Kansas, whose story I can recite in precisely two minutes if you would hear it."

When I nodded, he drew a deep breath and began: "The guts of this story aren't here; they're in and of west Kansas. The great wheat country is west Kansas. It's fighting country. Its war is people and wheat against weather—averaging about three drought years out of five, or two killer droughts every five years. The victor is wheat, millions on millions of acres; a whole damn' beautiful ocean of wheat. At threshing time in a fair crop year the whole countryside smells like a vast ovenful of hot, fresh-baked bread.

"West Kansas was opened mostly in the 1880s. The first lines of settlers tried the so-called spring wheat. There just isn't enough rain, including winter snow, to make crop with that kind of wheat. So the first lines of wheat farmers went down like infantry before machine-gun fire. Droughts, of course, were the machine guns. But they couldn't mow down all the infantry. The survivors got up and went at it again.

"Then the Mennonites came in. They had already learned the hardy merits of winter wheat—fall planted, with harvests in the beginning of summer. That kind takes advantage of winter rain and snow, gives a two- or three-out-of-five chance for making a crop. So a new wave went out to play the game of winter wheat. It, too, was a rough game. Drought met 'em. Sun seared 'em. But enough of their cattle could live on native grass to give them meat and a little milk to go with their bread. And God knows there was land! From one to a dozen sections for everybody who could take or even ask it."

The narrator swatted a fly with a copy of the first bulldog edition. An incredibly small telegram boy spilled his bicycle at the front door. "Western Union," he shouted. Bill White seemed totally disinterested in telegrams. "Then came the big wheat rush of the '90s. Gold in Alaska, diamonds in South Africa, McKinley in the White House, Republicans in luck. Folks who came West to buy a section of wheat land took two or three sections instead. And there were three bumper wheat crops in a row! That started the Kansas wheat-land boom—including the portfolio towns. The tidal wave of settlers drew out county maps on wrapping paper with lead pencils. Then they bonded the pencil-and-paper counties, built courthouses miles from nowhere. Some of the wheat towns turned out to be ghosts before they got built, leaving their bloody courthouses to stand out like carbuncles on the flat prairies and their hotbox hotels waiting to be burned for the insurance. Nobody needed the towns.

"Wheat was the real settler of Kansas, and, by God, wheat still is. Meaning, of course, that the Kansans are wheat-minded. You can beat 'em unconscious, prostrate 'em with the heat, but next year they'll plant more goddamn wheat than ever, and the year after that they will try for the all-time record. You can send the militia after 'em. They'll burrow up in sand piles, peep out of the dust, thumb their noses, and plant more wheat. So I say, 'Who the hell will ever control wheat crops in Kansas?' "

We strolled out into the blistering sun, loaded into Mr. White's black Packard, and proceeded to the immense brick box that was the Whites' house. "Sure, another drought is beginning to scorch our breeches. But we've still got the wheat crop. Neither this nor any other Western state has a climate that's literally, or even close to being uniform from one boundary to the next. As usual, we've got dry stretches where the wheat is thin and less dry places where the earth sinks under the new harvest. The world beyond here is like that, but here in Kansas, wheat in outrageous amounts is our life."

Bill White indicated his philosophical mood by lowering his spectacles almost to the tip of his nose and reclining in an overstuffed easy chair. He repeated that in Kansas, both over and under the wheat, the persisting and dominant "spirit" remained a lust for productiveness, a lust to grow one hell of a lot of grain to fill one hell of a lot of bellies. He repeated that the oncoming Kansas wheat crop, estimated as 100 million bushels, could unquestionably snarl up and sag down all the wheat markets from Chicago to Caledonia. But Kansas would keep up its orgy of wheat growing through fifty years after hell froze over. He called Kansas farming an annual pregnancy that simply would not be "sublimated." He believed that environment, above all else, sustains the will to change handfuls of grain to hundred-pound bagsful. Barring as many miracles as there are seed grains, Kansas would never go hungry or willfully conspire to permit anybody else to go hungry.

PLAINS OF DESPAIR

AS I journeyed on through western Kansas, the big harvest was begun. Great heading reapers, for the most part tractor drawn, were wallowing through the gold-topped tides of wheat like mechanized multi-ton monsters. I reflected that, given one Kansas in every principal nation, hunger ought to be as unknown as throwing bricks at grandmothers. I was also reminded by a cautiously meditative wheat farmer that a rainfall margin of approximately two inches frequently made the difference between a "bin buster" of a crop and a "dry draw." A belated, despaired-of half-inch rain had made possible the seeding and sprouting of the present crop. Subsequent winter snow and late winter showers had held the total precipitation just a hair above the vegetative lifeline for wheat. By the end of May the year's rain tally had reached approximately fourteen inches. Early June had brought another inch; even so, the total was barely half of the assumed water requirement for mixed-crops farming. The earth's message seemed to be that if man is to survive, he will do so with crops that make the best possible use of water.

On driving north into the Dakotas, I began meeting a seared and writhing earth that the rain gods had chosen to disdain. Seven years earlier, in 1924, the Dakota plains had greened with what the settlers had termed "normal" rain, an average of twenty-four inches. Then the long drought cycle began; since 1929 the Dakotas' average rainfall had slipped to eight inches, very near to what is commonly termed "total desert conditions."

By open admission the planted crops, mostly kaffirs, wheat, and barley, were going to hell in a saddlebag. I saw very few saddlebags, but despite the blowing dust I could see many horses equipped not with saddles or accompanying gear but with goggles or especially designed sunglasses. "We're too pore to buy sunglasses for ourselfs," a sad-faced cattle farmer assured me. "In this hell-weather, goggles don't benefit people too much nohow. But hosses soon blind away without 'em."

Horses were not all that were blinding away. The Dakotas' cattle population had already fallen to about a fourth of its 1924 totals and in due time would drop to an eighth. Sheep holdings were about one-fifth those of 1924 ("normal rainfall level") and the wheat yields were averaging about one-sixth. During the intervening seven years about a third of the Dakotas farmers had moved away; now, in 1932, about three-fourths of all farm lands in North Dakota were tax delinquent, and the delinquency score for South Dakota was only slightly better.

As anyone could see, the land-use practices had proved no real match for the drought cycles. Back in the 1880s, when these dry cold-and-hot frontiers were being settled, 640 acres, or one square mile, was the medium homestead size. By the never realistic tactics of dryland farming, one plowed under the sod, left half his acreage to "ketch water," and "grained" the other half. When the procedure proved suited only to supporting jack rabbits, gophers, and occasional open-range sheep, the Department of the Interior authorized and encouraged doubling the acreages of homesteads and the realtors followed suit, upping the medium to around 1,280 acres, two square miles. But when the short-grass prairie was destroyed and the distinctly addled procedures of half-and-half dryland farming were instituted, the "half-and-half spreads" were still far short of being adequate protection against the wrath of recurring droughts.

The farming ledgers simply would not show anything but telltale red. As Fred Symonds, the Bismarck newspaper publisher who would shortly flower as Dakotas counselor of the Roosevelt Administration, assured me, "If anybody should ever succeed in balancing any bloody books around here, these Dakotas will be just hell out of luck. Hereabouts, there are no break-evens left."

Quite undeniably, the brave dreams of earlier Dakotas settlers were blowing away in harsh, far-lifted dust that was clogging human lungs and auto carburetors, even while brushing aside the ever shaky theories of dryland farming. I pondered the likelihood that the plight of the Dakotas was one with counterparts on every continent of the earth and in scores of other countries. Their recurring paradox—of being listed as food-producing lands although most of the time they were not—struck me as typifying the nagging lack of dependability of farm statistics as a far-flung and too often direly misleading whole. Again and again I was viewing great areas where a reasonably capable man, working from dawn to dark, could literally starve on a thousand acres of duly listed farm lands. Here successive and merciless drought was the master enforcer of scarcity and accruing famine. But, as usual, there was man-caused and man-permitted hunger. My next assignment led me into a historic instance.

FOOD RIOT, U.S.A.

BACK IN Arkansas in 1932, the handling or mis-handling of state credit had thrown the "Wonder State" into renewed disrepute. A dour governor had recently asserted that Arkansas would not "be held responsible" for a $100-million highway bond issue that the previous administration had authorized and let be sold. Brokers were crying fraud and bewailing the plights of their clients, whom they tended to picture as hungering widows and starving children of nobly intentioned purchasers who had already recorded their inner emotions by dry-diving from high windows.

On both sides the background was baffling, cynical, and reported with outrageous disregard of the facts. To make the acrimonious fog even denser, the political "in's" had set up what was laughably termed a highway audit commission, which was using state's money to vilify the outgoing highway commission, all it had done, and all its principals. There were complexly interrelated side brawls that were further complicated by the continuing collapse of banks; at the time, Arkansas was leading the entire nation in number and proportion of bank failures.

As usual, my own situation tended to parallel the plight of a backhill juror in my home county who had confided: "Ef I believed what that prosecutor man says, I'd vote to hang the dee-fendant; ef I believed the dee-fense, I'd vote to turn him free. But bein' as how I don't believe a damn word either one of 'em says, I jest don't know what the hell to do." A *Gazette* editor suggested that some adequate meals could hugely improve the entire state, since most of the roars were in fact belly rumbles.

After spending most of a month striving to comprehend the mélange of half-truths, tenth-truths, and absolute prevarications (not incidentally, Arkansas did not renege on its highway bonds), I found myself still neck-deep in rumors, for the most part as polluted and ill-odored as the dirty brown Arkansas River.

They included prophecies of "lynchin' parties," though by then Arkansas had gone nearly five years without a mob homicide—the latest, in 1927, had been a broad-daylight lynching of a Negro in downtown Little Rock. However, some of the local newspaper men, who in the main were far more trustworthy than their respective newspapers, held the consensus that the rapidly worsening Depression would shortly be incubating racial violence. About 70 percent of all Arkansans lived on farms, and approximately half of them were cotton sharecroppers. More and more white "croppers" were taking over the better cotton lands formerly worked by Negro tenants. Some of the men were almost certain that white tenants would shortly be banding together to "scare the niggers off the land"; and the Negroes might not scare easily.

One dismal afternoon I received a cryptic phone call from Ellis Huff, the state editor of the *Gazette*. He suggested that I "light a shuck" for England, Arkansas, explaining that a "blowup" had occurred without forewarning.

At the time England was a rather morbid country town in the sharecropping country, about thirty miles from Little Rock. I went by rented auto, expecting to encounter a race riot; instead, I arrived on the late side of a food riot, which the Associated Press and International News Service presently listed, correctly or otherwise, as the nation's first recorded food riot.

Earlier in the day a crowd of country people, in greater part white sharecroppers, had assembled near the town and "made a march" on the larger of the general stores. They had stolen no money and broken no locks. Instead, they had made a mass entry and methodically looted the shelves and storage room of groceries, an estimated four thousand dollars' worth, along with several hundred dollars' worth of bolt cloth and readymade clothing and shoes. The "mob" was variously estimated as between two hundred and three hundred men and boys, but no Negroes participated.

The sheriff had reached the scene while the looting was still in progress, but explained that by then it was too far progressed to halt or quell. No, he hadn't made any attempts at arresting any of the leaders. He was far from certain there had been leaders; the looters had emptied the shelves on an each-for-himself basis, and the fracas appeared to have been quite spontaneous. Yes, the sheriff and his deputy had recognized some of the participants; all he personally knew were sharecroppers or other down-and-outers of nearby country. "They come hungry, they pilfered, and I expect by now they've et and fed their chillun and womenfolks," he summarized.

I sought out the proprietor, who still wandered about dazedly trying to count his losses. He confirmed that he had not been robbed of money. "Mostly they only looted eatables—practically all my canned goods, all the flour and meal and cereals and tinned meats, including sardines and salmon." He added that he, too, recognized many of the takers, that he had pled with them to "bee-have," reminding them he had never wronged them and had always treated them like friends and customers are supposed to be treated. "Still and all, they went right ahead and ruint me."

The sheriff helped himself to a big yellow apple that, presumably by oversight, had been left unmolested. "These ain't criminals," he repeated. "And I damn sure couldn't jest start shootin' 'em down like stray dawgs. Mostly they was home people, meanin' naturally they got no money. Most is tabbed up to the eyeballs with debts. They was fresh out of eatables and wearables, so they jest ganged up and took what they couldn't buy. Last two years the cotton crop hereabouts got bitched by droughts and whenever it rained, like everybody knows, cotton prices skidded to hell and six feet lower. Sharecroppers got no money and lots of the landlords can't borry none."

He repeated that as yet he had no intentions of making arrests. He insisted it was pointless merely to take in, say, one or two in a hundred. "Why should I? There ain't no money for holdin' trials with. That there's the case all over Arkansas and a lot further. And like I say, these people that done the ransackin' ain't the ones truly at fault. They worked their crops and didn't make nothin' except a little cotton they damn sure can't eat. Now they can't get money for it and the stores has quit givin' credit. These croppers, and by that I mean most of them, don't get land for gardens, ain't permitted to have pigs or hens or milk cows. All I'm blamin' is this ga-damned lousy setup of sharecroppin'. It just ain't right, and what's happened here is only wall-writin' that tells of wrongness past and trouble to come."

The sheriff repeated that this "ruckus" did not deserve "pointing up" as peculiar to Arkansas. He believed it might have happened anywhere that any substantial number of people were going hungry. He doubted that this was actually the first American food riot, and predicted vehemently that it would not be the last.

The sheriff's discourse regarding the excessive number of

sharecroppers impressed me as much more significant than the pathetic, overplayed story of our nation's "first hunger riot," for his denunciation of what he termed "mule-whip tenantry" rang with confirmable pertinency. Tenantry in the United States is much older than the nation. In Colonial times the preponderance of white American farmers, which some estimate as high as 85 percent of the total, were renters or tenants. The percentage was not greatly reduced during the first half-century of "independence." In 1816, when James Monroe, the former governor of Virginia and U.S. Secretary of State, led in crushing the Federalist Party and scoring the nearest to unanimous vote ever attained by a U.S. Presidential candidate, that remarkable Virginian described his fellow citizens fractionally, as one-third free, one-third slave, and one-third indentured or freed Negroes— and also as four-fifths farmers and three-quarters "renting farmers." The Civil War found the U.S. population still more than two-thirds rural, and more than half of those were renters rather than owners of the land they farmed. A full century after the American Revolution, and quite regardless of the "opening" of the West, an impressive majority of U.S. farmers were still tenants. The ratio held firmly until the years of the First World War, when farm tenanting in the United States began slowly to lose ground.

By 1930 about four out of every ten active farms in the U.S. were being rented. In the South as a whole, more than half of all farmers were still tenants, for the most part sharecroppers; the proportion in Georgia, Mississippi, and South Carolina was near 75 percent. Even in the more prolific farming states, including then "champion" Iowa (California is now our Number One), the tenantry ratio was close to a third. Could Depression-stagnant farming continue to pay the tolls of tenantry? There was strengthening evidence that it could not.

However, the burden of tenantry was still more or less worldwide. As of 1930, 90 percent of all active farms in the United Kingdom were tenant kept. Even in "wide open" Australia the ratio was 78 percent; in grass-happy Argentina, 40 percent; for Western Europe as a whole, around about 33 percent. Of all the principal farming nations, only four— Canada, Norway, Sweden, and Denmark—had markedly reduced their tenantry rates during the previous decade. In nations such as Mexico and Finland, the earlier shapes of national agrarian laws were beginning to emerge as way openers to dividing "stagnant" estates among working farmers. In Soviet Russia the state-owned collective farm was gaining scope and effectiveness but was still under siege of challenge and question, with many commentators asserting that the Kremlin's socialization of land was succeeding only in making all participants the equivalent of renters without privilege of management, or of even minimal participation in management.

Particularly in Germany, Holland, Belgium, and Poland, government efforts to assure tenants compensation for efforts or successes in soil improvements and maintenance of farm buildings and equipment were proving effective; "justice for tenant farmers" had long been a political tagline and in some part a *fait accompli* in the British Isles.

In all, a gathering of noteworthy generalities was gaining substance. The world at large was still hardly within radio distance of being a yeoman's world—if "yeoman" is taken to mean a freeholding farmer. Even so, there was a growing acceptance of the public weal advantages of permitting the food grower to own the land he tilled. Except in the colonial and Communist countries, farm tenantry was losing ground; at very least it was on the defensive, if not actually on its last legs. Consensus that the producing farmer was sufficiently burdened without dividing his harvest with a landlord was steadily gaining. Here again the United States was not leading, but we were beginning to follow. In many other respects, and with increasing clarity, agriculture was beginning to respond to international trends, whether encouraging or dispiriting. No seventh son of a seventh son, or other extrasensory prophetic gift was required to reveal that the 1930s were already taking form as a most definitive decade for agriculture. It was high time. In many nations, including substantial areas of our own, the chill, grim shadows of hunger were growing more chill and more grim.

ANOTHER PROPHET ARISES

AS THE early 1930s stumbled along, the paradoxes of food supplying grew more conspicuous and ever more international. As the world leader in terms of total tonnages of farm-grown foods, the United States was also well along in volume, immediacy, and total outrageousness of food-producing paradoxes. As of 1931 the nation had more than twice the now current total of operative farms— about 7.2 million, against an estimated 3.45 million as this book is written. By the end of 1931 the United States had more than a billion acres of farm lands in production, and the world's highest ratio of cultivated food crops per capita; in much of the country grain elevators and other food storages were crammed to overflowing; in instance after instance there was simply no space for the new harvests. Practically any traveler could see food crops waiting and rotting unharvested because, at least for the time being, they were not salable and could not be stored. Here and there corn was being burned in lieu of coal.

For most of the nation there was plenty of land, more than plenty of farmers; a U.S. Department of Agriculture survey completed in March 1932 indicated that between 800,000 and 1 million additional Americans were "going back to land." In "fat land" regions, particularly in the Midwest and Great Plains, there was a straining abundance of already produced foods. Yet never before were so many of our people going hungry or ill fed.

There had to be reasons for this most dispiriting maze of contradictions. The most conspicuous was the catapulting number of factory stacks without smoke; the industrial payrolls were collapsing, and at least for the time we did not have a blazing foreign war to revive them.

For great numbers the traditional American routine of leaving the farm to seek gainful employment in the city was being reversed. The ensuing migrations were demonstrating once more that the widespread movements of people usually worsen the supplying of food. Great numbers of rural people continued to venture out in quest of jobs in towns or on the road. In most instances they returned to their homelands even poorer than when they had left them.

In time most of the returners were finding that hustling one's food from Uncle Rufe's abandoned homestead is no bed of roses. Others were confirming that the surest way to eat well was to find work in a successful shop or factory, if that were possible. And while industrial payrolls were still downward bound, farm earnings were keeping far below them. By December 1930, when unemployment passed the 15-million mark, the national average of annual earnings from growing principal crops was barely $8 an acre; at least temporarily, average U.S. farm incomes were about only $400 per year per family.

The argument that a family was better off growing its own food collided with other contradicting realities. Living on hurriedly planted gardens and wild strawberries, with an occasional boiled rabbit, sucker fish, or squirrel stew on the side, was less than idyllic and far short of being dependable. But the prevailing occupational upsets and the uncertainty of the hoped-for reopening of the assembly plant, or machine shop or mill or factory, made the difficulties of a retreat to the land even more formidable. However humble or compelled, a farm establishment cannot be vacated like a hotel room or an overnight guest house.

Though the provable effects of weather on food production are almost habitually exaggerated, for several regions of the United States incompatible weather continued to be a dogging aggravation; most evidently, the droughts were not preventing the decimation of farm incomes. The closing 1920s had shown distinguishable beginnings of what lingered as a prolonged and spreading drought cycle. This had emerged strongly in the Southwest and upper Great Plains during 1929; during 1930 it had spread over some twenty states, including most of the Great Plains, the western South, and the Border South. The encroachments continued throughout 1931, with the first development of extensive dust bowls, principally along the Great Plains fringes of the Rockies. The rapacious dry-land grain farming of the First World War period was still dealing its lung-clogging aftermaths. Reddish dust, blown from Colorado and adjoining grassless plateaus, was literally falling on the national capital.

But the berserk weather was but one lesser aggravation. Great droughts, like major floods, had molested many times before, and interstate dust storms had been graphically recorded as long before as 1816, the calamitous "year without a summer."

Inevitably, the newspaper trades were feeling their share of the cruelly hard times. One moderate and inconsequential item of evidence was my own finding that the *Times* had chosen to relegate its misfit from Arkansas to a distinctly thin spot as an "area correspondent" for the western South. That provided both the time and need for my seeking additional outlets for my reportorial efforts. Surprisingly, a first taker turned out to be *Wallace's Farmer*, a self-termed "weekly farm newspaper" published in Des Moines.

"Uncle Henry" Wallace, who had founded the weekly magazine back in the 1870s, had been a country preacher and self-made Bible scholar before going into publishing. His editorials invariably opened with a quotation from the Scriptures and usually closed with an exhortation to do right by others. Preacher Wallace's son, also named Henry, whom some remembered as Harding's Republican Secretary of Agriculture, had prospered as editor-publisher and changed the solemn weekly tract to a substantial wealth-earner. The second Henry's son, Henry Agard Wallace, shortly to be F.D.R.'s Democratic Secretary of Agriculture and presently Vice-President, had temporarily left the paper to go to college and major in plant genetics. After a stint of teaching at Iowa State and joining in a hybrid corn seed business that would presently make him well-to-do, young Henry had succeeded his father as editor-publisher of *Wallace's Farmer*, which had already sagged dangerously. In the 1928 campaign the dissenting and uncombed third Henry Wallace had supported the losing cause of Alfred E. Smith, an action that did not benefit the family magazine. Even so, *Wallace's Farmer* somehow managed to stay alive and keep on preaching.

In the course of a brief pilgrimage to Des Moines, the managing editor, Donald Murphy, whom I instantly liked, confided that his boss was "out and around politicking" but in due course would look me up. From Iowa, I returned to my parents' home near Fayetteville, and there set up working headquarters in the attic.

This led to my first emphatic disagreement with my father. I was obliged to have a telephone installed. My father, who regarded the contraptions as unsafe and dangerous, was against it. But with my mother's devoted support I nevertheless got a telephone installed. The first incoming call was from Donald Murphy of *Wallace's Farmer*. "My boss and I drove down to check on your purple prose. We've found it generally accurate," he said reassuringly. "But I should tell you the boss thinks you're tending to soft-pedal. He sees this famine deal down here as absolutely catastrophic and wants to talk with you right away."

The transient managing editor explained that they were camping in a mountaintop cabin a couple of miles from Fayetteville. There I found Don Murphy, garbed in a business suit that appeared to have been slept in for several restless nights, and preoccupied with swatting wasps with a tightly rolled copy of *Wallace's Farmer*. In the smokier corner of the room a slender, narrow-shouldered, tousled-headed figure, clad only in underwear shorts, was stooping over a badly misbehaving kerosene range. Without looking up, he commanded me to be seated, apparently without having noticed there were no chairs. "The beans are almost cooked," he added, "and we'll have us a feast."

With a rather loud sigh Don Murphy began improvising a table with two orange crates and searching a littered corner for some wooden boxes. "Have a chair!" Henry Wallace repeated, his voice again changing quite surprisingly from self-assured baritone to a squeaky, almost pre-pubescent tenor. He next produced three paper plates and began loading each with a slice of rye bread almost covered with canned beans. He sampled the intemperately hot beans, frowning darkly. Between bites he began recounting that he and his companion had found hard-times cases far more extreme than any I had listed. He had observed many malnourished children. "We ran across a Negro family practically starved," he recounted. "We brought 'em six dollars' worth of groceries and darned if they didn't gulp down the whole boxful before we were out of sight."

Murphy recalled that only a half-hour's drive from where we were, he and his boss had met a distressed "backhiller," who explained that he had fifteen calves that were practically starving and therefore was "hurtin' " to sell the whole lot for fifty dollars. "The boss suggested that we drive into Fayetteville and see if we could find a bank that would lend the poor Joe some money to buy some feed with. So what happened? Well, that thus-and-so of a banker took down the backwoodsman's name and address, then cruised out and bought up the little herd for a lousy fifty dollars. Figured he could turn a fast dollar by reselling them."

Young Wallace's frown deepened. He gulped the remainder of his open bean sandwich and began stating what he termed his "special pitch." Iowa grain elevators and grain buyers were "glutted" with old storages of wheat and oats and shelled corn. Without buyers, the potato storages were similarly crowded to the ceilings. He believed that many of the Iowa farmers would welcome a chance to give away their "stagnant surpluses."

"How's the best way to get the glut stuff down here?" he demanded.

Don Murphy swallowed diligently. "I've told you at least ten times; the railroads have been authorized to give free haulage—frankage, that is—for relief foodstuffs. I'm sure the cooperatives would take over the loading out. The National Red Cross would do best as distributors. We could begin with a trial shipment of, say, ten carloads of mixed grains and two of potatoes. We could pick out six of the worst-off counties down here, and consign each a couple of carloads, care of the county Red Cross chairman."

Young Henry Wallace viewed his assistant approvingly, like a tense professor weighing a bright student's recitation. "You understand I'm only suggesting a trial shipment," Murphy continued. "If it works out, God knows there's plenty where that came from. I'll bet we could recruit five hundred carloads in a week."

Wallace was nodding with great vehemence. He questioned me on what I knew about the American Red Cross. I answered that the career employees seemed exceptionally competent and I liked what I saw of the local county chairman.

The senior host wagged a finger at me. "If we try this, will you follow through and report on what happens?" I said I would be glad to.

Don Murphy had begun recalling the principles of earlier proposals for distributing foodstuffs to the hungry. He mentioned the platform of the Agricultural Wheel, as devised in a country schoolhouse near Beebe, Arkansas, back in 1890; then recounted the 1892 Sub-Treasury Plan of the then new Populist Party, which, led by General James Weaver, had actually polled more than a million votes.

"The choice is between agriculture birth control and artificial transfusion of foodstuffs," Henry Wallace summarized firmly. With that he got to his feet and pumped my hand rather violently. "See you later. Keep alert."

About two weeks later I watched the arrival at Springfield, Missouri, of the first six carloads of the giveaway surpluses from Iowa. A Red Cross representative from national headquarters was on hand to receive the shipments. He had mapped out a distribution plan that included a mixed carload assignment to a siding in the mountainous backwoods of lower Washington County, Arkansas. He suggested that I ride the car, more literally the caboose, to the destination in the area of Winslow, and help the county Red Cross chairman distribute it. "I predict you'll find plenty of takers," he added prophetically, and pointed out that he had chosen the discharge site because the rough mountain country had been relying almost wholly on the now collapsing hardwood trade.

I viewed the reloading of a "relief" car with twenty-five tons of shelled corn in hundred-pound bags, about ten tons of oats in fifty-pound bags, and storage potatoes in the rest of the space. Late the following day the local freight deposited the food car none too gently on a siding near a mountainside hamlet: Brentwood, Arkansas. The depot, not much bigger than an old-fashioned privy, was already surrounded with people, for the most part ragged, sunburned men and lanky youths in faded and patched dungarees. Several of the men were carrying double-bitted axes, then standard equipment for free-lancing tie hacks; their earnings ranged from about fifteen cents a day to nothing.

I had no way of knowing how many of the standers-by were local residents, or which ones were family heads, or who had livestock to feed. The instructions were to issue an additional hundredweight of shelled corn and a bag of oats to livestock owners and to distribute the potatoes among the family heads when "call tickets" previously issued by the county Red Cross chairman were presented. Others were to receive their choice of one bag of corn or two of oats. But nothing was to be given out until the county chairman arrived.

Only a few of the not especially patient waiters had received tickets, and quite obviously the car did not hold enough to accommodate all who had come to receive. When I suggested that all wait the arrival of the Red Cross man, I heard a chorus of protests; some had already been waiting since early morning, and those who would be obliged to carry home their share wished to get going while there was still daylight. I noticed there were only a few wagons at hand, and no more than a half-dozen or so bony horses, mostly saddleless, and only one visible auto, a badly battered pickup truck with a roughly lettered sign on its backgate: JESUS SAVES.

A tall ax-man stalked toward the loading door, which was hasped and padlocked. "You aim to open hit, or do we bust hit open?"

I repeated that I would open the car just as soon as the Red Cross chairman arrived, but I heard my final words being punctuated with ax blows. Another ax-man trotted to the door and joined in an extremely effective job of chopping around the hasp base, avoiding the metal facing and thereby cutting away the lock.

Seconds later they pushed the door open. The fierce rush began. When I tried to quell the stampede with assurances that everyone would get a fair share if only the crowd would wait turns, I was shoved aside with such violence that I lost my balance. As I tried to rise, a skinny citizen tottering beneath two hundred-pound grain bags fell over me. I saw red blotches and felt a succession of heavy feet stamping my chest. When I tried crawling away, I saw an auto with a Red Cross emblem on its door bounding up the rutted hillside road. By then it was too late for any further attempt to distribute the cargo equitably; the strongest were taking away the most. I stumbled toward the auto, thankful for having survived my first direct entanglement with the brute force of hungry people.

I recall waking next day most unhappily in a hospital bed, head throbbing, chest stiff as a clay tile, eyes smarting violently. Somewhat dimly I made out the barrel-like form and the expansive grin of old Doc Gregg. He was speaking in his usual sepulchral bedside voice. "Nice going, Buster Boy! Your squirrel-chaser cronies sure gave you the business. Two broken ribs, a dislocated shoulder, and enough bruises to color a two-bit eggplant. And those orbs of yours are red as the tail lights of my autymobile. Along with other donations you've picked up a lulu of a case of the pinkeye." He opened his bag and took out an oversize eyedropper. "Steady now, beautiful redeyes!"

Before I took leave of the hospital Matt Reynolds, the county Red Cross chairman, dropped in to see how I was "farin'." He explained that he had no funds for paying hospital or medical bills for well-intentioned volunteers, but that he was awarding me a pocketful of "give orders"; any time I came on a needy case, I had authority to write out an order for gift food.

"I expect you regard all this as being something new and unusual. Well, it's not. What we've both been seeing is certain to happen again; God knows there've been hungry people in these parts as long as I can remember. When the Depression eases, I predict the return of normal hard times. However, I'm absolutely convinced our children, certainly our grandchildren, will be growing up in a world with hunger on practically every side."

NEW DEAL FOR AGRICULTURE

HUNGRY MONTHS followed hungry months. In measure of public heed the Border South and from West Virginia to Oklahoma (most particularly Arkansas) continued to get the hunger headlines, but hundreds of cities and towns were being obliged to sustain the bread lines. The sad, people-rotting affliction continued. There were many self-proclaimed doctors but as yet no widely proved remedy.

The revolt against the dreary presidency of Herbert Clark Hoover and company was duly expressed by the landslide election of Franklin D. Roosevelt, the engaging promiser from Albany, Hyde Park, and better-heeled Manhattan. The "New Deal," as a taglining replacement for an earlier Roosevelt's "Square Deal," promptly turned to agriculture as a primary field for the seeding and harvesting of votes. Early in 1933 the already announced New Deal for Agriculture began emerging as a potpourri of rather direct lifts from already effected moves by other governments to participate directly in farm planning and, less directly in most instances, in the processing and distributing of foodstuffs. The lifts were being mixed, in some instances quite bafflingly, with various themes and credos from earlier American sources. The real importance, many scholars believed, was not so much in precedences as in a first direct governmental participation in agriculture and disposal of harvests. But the Roosevelt choice of Henry Agard Wallace as his Secretary of Agriculture offered no implicit clarification.

In unimportant parallel, there was no announced purpose for my assignment to Washington duty by *The New York Times*. Arthur Krock had succeeded in finding (his term was "stirring up") some work for me in connection with the immediately oncoming Rooseveltian take-over, then being labeled by some of the working press as the Great Greenwich Village Invasion. As usual, the reshuffling of personnel cards occasioned some delays. When I finally set to news-digging in and around the national capital, the New Deal for Agriculture was a month old.

Henry Agard Wallace was off to a precarious start in national politics; the deeply confused Capitol press corps was listing him quite variably as something between the new doctor and the new commissar for American farming. In general the farm press was speaking fairly tolerantly of his initial handouts of propaganda; most major city newspapers and conservative columnists were vehemently blasting Henry Wallace, the erstwhile pampered brat and loner from Des Moines. For better or worse, as an exceptionally diligent self-publicist the new Secretary of Agriculture was busily spinning together at public expense what impressed me as being the most able force of publicists then in publicity-spouting Washington. Milton Eisenhower, the engaging younger brother of an even more engaging Major Eisenhower (whom I overheard remarking: "Man, I detest being stuck here even temporarily, but I guess us Democrats have got to stick together"), was still serving very capably as the Department of Agriculture director of "information." But Henry Wallace was stocking his own kennel of image-shapers. These were pivoted about a circumspect, bespectacled, ponderously trite fellow Iowan, Paul Appleby, the new administrative assistant to the new Secretary, and an extremely imaginative and abstruse mathematician, Louis Bean, who was listed as Department statistician.

Wallace's special apologist was a young ex-taxi driver from Des Moines, Ferner Nuhn, husband of the then heeded Iowa fiction writer Ruth Suckow, and poetic rationalizer of what some of the less sympathetic news tyros described as Iowa-style smugness and rudeness, personified and maintained in top-heavy surplus by the new Secretary of Agriculture. Wallace's Dr. Jekyll-type thinker and speech writer was the meditative, ever gracious Russell Lord, a likable word farmer from Maryland, who had studied agriculture at Cornell and worked for Crowell's *Farm and Fireside* until that journal had determinedly plowed itself under.

Russ Lord, who was gradually awakening to the fact that food must be produced by people as well as on acres, was distinctly aware of the depth and reach of the Wallace opposition. He was disposed to agree with the mighty Des

Moines *Register* that as an open-field candidate in his home state Young Henry could not win an election for dogcatcher of Muddy Bottom. In private young Mr. Lord agreed that the younger Mr. Wallace was appallingly rude, that he had remained a spoiled brat, that he was beginning his regime by making unnecessary legions of enemies, from Cordell Hull, the accomplished politician Secretary of State, and Bill Borah, the Senate's giant-killer from Idaho, to the enterprising proprietors of the Jones and Jones Odorless Slaughter House of Steadfast, Iowa.

The new Secretary's most cogent speechwriter and thinker also granted that Henry Wallace reeked with inconsistencies, including the personal foible that while crusading for reduction of what he alleged were ruinous corn surpluses, Wallace was rebuilding his private fortune by means of the extremely profitable development of much higher yielding strains of hybrid corn. But Lord pointed out persuasively that Wallace was mustering a "crusade of concern" about the fundamentals of food production. He smiled off Wallace's rabble-rousing insistence that the twentieth was at that point the century of the "common man"; he agreed that entirely too many common men were going hungry even while too many great food crops were going unharvested.

Early in May 1933 Franklin D. Roosevelt recommended to Congress the newly devised Agricultural Adjustment Act, describing it as a first step along an untrodden path. As an attempt by the federal government to institute a correlated planning of federal farm legislation, the AAA was indeed a first step along an untrodden path. The path was being needlessly roughened by clumsy writing so conspicuously without American legislative precedence that almost any law student could have predicted correctly that it would not get by the U.S. Supreme Court. But the relatively easy passage of the bill was a recognition of the fact that farm legislation was no longer avoidable and that the United States' agricultural and related food-producing problems were of readily accepted international significance.

If the AAA was not good legislation, it was at very least a world document. Its tenets included the Hebraic ever-normal-granary strategy of Old Testament times, and very early Roman Empire land-use laws that also took for granted the right of government to protect or, as needed, direct, procure, and distribute public food supplies.

On June 12, 1933, the so-called "Emergency Farm Bill" became law and the Agricultural Adjustment Administration was officially incubated. It was not conceived as a device for feeding the hungry; its professed goal was restoration of farm income, or "purchasing power," by way of a forced revival of the 1909-14 average prices for nine designated crops: wheat, dairy products, tobacco, cotton, rice, corn, sugar, hogs, and peanuts. There was no "direct coverage" of beef cattle, the foremost source of meat, or oats, by common knowledge the most nutritious of the cereal grains, or rye, known to be the healthiest and most efficiently harvestable of all the great grain crops. From a food-supply standpoint, the perhaps epochal farm act was more impressive for omissions than inclusions. It ignored potatoes (the Number One vegetable of the country); soya, already the Number Three field crop; the rapidly gaining kaffirs and sorghums; all the commercial fruits; also sheep, poultry, and a score of other distinctly important food harvests.

Furthermore, most of the chosen subjects for "domestic allotment" were concentrated in restricted areas of the Midwest, the Great Plains, the Middle Atlantic, and the cotton-growing South and Southwest. By 1933 about 95 percent of the nation's wheat crop was being grown in only eleven states; dairying was strongly concentrated in six; cotton growing in nine; tobacco growing in five, and so on. Although corn and hogs, which the Wallace pundits rated as substantially the same crop, were widely distributed, their decisive concentrations were in only nine states.

Even more damaging was the fact that the concept of domestic allotment invited its own profitable violations and functional collapses. The working (read "unworkable") routine here was geared to encouraging farmers to voluntarily reduce their harvests of specified "allotment crops," and to permit the planting of the eliminated acreage to soil-restoring cover crops for "carrying" foraging livestock. Farmers who joined in the government-prescribed reductions of the nine chosen crops would receive U.S. Treasury checks covering the difference between the 1933 prices and the so-called "base prices" that had obtained from twenty-four to nineteen years earlier. The "differentials" would be collected by way of government-licensed "processors" of farm crops, i.e., millers, packers, and ginners, as based on Department of Agriculture estimates of the total unconsumed harvests of the specified crops. Although farmers could not be literally forced to enter the agreement, they were being powerfully encouraged to do so.

The professed and strongly publicized goal was that of restoring farm buying power, or parity. This was patently unattainable. As of June 1933 growers' prices of the selected crops were averaging somewhere near half of their 1909-14 levels. But consumer prices for most processed or manufactured goods had remained well above 1914 averages. The so-called farm parity had changed to a myth. In 1909, for example, when the farm price of wheat was 99 cents a bushel, work shoes cost about $1.75 a pair; two bushels of wheat would buy a pair of shoes. In 1933 work shoes were averaging about $4.00 a pair and wheat about 44 cents a bushel; a

pair of shoes was costing the farmer at least nine bushels of
wheat.

There were other *non sequiturs* and inevitable imbal-
ances. In repeated instances these were aggravated by appallingly stupid administrative moves. This was typical: since
the New Deal farm bill was enacted after most of the 1933
crops had been planted, Wallace directed that limitation
procedures "retrogress" at least to the extent of the immediate slaughter of 400,000 already farrowed pigs and the
plowing under of about a third of a million acres of planted
cotton. Particularly in the Midwest, the press loudly protested the arbitrary massacre of "innocent baby pigs." No
less understandably, the ludicrous command to plow under
half-grown cotton was also deplored. In this, my own sym-
pathies were with the cotton-plowing mules. Through years
and generations the plow pullers had been whammed and
whacked for stepping on or causing the destruction by plow
of the cotton plants. Now that the mules were being commanded to plow under entire rows of the plants, they were
presumably completely baffled.

This confusion held for great numbers of Depression-
weary farmers also. Their choices, provided of course that
they were growing one or more of the specified allotment
crops, now were three: to accept the AAA plan literally, to
exploit it to their own advantage, or to refuse it. The fact
was self-evident that among all accepters the Midwestern
grain farmers had most to gain. On that basis the *Register-
Leader* of Des Moines put reporters to interviewing individually 30,000 Iowa farmers. In the beginning, 77 percent of
these were opposed to the plan. After the allotment checks
began to pour out of the U.S. Treasury, the vote changed to
51.94 percent in favor, with the remainder opposed. Practically none said, "No opinion." The national total of ac-

ceptances presently rose to almost 4 million farms, about half of what was then the U.S. total.

Significantly, the accepters included most of the larger farms and comparatively few of the subsistence farms. Anticipating this, beginning in April 1933 the Roosevelt Administration had pressed to quick passage a $25-million "emergency" loan fund for helping citizens gain possession of lands for establishing subsistence farms. Within three months the loan applications totaled more than a thousand times that amount. The self-evident choice of the small farmers was to grow more food, not less. The back-to-land movement continued to stumble and reek with pathos, but also to produce food. By midyear the Department of Agriculture's highly respected Bureau of Crop Estimates boldly predicted that the "controlled" harvest of that year would substantially exceed the "uncontrolled" harvest of 1932. Henry Wallace replied pompously that the federal government could well afford to "build a sound agriculture future by protecting the farmer against the more predatory results of his own individuality in planting and harvesting."

Franklin D. Roosevelt, meanwhile, expressed his "moral approval" of what he proposed as a new and permanent policy of federal purchase of submarginal lands for retirement from active use and conversion, where feasible, to publicly owned forests and water sites. Thus was born the Resettlement Administration, with initial Treasury grants for purchasing about fifty million acres of these lands at an average cost of $7 per acre. Rexford Tugwell, then Assistant Secretary of Agriculture, took over as director of the Resettlement Administration. The former Columbia faculty member opened with the public statement that poor-land retirement "seems much more reasonable than the present emergency program of blanket crop reductions"; he added, even more significantly, "It may be expected that . . . the emergency efforts will evolve into some kind of complete control and efficient utilization of all lands within the United States . . ."

That trial balloon phoofed out; Congress finally balked. Senator Borah, the veteran political philosopher from Idaho, reflected on that while treating me to a dish of cheese and crackers in the Senate restaurant. "Mark my word, sonny, that purple-eyed upstart from Columbia College has it all wrong. Nobody's going to snuff out independent food production in these United States. It's doubly important because in farming we set worldwide patterns."

Evidently there were functional reasons why the AAA was destined to be replaced by a prolonged and perhaps unending succession of farm plans. The AAA's faults were big faults: it definitely favored larger landholders and corporation-owned farms; it gave landowners inequitable advantages over tenants; it gave no real heed to possibilities for improving the badly lagging merchandising of food harvests, or to strengthening crop production by means of encouraging the development of additional cash crops better suited for use as industrial materials.

Another grievous fault was its deliberate bypassing of international markets. Wallace continued to recall that World War I had "thrown American farm production in high gear," and followed with the kindergartner's *non sequitur* that it should be returned to low gear. This was mismeshed with the almost ludicrous assumption that, at least in the United States, food demands are essentially stable both in variety and volume. The self-evident truth was that food demands were and are insistently and unendingly changing. Even as the first New Deal for Agriculture thundered to a premature climax, food-buying patterns in the United States were rapidly shifting toward larger intakes of red meats, particularly beef and pork, and steadily expanding the consumption of fruits, green vegetables, and dairy products. As industrial earnings began to revive, foods and food merchandising were the first principal recipients of the slow uptake of earning power. The would-be-epochal federal ventures in crop restriction did not even begin to restrict the food supply; month by month they were expanding them.

HEAPS AND HEAPS OF PETATERS

AFTER A laborious, hard-tripping eighteen months of Washington news-chasing I shifted to farm-magazine reporting. Though quite deliberate, for a hardup journalist the choice was neither easy nor without financial perils. Farm magazines were blundering into hard and danger-ous times; about twenty had already closed shop, and several of the erstwise plump weeklies had changed to slender monthlies. The advertising revenue continued to slough away, and most of the editors were steering by guess.

Farm viewpoint, to exhume that somewhat hypothetical phrase, was also in mutation. However dubious of Henry Wallace and the tumultuously publicized New Deal, farm readers seemed above-averagely well aware of the unfolding revolutionary era in terms of farm planning as well as coun-try living. The editors, in great part town- or city-office rou-tinists, were rarely apace with their readers, much less ahead of them. They were, as the saying then was, sweating bullets about what to print. In earlier times farm magazines had been simplified digests of agronomy bulletins interspersed with fluffy nothings, usually on the saccharine side, and sprinkled with recipes that required buying groceries at the store, "woman stuff," frequently impregnated with slightly veiled admonitions to buy advertised products, from crocheting thread to floor wax, and less designing expositions on how to organize a squat-tag team for wholesome girls, or how a future farmer might excel at pitching horseshoes, baseball, or whatever calls for pitching. The editorial messages were most often concerned with getting more crop per acre, upping the corn yield, weeding out scrub bulls, getting the hogs fatter in less time, and otherwise Being a Live Wire in the Country. But now that the direction of political controls and Treasury subsidy was toward artificial scarcity, the time-proved editorial approaches were gravely queered.

My next less-than-jubilant employer was Crowell-Collier's farm magazine *Farm and Fireside*, better known to its hired hands as *Barn and Bedside*. During the 1920s this "farm book" had netted millions under the remarkable editorship of an uprooted Ohioan, George Martin, who had changed to the most ardent New Yorker I had ever encountered. He freely revealed that when obliged to journey north of Fifty-seventh Street or south of Forty-second, he felt positively lost in the backwoods. He had lately moved from his long-time home in the Roosevelt Hotel to what he deemed a less countrified location, the then new Waldorf-Astoria. From that stronghold he revealed to a forum of the Rural Life Association that the one and only justification of a farm magazine is to make a whole hell of a lot of money and to bear in mind that quite regardless of latitude or longitude, region or nation, farmers fall into two absolute groups: go-getters and slobs.

Under duress of withering Depression Crowell-Collier changed *Barn and Bedside* to an outrageously improbable spread called *Country Home*. George Martin discreetly bowed out of the befogging picture to find work publicizing

Radio City for the Rockefellers. Thereafter, and somewhat blearily, *Country Home* was two-stepped away from real farmers and farming and set to recruiting an improbable audience of well-to-do farm owners and suburbanites "with rural interests."

In the quest of what its proprietors termed the nonurban moneyed group the former farm magazine was doing an impressively effective job of severing all liaison with its readers—if by then there were any. This siege of dunderheadedness involved faking even the contents of the page captioned "What Our Readers Write." In my previous journalistic employment, reader letters had been handled in reasonably good faith; certainly that held for the *Post-Dispatch* and the *Times*. On both papers I had filled stints as "letters editor," thereby gaining conversion to the belief that despite their foibles and, not too infrequently, their ax-grinding or other ulterior motives, reader letters usually provide revealing and worthwhile reading for all concerned, even editorial writers.

But at my next place of employment I learned with very real dismay that reader mail was being faked outright and quite officiously. For an extra $200 per published page an objectionably fat and surly associate editor was not only inventing the letters but extemporizing the replies. Example:

M. J. of Illinois: My parents and grandparents as well as myself are lifelong subscribers to your wonderful magazine and its predecessor. Recently, at the home of my grandparents, my grandfather having recently passed away, my wife and I found all issues since January 1901, neatly stacked in Mr. J.'s reading room. The pile was six feet, four inches high.

(*Reply*) Thanks, M.J. of Ill. We knew we rated highly with the farm family but until now we didn't know we rated 6 ft. 4 high.

As an extremely junior deckhand, I felt myself hopelessly walled off from readers, whoever and if they were, and felt no modicum of hope for gaining so much as a glimmer of bona fide farmers' viewpoints. Indeed, by then I found myself surmising that Crowell-Collier's publishing was beset by a lingering cranial blackout. Accordingly, I set out to find another job.

Country Home's principal rival was the Curtis Publishing Company's *Country Gentleman*, then propagated in Philadelphia and by its own admission holding sway as America's Foremost Rural Magazine.

Philip Rose, the "Gent's" editor, was a former civil engineer. Despite that and his Curtis employment, he was dually endowed with a deep and affectionate interest in farming and a rare, refreshing intellectual honesty. He applied both in arriving at what he termed a working definition of a "real farmer." "He fits no stereotypes and has no absolute hallmarks beyond being a man or woman who prefers to spend his mortal span, or most of it, in the country. He likes to produce things, particularly food, and regards this as basically reasonable and honorable. He is not a politician; he would rather make his own living than mooch it. . . . He has his own ideas about the best crops and the best use of his land."

Phil Rose confided to me that he regarded the prevailing exploitation of planned scarcity as economically ruinous to professional agriculture, grossly unfair to the majority of poor people, both on and off farms, perilous in terms of adequate food supplies, otherwise unnatural, and below par morally.

"I agree with old Georgie Martin that all farmers have considerable in common quite regardless of their particular community, county, state, nation, or whatever. Farming's a worldwide trade; judging by what of it I've seen, farming's getting to be more or less similar—more and more like other farming, regardless of country or continent. Unlike Georgie, or Henry Ford, I believe we have to look on farming as primarily food growing. I believe this country and the world at large are still a long way from effective farm production of great numbers of industrial materials. Food's still the big factor. Here in the United States we've taken for granted that there will be heaps and loads of food as long as there's a dollar to buy it with.

"I don't agree with that. I can imagine situations where food could get as scarce as snowballs in hell. . . . Down in the Ozarks you grew up with God's own plenty of unused lands and the devil's plenty of hungry people on every side. I grew up likewise in the Upper Peninsula of Michigan, where there's still a lot too much land and a lot too many hungry people. So I say people, not land, have to do the food producing. By and large, people should and must get it done their own ways; meaning that some need to concentrate bigger production on fewer acres, while others find themselves obliged to spread over a lot more acres.

"There are general and special situations, granted, and likewise different tempos. As for farmers' viewpoint, it's got to keep changing even if from fixed pivots, like the calf that grazes around a stump. So, my idea of running a farm book is to try to fill out the farming murals with big, broad strokes of what the bright boys call contemporary perspective. Somehow, trying to state this case leaves me feeling silly, but this is all the advice I'd care to offer."

My first assignment was to another enduring American frontier that has survived as an oasis of uncompromising abundance. It was and is still the nation's and the world's particular and persisting stronghold of potatoes—Aroostook County, in far northeastern Maine. This farthest northeast prong of the United States is a whopper of a country, ap-

proximately the size of Massachusetts. About four-fifths of
the land is in forest, in greatest part cut-over conifers. Only
about a quarter-million acres, roughly one-tenth of the
country's total area, is in farms, and about five-eighths of all
its cleared land is planted to potatoes, locally known as
"petaters."

There is no other crop of consequence. The continuing
planting of about 150,000 acres is the nation's largest, and
Aroostook has the world's greatest concentration of high-
yield potato lands. During the present century the average
yields have approximately tripled, edging persistently from
around 100 bushels an acre to well over 400 bushels, for
calorie yields at least double those of any other principal
food crop grown in the United States. As practically any
Aroostooker will confirm, the county grows potatoes because "it's got to." The cool wet summers produce luxuriant
forages but the grazing seasons are too short for successful
dairying or beef-cattle production. Efforts to grow peas, as-
paragus, rhubarb, and other north-country vegetables here
have never been sufficiently successful. Excessively long
haulage to market remains a major impediment to other
perishable harvests; except for rye and buckwheat, the grain
crops do not thrive, nor do fruits or berries.

Potatoes remain the "natural"; Aroostook continues growing them at the rate of a packed carload for every ten minutes, from first plowing time in April to the unremitting
November freezes, to help potatoes keep their place as the
foremost food vegetable of the United States and the Western World. With a planted acreage of about one nine-
hundredth part of the nation's total, Aroostook frequently
produces about one-fourth of all potatoes consumed in the
United States; for added measure, its magnificent productiveness relates to the more global conquest of hunger.

As usual the enduring reasons are strongly human. One is

that, comparatively speaking, Aroostook is durably settled. Except for harvest labor, principally from the adjacent Maritime Provinces of Canada, the movement of people is severely limited. The root population begins with the Yankees, in great part descendants of stout spirits who went northeast into a wilderness while many of their kin and neighbors were pioneering to the west. There are also the descendants of earlier generations of once itinerant Yankee peddlers, preachers, teachers, soldiers, and the post-boundary Acadians. About 1784, after Britain had forcibly removed the people of Evangeline from Nova Scotia and lower New Brunswick, some of the Acadians followed the St. John River beyond the threat of British warcraft or land garrisons and there built settlements on fertile Aroostook prairies. French Canadians from Quebec and Italian railroad builders also joined in the colonizing. For the most part they, too, came to stay.

All took part in pioneering and stabilizing an agricultural frontier. Aroostook is no habituated showplace. It is distinctly removed from the castes, classes, and snobberies of the ocean fronts; also the crab cakes and soused clams, the yacht harbors and summer estates guarded by high hedges so that neighbors and *hoi polloi* may be duly discouraged from gawking. In Aroostook a gawker may gawk to his heart's content, and he will not be gawking alone.

On entering the petater strongholds one travels through magnificent vistas of great green spaces, of fast-shifting acres of shadows, of bluish hills and enlarged wastelands. As one nears Houlton, the county seat, the farm houses grow still bigger and better painted. Woodlands give way to fringings of conical spruce and the big fields begin—rolling, plenteous fields, some starchy green and white-flecked with potatoes in summer blossom, others sleek with alfalfa or partly red with blossoming clovers, or spread with a golden carpet of wild mustard, the foremost weed pest of the region.

"With petaters you got to rotate—a year or two in petaters, then plant the ground to grass and clovers. Load your seed drills with oats and clovers and orchard grasses. Oats come first. You mow the crop and by then the clover's beginning to start. Next year you get clover and next year mixed grass. Also you get mustard. It works in and seeds itself and pesters you worse than the lingerin' itch."

The farm homes keep growing bigger. The lightning rods become more numerous, in some instances rising in virtual hedgerows from housetops and barn gables, and the arched roofs of the giant-size potato storages. The houses, hit-and-miss Victorian in architecture, show a remarkable affinity for bright-colored paints: yellows, blues, bright browns, rich grays. Red is preferred for barns and potato storages. White is the color of the wood-built Grange halls, the Masonic "temples," and country churches.

Throughout the summer the fields stay green and luxuriant. Droughts are virtually unknown. Winters are long and deep with snow. Spring comes late but with quick magic. As soon as the deep snow melts, the frost is pretty well out of the ground. Grass "rises." Abruptly, sleds and sleighs are replaced with plows and tractors drawing oversize potato seeders. As long ago as 1920, potatoes had won absolute acceptance as the sustaining crop of Aroostook; as with all one-crop farming, winnings and losings alike come high.

In lucky potato years, the exceptionally remote county became the first farming center in the United States in which individual farm incomes exceeded a million dollars a year. Unquestionably, the large size of individual farms resulted in intermittent flooding of markets and the submerging of prices. On the constructive side, the big-earnings years that have tended to recur somewhere near four years in ten had already made the county a "potato capital." By the early 1930s it was a successful proving center for all kinds of tractive machinery, including tractor-drawn planters, cultivators, and diggers, and sorters, sizers, boxing-and-bagging machines. By the early 1930s the Aroostook potato fields were also proving grounds for airplane dusting with pesticides and for the continued use of chemical fertilizers, particularly nitrogens, phosphates, and lime. Better use of improved fertilizers, from two hundred to five hundred pounds an acre yearly, had already doubled the average potato yields of 1920 and was in the process of doubling them again.

But the economic groundwork comprised the really decisive story and work pattern. There was no tenable place in the Aroostook scene for "controlled scarcity" or any other deliberate policy of reducing harvests.

Geography and indispensable transportation had long since shaped this absolute. The unavoidable rail haul of at least five hundred miles to the nearest substantial markets (beginning with Boston and New York) and subsequent haulage to most of the U.S. East, at least as far south as the Virginia Capes and Atlanta, and necessarily including the metropolitan Washington area, made up about half of the prevailing retail price of the harvests. Quite regardless of the eventual distribution, which by then included most markets east of the Mississippi, the first long haul required big-volume supplying along with excessive investments in storage facilities. The principal and best proved carrier was the Bangor and Aroostook Railroad, built, equipped, and operated primarily for handling the Aroostook potato crops. The railroad could not possibly survive any substantial reduction of its basic freight; neither could the competing trucking lines. The formidably big private investments in storages, already averaging around $30,000 a farm, were likewise predicated on undiminished harvests and paid for out of truckloads, carloads, and trainloads of potatoes actually shipped and sold.

Thus the reward and penalty for growing potatoes was, and from all reasonable indications ever will be, growing more potatoes. The quandary and advantages were being shared in more and more countries by more and more crops, particularly perishable crops. Once vitally established, the production tempo cannot be successfully slowed; perishable harvests, like water, must seek their final levels, with rates of flow augmented by volume as well as topography, including those influenced by man. Once aflow, there is usually no convenient economical magic for shutting them off or throttling the flow.

Very early one morning I joined Phil McDonald, one of the "oldliners," who had early sold one of his own potato harvests for more than a million dollars, in watching a daybreak experiment in airplane-spraying. The boy pilot had checked his sprayload and dust ejectors; he puffed a cigarette while watching his engine warm. We noticed that the youth was laughing. "Be we that fool funny?" Phil McDonald inquired.

The youth readjusted his goggles. "I was only thinking of what my mama told me last birthday party day when I was fresh back from flyin' school down at Fort Worth. I was trying to tell her I could fly safe, bank sure, and get the good out of height and speed. She plain couldn't understand that in flyin' height and speed make for safety. So she grabs me around the neck and says 'Billy Boy, promise me you won't never fly high and fast. Your mommy wants you to fly low and slow." He tossed aside his cigarette and rebuttoned his leather jacket. "I was sort of wonderin'," he continued, "if them politicians down in Washington ain't tryin' to tell you growed-up farmers what my mama was tryin' to tell her growed up Billy Boy: 'Fly low and slow—and watch yourself bust up.' "

A WHIFF OF FISH

ON A dreary day in Philadelphia the editor was reflecting on alternative food sources, those not directly related to land or living soils.

Phil Rose gave notice that his meditations were somewhat subjective; he had a headache, lingering indigestion, morbid concern about the politicians who were farming the farmers, and the contriving leaderships of certain would-be farmers' organizations, country slickers out to farm the politicians. But first and last he was concerned about food.

Like other of the Curtis Publishing Company's upper deckhands, the *Country Gentleman* editor regularly took lunch at the restaurant in the grimly elegant marble-piled Curtis mausoleum on Independence Square. The food ran heavy there. George Horace Lorimer, then president of Curtis and editor of the *Saturday Evening Post*, liked heavy midday meals.

"Every time I swallow this goddamned brick plaster," Phil Rose revealed, "I feel like singing sad spirituals about Sister Hog Slop, then swinging from vines and going fishing. I seem able to think about farming only while fishing. Now this could be the primitive in me or it could be history having out, as with Independence Square. American farming began as a landside provisioner for offshore fishing and as such presently grew to be the tail that wagged the dog.

Any fool knows that commercial sea fishing could conceivably take back the brunt of the people-feeding job. I am told that life began in the sea, and quite conceivably in due course might go back there.

"The more immediate point is that the beginnings of these United States as we now try to know them were largely by fishing. Most of the white men who presently took over the land—I mean from the times of Champlain on through those of the lobster fishermen now known as the Pilgrim Fathers—fished first, farmed later, meanwhile living mostly on and by fishing. It's possible that at least in some part this sequence could be restored."

He granted that the proportion of the nation's food supply taken from the sea had dwindled to relative insignificance, probably no more than 1 percent of the total. Nevertheless, the editor had given thought to possibilities for effectively feeding both people and domestic livestock from the oceans and restoring soil fertility with volume catches of fish. He had therefore decided that the farm magazine might make a try at making some layman's appraisals of ocean farming. He further believed that a gawking landlubber from some benighted inland locale, such as Arkansas, might best have a try at seeing ocean farming for others who likewise know nothing about it.

Accordingly, from Rockland, Maine, I set forth for the fishing fronts in a fish warden's boat captained and crewed by a State of Maine fish warden, Gene Loud, a former lobsterman from Loud's Island—no national affiliations; Maine had declined to adopt it, Canada wouldn't have it.

Gene Loud believed that these attitudes toward his homeland symbolized the continuing public regard of the historic trade into which he had been born. Americans still thought of fishing as freshwater fishing; the kinds Gene knew were hard, skimpy, frequently perilous quests for livelihoods from the sea.

A first brief glimpse showed that ocean fishing at least was trawling along. Along the upper Atlantic coastline it was still the trade of about 150,000 men who used about 3,700 duly registered vessels and perhaps 70,000 small boats to lift catches between the Virginia Capes and Grand Banks totaling above a billion pounds yearly. Along the self-entangled Maine coastline, Gene Loud pointed out dozens of islands or coastal communities where fish is still Lord High Everything; where the women rise at two in the morning to cook breakfast for men who put out by three in order to "count catch" by mid-morning.

My salt-sprayed warden friend recommended that as a first-timer I begin at the top by boarding the *Buena Marda*, a 90-ton seiner, Diesel driven, that was then the figurative flag ship of the long renowned Gloucester fleet, which then included about 135 registered fishing vessels ranging in size from about 10 tons to 125 or more, all naming Gloucester, Massachusetts, as home port.

Accordingly, I went aboard as a "dead herring," i.e., a rider without a working share in the catch. The matter of shares, I learned, is of great importance; the boat owner (in many instances the "working skipper") takes half the catch, or stock, as rental, food, and fuel costs, plus the cook's and engineer's wages. As a rule, the other half of the stock is divided in equal shares for all crew members, with extras for particularly important functionaries. Thus, open-ocean fishing has remained one of the more democratic of all the food industries, as well as one of the more diligent. For good measure, as I soon learned, one's stature is not marred by such feminine-slanted decadences as face washing and shaving, or luxurious quarters. One "flops" down in the fo'c's'le on a narrow shelf. Work assignment permitting, at dusk usually one climbs into his bunk, wraps himself in a cocoon of somewhat odorous blankets, and expects to be roused out in pitch darkness around 3 A.M. This is not necessarily so bad as it sounds. The galley stove is booming and the mess table is within easy lunging distance of the bunk shelves. By long-time "fishee" tradition the food, at least what I ate of it, was excellent.

Most of the fishing craft that name Gloucester as home port were (and still are) "skimmers"; about half were principally concerned with taking mackerel. The skimmers are the most abundant harvesters. Their school-fish quarries, particularly mackerel, are usually best taken near or somewhat before dawn, when vast sweeps are most likely to be breakfasting on floating plankton or other near-surface foods. The ship's lookout is disposed to seek out the big schools in part by gathering testimony from eyes sharper than human eyes—including those of gulls, gannets, porpoises, and dogfish, which likewise wait for the schools to plow surface.

Sometimes, if the wind is right and the sweeps are plentiful, a lookout can even smell the fish; more frequently, he can spot the phosphorescent patches that mark the whereabouts of the big schools. Whatever his sighting technique, when the lookout calls "fishee," the skipper takes command, crewmen reach for rubber boots and begin pulling on oilskins. The first play is to bring alongside the seine boat, usually an oversize motor-powered dory big enough to carry eight or nine men and as many as twenty tons of fish. In routine practice, the skipper directs laying of the "purse" seine, a mesh net usually twelve to eighteen feet wide and sixty to eighty feet long, floated by means of a topline buoyed by hundreds of cork floats. The technique is to encircle the fish school and close in the net, somewhat as one closes a billfold. With great skill the catch is first scooped into the dory boats, then hoisted aboard the mother vessel to be packed in ice, or nowadays to be quick-frozen. Whatever the equipment and however expert the crew, the work is chancy: the excessively lively harvest may dunk out of net reach or abruptly change directions. Either maneuver produces a "water-haul."

Whatever the specifics, fleet fishing is usually directed toward the more plentiful catches; it is, in a sense, the ocean-front equivalent of big farm or ranch operations. Shore fishing is more comparable to subsistence farming; it is centered on trawling, or line fishing, in known "grounds"; its most historic strongholds include the Atlantic coastline from Cape Cod to the Newfoundland banks. Its most historic quarry is the cod. Nobody knows for sure how many centuries these chill offshore waters have been fished for cod; the telling point is that they are still being fished, for cod and range-related shore fish.

One also learns that the sea, like the land, keeps unveiling new or revived crops of profound benefits to man. During the 1930s the briny Eldorado of the offshore North Atlantic was scallop mussels that grow in ocean beds from which they await dredging out and loading aboard ships, where crewmen shuck or husk out the hinge muscles, the white button of edible meat, and toss the bulk of the catch back to sea. The opening of new scallop shoals is usually by way of knowing hunches and bold risks. The then most productive beds (off George's Bank) had been opened during 1930 by a partnership of two Maine fishermen and boat owners, captains Charles Carver and Sumner Whitney. The fishing skippers had pooled their savings and mortgaged their homes in order to raise the $22,000 for building a boat especially equipped for "draggin' deep bottom." It was long-odds gambling that paid off. The first three days of dragging brought up 5,000 gallons of shucked scallops; the season's earnings repaid the boat costs, plus wages and supplies for a crew of ten, with lush bonuses for all. Portentously, the two fishing captains opened by instituting a reseeding program, returning to sea all scallops too small for commercial use and voluntarily refraining from "taking crop" during the summer spawning period.

There were other sea-front practices that showed significant similarities to food production on land. For one instance, clams, particularly the preferred softshell types, were being planted extensively along muddy or sandy tide fronts of the upper New England coast. Maine's Department of Sea and Shore Industries was leading in this endeavor, which the marine-industries department of the French government had pioneered about a quarter-century earlier. The Maine pioneers demonstrated that clam production responds to routine techniques of land farming. Clam spawning usually takes place during the mollusks' second year. The newly hatched embryos float free for a time, then anchor themselves in tide flats to feed on suitably sized marine life carried by the tides. Like landside fields or gardens, the ensuing clam beds can be "dug to death"; tens of thousands of acres of once bountiful clam beds were no longer producing.

Maine, with an estimated half-million acres of clamming flats, had already established a clam-experiment station and was leading the way to a workable procedure of clam farming. This included tractor "scratch plowing" of the more promising sites, planting them with seed clams (usually about the size of a garden pea), and covering them with sand or mud, available at low tide. The usual growth period is two years; the yields varied between a few bushels to as many as a thousand bushels per acre. The planting was principally by state governments, since most of the sites were in public domain. But Maine, with Massachusetts following suit, was seeding clams for the public to harvest on a diggers-are-takers basis.

Clams are most literally a planted crop of the ocean edge. Lobstering was holding its longtime place as an open-range livestock resource. For the United States and much of the gourmet world beyond, the lobster range includes an off-shore Atlantic strip extending from the Virginia Capes to upper Labrador, though the more effective lobster fishing keeps moving north. Back in colonial times lobsters usually were scooped up with hand seines, or speared, or hooked with special tongs, all done within wading depths. But that was long ago. As any coast stroller knows, lobsters must now be caught in deftly rigged traps, or pots, which are weighted and lowered to the nearer sea floor, frequently several or many miles offshore. The usual lobster trap is a slatted crate with a hinged door, and a head equipped with a funnel bow directed upward. To reach the bait, the lobster must crawl through the center ring of the netted funnel; that leaves the crustaceous dimwit a prisoner. As a rule the lobster fisherman functions considerably like a fur trapper; he keeps a string of pots—sometimes upward of a hundred—marks them with miniature buoys of distinguishing colors, and regularly pulls the traps, takes the catch into his dory, rechecks the bait, and relowers the traps. Most dories now have outboard motors.

My companion, Gene Loud, spoke authoritatively of lobsterin'; back on Loud's Island, he had taken to the trade when he was only nine. He had no chance to go to school; there was none on Loud's Island. So at nine Gene became dory helper to his father. By the time he was fifteen he had his own string of traps. He took live lobsters to the nearest island store and there sold them for whatever was offered, rarely more than a nickel apiece in cash. In those times most seafood buyers kept general stores and bartered without immediate heed of market quotations. This changed only gradually. Ironically, lobstering, one of the more toilsome of the fishing trades, stays among the worst paid.

Gene Loud recounted matter-of-factly that even though he had been a 150-pot man, he had never earned enough to feel secure about becoming a family man. He found that, as a year-around average, his working overhead, including dory boats, engines, traps, rope, and miscellaneous upkeep, claimed about half of his average gross take of around $2,500 a year. Appropriately, Gene Loud never expected lobsterin' to be any briny bed of roses. He knew how it feels to rouse out at three in the morning, put one's dory to a rough sea, and face an "easter" at, say, ten below zero. He recalled two lobsterin' neighbors who got lost in a winter fog and hit a squall. One froze at his oars. The other rowed in and hove into port with his hands and feet frozen. But at least Tom Robbins of Robbins' Island lived to tell about it. "A bold clear Voice calls to me from out of the darkness. And I follers, and the Voice steers me true, so I pushes to home, landin' with a pack of angels a-hiverin' in my bowsprits."

One noted that the hiverin' angels had not as yet shown the way to economic anchorage for the fishing fronts. Shore and ocean fishermen had remained in strong contention for last place among the most poorly paid of food producers. A gentleman trawler based on Deer Island, off Maine, assured me that "of a good month" he netted up to $25, but since 1930 his annual income had never gone above $200 a year. At the time average earnings for able crewmen of the Gloucester fishing fleet were less than $300 a year.

Any way one gauged it, ocean-front farming was floundering and gasping. Shore fishing, particularly of historic standbys such as cod and halibut, was steadily losing supply; eminent school fish such as Atlantic mackerel and Pacific tuna appeared to be shifting southward. I kept meeting old-timers who would not change trades, yet reiterated their hope that their sons would choose more provident trades. "I'm seventy-two now, and still at trawlin' cod," a veteran bait puller told me. "I live mostly on fish I catch and potatoes I raise and pipedreams for a upturn on the fishin' coast. My wife is long gone dead, my son is growed up and teaching at Bowdoin College. He seen the true light in time —he fishes only because he likes fishin'."

One also noted that the number of indigenous American personnel was waning on most of the fishing fronts. In ship or fleet fishing Portuguese were the majority personnel; about half of the farther ranging fishing crafts were "guinea"-crewed. Italian, Greek, and Middle Eastern personnel were also replacing the fishing Yankees; Scandinavians were taking over as the most numerous fish butchers.

The working internationalism in ocean fishing was encouraging. But the first-line processing at sea-front packing stations was durably discouraging. Salting and sun-drying, the traditional and in many instances the most economical curing processes, were being replaced by freezing or "hard packs." But the Latin American preference for salt fish—the Caribbean was the most important of export markets—had not yet shifted to the frozen product. The American sardine industry was also fumbling and faltering; its technically lagging "bakeries" and packing sheds were unable to compete effectively against the able competition of Norwegian fisheries. But the more weighing faults were with fish processing and marketing within the United States. According to Maine's Department of Sea and Shore Industry, more than 90 percent of total seafoods sales were in towns and cities along the coast; inland markets were still of very slight consequence.

Another obviously lagging area was that of fish butchering, which remained appallingly wasteful. At a fairly typical

packaged-fish plant near Rockland, where catches were purchased directly from trawlers, only about 40 percent of the
bulk weight was being processed for markets. The U.S. Department of Agriculture then estimated that field crop
losses occasioned by insects and other pests, together with
harvest and storage wastes, including rat losses, averaged
about 23 percent of potential harvests of the estimated total
of field crops. Harvest losses along the fishing fronts were
averaging at least double those of "landside."

No less regrettably, the fishery wastes were not being recovered extensively for livestock feeds, fertilizers, and other
fishery by-products. One after another, fish processors insisted that the conversion of fish wastes to commercial livestock feeds and fertilizers required investments in processing
equipment that very few of them could afford. Moreover,
the groveling prices of marketable fish did not encourage an
extensive increase of capital investment in any other expensive equipment.

There was evidence, however, that as declines continued
on American fishing fronts, significant gains in fishing industries were being reported from such diverse fronts as Norway, Denmark, Finland, Greece, Italy, Soviet Russia, and
Japan. Canadian fishing industries were holding their own.
But in terms of United States food supplies, fish and seafoods were still losing ground: the total consumption had
fallen from about 2 percent of the nation's food supply to
less than 1 percent. At best mediocre, the merchandising
of sea food generally remained extremely bad. As yet there
were no impressive exceptions. American food supply was
being pivoted on land. The same held for most of the world.

THE FARM COMMUNITY

BEFORE THE mid-years of the 1930s arrived, there was no real doubt that the decade was one of profound agricultural significance, or that the scope of agricultural changes prevailing in the United States was in at least some part international and inter-hemispheric.

But the gist of the changes did not include the New Deal for Agriculture's sought-for economy of scarcity. The awareness of potential food shortages was alive in most countries, certainly not excepting the United States. Every principal region of the country showed increasing food harvests.

Undeniably, U.S. agriculture was in mutation. Interrelated was a renewed incubation of rural communities—along lines that were generally less than compatible with the credos of the New Deal.

Throughout the 1920s U.S. farm realms had been unrelieved targets for open-season bombardments of non-agrarian doctrines and points of view. In the United States, as in much of the Western World, the 1920s had turned out to be an unrelenting marathon of lures, appeals, and exhortations directed to persuading farmers to buy more goods and services and pay the tabs with increased production of crops. Industries, politicians, business clubs, even government agents had joined in urging the farmer to step out of his traditional furrow as a food producer into the show pen of ardent consumer. Unquestionably the frequently audacious solicitations had contributed to the readily materialized fact that the United States, then with about 6 percent of the world's population, had been consuming approximately half of the world's total of manufactured goods.

But the decade of the 1920s, which Westbrook Pegler had termed the American decade of wonderful nonsense and William Allen White had included in his designation of the

American epoch of supreme goddamned stupidity, was primarily an interval of the city or townsman. The agrarian goose, with proved talents for producing golden eggs, was expected to yield to industries and cities not only the decisive margin of buying power but also the best of its youth. The Horatio Alger, or some would have it, the Abe Lincoln tradition for leaving the farm to find fortune in the cities remained regrettably powerful. As one inevitable aftermath the farm realms, even the more fecund, had been left with an outrageously high percentage of culls and an unnaturally low proportion of talented youth.

For most of the nation, country schools had remained inadequate for minimal needs; at best they had endured as penny-whistle imitations of town schooling rather than indispensables shaped to the needs of farming and rural living. Again using a broad generalization, the country schools had contributed disturbingly little to the life and economy-sustaining professions of food production. Yet somehow, as practically any chamber of commerce secretary would admit, the farm dollar kept right on turning the wheels of commerce. Farm buyers continued to spell the difference between success and failure in crucial industries—auto making, steel, shoes, electricity, and many others. But even more basically, farming and food-processing industries had somehow succeeded in producing and supplying in steadily increasing volume the absolute first need of man.

The American era that separated the World War I armistice from the collapse of Wall Street was lopsidedly urban— an interval of city and town dominance in population growth, commercial gains, and advances in trades and professions. Yet farming survived this and its many related inequities. Even while crop prices had limped farther and farther behind the averages of manufactured goods, crop acreages had continued to increase. Food exports had tended to fall, while farm mortgages doubled. These same contradictions were obtaining in other principal food-producing nations.

Though the years of the First World War had seen U.S. farming changed for the first time from a majority to a minority occupation, great numbers of Americans still coveted farm lands and sought to make them more productive. Now, in the 1930s, quite regardless of the mighty ado about controlled scarcity, the nation's farm plant as a whole proceeded to increase its harvests, particularly of foodstuffs, as the strewing of federal bounties for not growing crops remained at conspicuous cross furrows with the stubborn expansion of planted acreages, particularly of food crops. Again the U.S. Department of Agriculture's own crop statistics were proclaiming that as more thousands of tons of food were being harvested, more thousands of tons were being consumed.

Though food production continued to stay well ahead of the still dawdling food prices, the first two years of the New Deal for Agriculture found the nationwide average farm income rising in almost direct proportion to the harvest increases. As 1935 began, about a third of U.S. farmers were receiving or committed to receive U.S. Treasury money for *not* growing crops. But this was once more a minority of U.S. farmers and farms; the national farm income was rising in greatest part because an estimated 43 percent of food growers were planting, tilling, and harvesting more boxes, crates, bushels, truckloads, and carloads of foodstuffs. Why? I went my way seeking answers. The first and most general were, and still are, the absolutes that food growers as a great group were barely beginning to envisage the attainable productiveness of the living soil, and that by fundamental biology as well as economics, valid agriculture is implicitly opposed to reduction of harvests.

Another powerfully contributing factor, one more easily

explainable, was the revival of the farming community. The New Deal for Agriculture itself was proving an influential contributor to the widespread reawakening of the rural community. By 1935 county agricultural agents, on duty in 2,506 of the then 2,812 counties of the United States, were serving as clerks and referees (or, some declared, office boys) for domestic allotments. Their labors and miscellaneous participation were being supplemented by hundreds of local committees and boards that, whatever their specific functions or nonfunctions, were serving to bring farmers and landowners together in the quest of individual or common benefits.

Some onlookers, including this writer, saw the foregoing as the most worthwhile contribution of the Agricultural Adjustment Administration and its immediate successors. Regrettably and in some part ironically, the duress and wholly independent efforts to found subsistence colonies had not cropped out effectively, though some of them, probably 700 to 800, had endured for a year or more—long enough to prove once more the willingness of Americans to stand together against forces that would destroy them.

As a great deal of firsthand reporting was pointing out, the revival of rural community status and relationships far exceeded and outlasted the frequently valiant but pathetic ventures in setting up subsistence colonies. In many impressive instances the revival of rural communities was proving successful. By 1935 a hundred or more instances were becoming observable in what may still be listed as Mormon country. Late in 1935 I set out to report the then in-borning rural welfare ventures of the Church of Jesus Christ of Latter-day Saints. The seed beds here were of living companionship and community, built on or attained from a common faith and will to be self-sufficient. I began to view the most remarkable story in what earlier Mormons had called the State of Deseret; it includes most of what are now Idaho and Utah.

The most renowned leader of Mormon colonizers, Brigham Young, had believed, with Thomas Jefferson, that tillers of the earth make the best citizens. As an opposed minority, his fellow believers were long since resigned to seeking sanctuary in desert fringes or other undeveloped fringe-lands that the run of land seekers had spurned or selectively bypassed.

The Mormon pioneers had moved and toiled by communities to change the so-called "bad lands" to enduring farms and town sites. They had caused the deserts to blossom and bad lands to be born again as good lands. Now, a new generation of Mormon pioneers, sorely oppressed by depression and threatened with unwelcome inclusion on relief rolls, was once more colonizing deserts or near-deserts by means of working communites of member peoples.

My first close look at the renewed Mormon pioneering of rural communities was centered on the long-idle Keogh Ranch, in the grim drylands about three miles from the village of Malta, Idaho. The testing ground was a 4,000-acre spread once operated for cattle raising and later, when the grass began to fail, as a sheep ranch. Late in 1934 the Church had purchased the glum remains for use as a colony site. Early the following year a first group of pioneers, settlers with firm intentions of becoming landowners, had been "assigned."

I arrived at the one-time cattle and sheep ranch during the doldrums of an autumn noon, picked my way among empty corrals, and stopped at an aged bunkhouse built of mud-chinked logs, which had once been headquarters for a hell-roaring bevy of open-range cowboys. There was no noontime lull. Six of the newly arrived colonists were at work. One was driving a shiny new tractor plow over an extremely dusty field. Another was driving a team of horses to plow out a badly neglected irrigation canal. Two more were digging a well for supplying irrigation water; the other two were at house building.

A month earlier the first half-dozen "saints," all with previous farming experience, had taken over the abandoned ranch and set themselves up as a farming colony. Already they had plowed and planted about 150 acres to grasses and grains, opened about three miles of dirt roads, which were practically indispensable for establishing new homesteads, and completed two of the five wells that were required for irrigating subsistence plots. The first season comprised a tryout. Having endured the tryout, each colonizer was to "work out" a 30-acre plot of land; the Church would supply him rough lumber for building a cabin.

On arrival they reported to the Church-appointed supervisor, an elderly cattle rancher and former agricultural director of a sugar-beet company; seventy-two-year-old Mark Austin served as supervisor without pay. The six pioneers came to the land virtually without money. All bought the necessary food, clothing, and household goods on credit extended against the first crop. The Church made them a loan of implements, a tractor, and two teams of draft horses. No member was permitted to begin buying land until he had successfully finished his tryout year. Then his purchase was limited to what was regarded as a subsistence farm. Now that the irrigation canals were being repaired and river water sources supplemented by the newly completed wells, plans were under way for admitting additional colonists.

These, too, would find the living on the former Keogh ranch lands one of hard work and few diversions other than neighborly company. But the people of Joseph Smith still responded to the call to join communities of land owners.

They followed again the same hard way; some faltered, some fell, but a countable majority was winning. These were again writing lastingly in the dust and hardpan and blown tumbleweeds. In part theirs was a world story of a directioned minority.

Through the generations the Church leadership had grown convinced that the prerequisite liking for owning land and growing crops is better born in a man or woman than thrust on him. More than nine-tenths of the Mormons who had lately taken over farms had done so on their own resources, including farm experience, receiving no help of the Church beyond expert counseling and community benefits such as the building of new churches and schools.

As a routine step in proving the settlement possibilities of untried land, the Church encouraged first pioneer groups of single young men to open the way and make a first crop. This procedure was being accentuated by climatic changes in various parts of the intermountain West. In some areas, failing rainfall had already erased the continuation of dryland farming. In the one-time prosperous community of Vernon, Utah, rainfall had diminished until now all the dryland farms were abandoned; the same held at Widtsoe, a high-plateau farm community near the Powell National Forest. The Church was helping farmers to locate more dependable land by dispatching farm experts throughout the great area to make surveys of favorable lands then available for purchase. These investigators appraised the land, its water resources and price, then publicized the information through the various wards and agencies of the Church. In all instances members were being urged to colonize in groups. The laborious foundings of these independent farm settlements were in progress in various parts of Oregon, Montana, Idaho, Colorado, Arizona, and New Mexico; for the time, at least, the colonizing was most active in southern and central Idaho.

For members unable to afford land the Church was buying tracts for trial settlement and resale. Since 1930 about ten thousand acres, allocated in small strips of usually no more than fifty acres to the family, had been so bought and sold, in all instances at low prices. Usually the Church chose sites where water could be brought to the land by means of settlers' labor and community enterprise.

On that basis the Church had lately helped locate a twelve-family farming community about one hundred miles east of Calgary, Alberta, and five hundred members in the area of Salmon, Idaho, a once-thriving livestock country that had fallen prey to drought. The apportionments were principally to groups of ten to twelve families. Any visitor could see that new spans of irrigation canals were changing mustard-brown ranges to green fields.

By 1934 Mormon colonizing had been in progress for almost a century; it continued to change deserts to secure farm lands. I reflected on this while visiting Hurricane, a Mormon community in the mesas of southeastern Utah. The life and green fields of Hurricane depend on a home-made irrigation canal that taps the rambunctious Virgin River. The canal is about eight miles long, nine feet wide, and four feet deep. It continues to carry enough water for forty-five farms, and irrigates about two thousand acres that support twelve hundred people.

Mormon settlers had spent fourteen years digging and building the canal. They dug it with picks, shovels, and drills; prodded and blasted through nine tunnels, guided the precious irrigation water along sheer cliff walls hundreds of feet above the mesa table, in part by building wooden flumes on high trestles. There is always water in the Virgin River.

Eight miles away, rich soil awaited the water. Earlier, about a hundred Mormons joined in a "drive" to bring the precious water and the dry soil together. They issued blocks of twenty shares each, all payable in labor. Each share entitled the owner to one acre with "primary water rights" and an equity in a town lot, exact choice of land to be decided by drawing straws. The length of the proposed canal was marked off into stations of four rods each; these were assigned to stockholders, who pledged themselves to work out their stock payments with labor credits decided on a basis of the difficulties to be met, whether solid rock, loose rock, or earth.

In summer the settlers took recess from canal building to tend their precariously dry farms. Between November and March all able-bodied men and boys packed "grub boxes" and went to the mountains, leaving the women to tend the homes and livestock. Workers labored and wintered in the rough lands until at long last the canal carried water to the fertile drylands below. The first ten families to move in elected to live in tents and sod dugouts until they had made first crops. By 1930 the Hurricane desert was flowering and bearing. Its fields were green and heavy with harvests. Even at Depression prices the sales of special foods, including peaches, grapes, and pecans, each year repaid the recorded cost of building the most unusual canal.

Back in 1857, while giving counsel that it is cheaper to feed Indians than to fight them, Brigham Young pointed out that the terrors of the wilderness, such as Indians, man-eating grizzlies, and uncrossable rivers, were but temporary drawbacks. Indians would grow accustomed to white men. Mormon hunters would soon wear down the bears. Ways and means would eventually be found for bridging the more troublesome rivers. But Prophet Young never entertained any illusions that wilderness-fighting is a game for softies, or that the intermountain West, even when won, would be easy to hold.

Flood damages and wind erosion are forever menacing. Cheap lands capable of growing crops become ever scarcer. Most of the good land accessible to water was already either in use or being held at prices beyond the purse of a poor colonizer. Capable colony founding and the successful return of men to land had never been more formidably difficult. But the Church, which during 1931 had about 12 percent of its 750,000 members in the United States on relief rolls, in less than two years had helped about 33,000 of its members to find self-sustaining places in farming communities. The specifics were highly localized, but the total enterprise was of enduring world significance. Already at least fifty other countries, from the Andes to the Urals, from the Sudan to farthest Australia, were instituting irrigation as a *sine qua non* of food production. But the Mormons continued to lead with this earlier lifeline to preassured harvests.

In its practical sense, farm irrigation in the United States began in what is now Salt Lake City back in 1841, when Mormon pioneers undertook to plow a first dry furrow to carry water. One plowshare broke. The second dug into the dust and hardpan and opened a way for water that irrigated a first crop of potatoes. Since then the irrigation ditch has remained the Mormon trail to survival.

For the best of reasons the Church had grown to be an international reservoir for scientific information about irrigation and food supply. Church-directed research had already set in work a master manual of watering based on accepting the idea that by no means all lands can be effectively irrigated, even when water is amply procurable. Dr. John A. Widtsoe, the foremost Church authority on dry-land utilization, was one of the first students to demonstrate that by cutting off water from wheat immediately before harvest time the protein content of the grain can be materially increased, and that food values of many other crops can be improved by the more exacting use of minimum irrigation.

Church scientists were even then demonstrating that improved fertilizing of land can greatly reduce the amount of water required for successful irrigation and that tilth or structure of soil is of primary importance to effective water use. Meanwhile, the progress and demonstration of crop irrigation were expanding apace with the hard, long-time procedures of wresting farm sites from the deserts or the terrestrial wreckage of earlier farms and ranches that had failed. Undeniably, the land-earning Mormons were exceptional Americans of an exceptional Christian faith. By census the Mormons were only about six-tenths of 1 percent of the U.S. public; their farming members were barely 1.5 percent of the prevailing farm population. But Mormon farm communities were even then at work in five other American nations, while their missionaries dutifully proselytized in a dozen more. Stubbornly and devotedly, they were writing their own saga on hard but enduring earth.

MORE GRASS—MORE MEAT

THE ALL-but-invincible zeal of outer-fringe Mormon farming communities impressed me very deeply. I could only regard their story as an American epic that revived the past and stepped determinedly into the future. To my chagrin, what is laxly termed "general readership" turned out to be glumly disinterested. Even the Curtis editorial staff, which then abounded in professed

Western-enthusiasts, post-mortemed my reportorial labors as a passable struggle with an impossible subject. One of the associate editors noted that this was the first he had ever heard of the Church of Jesus Christ of the Latter-day Saints. Another confided that he knew only, but surely, that Mormons are a cracked remnant of fanatical sectarianism —partly-alive contemporaries bent on defying what he termed "agronomic rudiments."

The obese analyst elucidated over a large Philadelphia beef pot-pie with boiled onions and tallow sauce: "Look, brother, your copy shows entirely too much sympathy for those bucolic crackpots. You insistently overlook what ludicrous dust-scratchers those self-alleged saints really are. Consider the salient facts: the United States is officially striving to institute agricultural birth control. So the Mormons officially strive to increase food production. The U.S. government is trying to withdraw marginal lands from farming use. So Mormons are once more hell-bent on bringing back bone-dry lands where more rational Americans have long since been starved out. These mis-timed saints keep plugging along, trying to make the deserts flower and all that malarkey, while the rest of the country tries to get on to admitting sensibly that we have maybe half-a-billion acres of nondesert lands that by all that is reasonable and right should be passed back to the Indians or maybe the U.S. Bureau of the Budget. You extol the Mormon 'community,' but what's so bloody wonderful about communities of desertside goons?"

I murmured something about there being no real point to further arguing; as a non-Mormon I had to concede that these somewhat less-than-literal Latter-day Saints and their followers and leaders were indeed at cross furrows with the prevailing clamorings and incantations of the no-longer-new New Deal: wherever official Washington was saying "is,"

Mormons were saying "is not"; where the officialdom of the Potomac Flats was saying "is not," Mormon leadership was repeating, "Only God knows and can reveal."

Yet, as any onlooker could perceive, these sons and daughters of Deseret, by a wondrous admixture of common man's pragmatics and uncommon faith, were once more shaping farming patterns of worldwide consequence. While the United States at large was being harassed by political epidemics of extreme nationalism and favored regionalism, the Mormon farming community continued to devise and prove ways and means for reclaiming near-deserts and causing them to live and be fruitful. The reclamations were not huge in spread; the Mormons had remained comparatively few in numbers (the American membership at the time was only about 800,000). Yet Mormon colonies or renovated communities were enduring, in great part thriving, in seven states of the U.S. West and Southwest; in Canada, Mexico, Brazil, Argentina, and Peru; and to visible degrees in five other American nations. Mormon missionaries were very ably proselytizing throughout most of the Christian and partly Christian world; Mormon credos of land use were respected in scores of nations.

Whatever the specific place, the working goal in Mormon colonization was the community development of "pockets," or special vantages, of high-yielding, usually irrigable crop lands, interspersed and supplemented by improved grass lands provided with well-chosen grazing livestock. This was, and it remains, ably definitive of new shapes in increasingly worldwide food production, an American progress story self-proven as a world progress story.

During the epochal 1930s the range agriculture of the American West, particularly the western Great Plains, the Intermountain West, and the more rugged Pacific West range lands, managed to endure and typify in ways that were at least akin to what many foreign appraisers were listing as Mormon ways. Cattle, which had done most to "open" the North American West, one of the earth's maximum strongholds of indigenous grasses, had continued to "save" the greater part of the U.S. West, insofar as it was then being saved.

However much frustrated by the prolonged siege of Depression, the consumer's desire for red meats, particularly beef, had remained practically invincible. Depression or no, the per capita consumption of beef and dairy products had been showing persisting gains averaging 2 to 3 percent for each successive year of the 1930s. It was not a "smooth" gain; because of appallingly low prices for meat animals, there were no financial beds of roses for either cattle-raisers or dairy-farmers. Even so, U.S. consumption of both beef and dairy products was gaining more rapidly than the census, and this held for substantial areas of the Western World, particularly Russia, Northern Europe, and Scandinavia, and also Australia, New Zealand, and several regions in Latin America. In the latter, and somewhat abruptly, Brazil was taking a place on the roster of principal cattle-raising nations; Mexico, Venezuela, Colombia, and Cuba were gaining, cattle-wise; Argentina could count more beef cattle than people, as could its backwoods neighbor Paraguay (now the only nation on earth with more cattle than people). In all instances the ascendancy of cattle-raising confirmed an upsurge of grass-lands dependence and development.

By the middle 1930s meat production was trending upward on every continent except Africa. Once more, pedants and academic theorists chorused that this simply could not continue. But numerous agricultural censuses insisted it was continuing. As usual, the Malthusians were murmuring and revising their credo of eventual world hunger. This time their prevalent chant was that as the financially favored consumed more meat the more impoverished would be left to hunger.

Evidence to the contrary was gaining scope and impressiveness. Undeniably, planet Earth had far too many blotches and shades of hunger, but the rapidly expanding changeover to higher ratios of meats seemed to be improving nutritional balances and averages. As the 1930s moved along pork was holding second place (to beef) in the United States and gaining strongly as a basic red meat in Scandinavia, Northern Europe, and great areas of East and Central Asia. China was far in front as the world leader in swine-raising. Soviet Russia, where artificial insemination of both cattle and sheep was being ably pioneered, had already taken over as world leader in sheep-raising, and held third place (after India and the United States) in cattle numbers.

The crux of the development, so it seemed to me, was in the areas of land used, particularly the improvement and renewed pioneering of grasslands, and the gradual, sometimes bumbling, but largely inevitable fostering of hardier and more adaptable types, breeds, and strains of grazing livestock. In the United States the Mormons were very noteworthy way-blazers for this largely unpublicized transition.

Especially for the Western Hemisphere, cattle was leading the fairly gradual changeover to larger proportions of meat in prevailing diets. But, as already noted, the 1920s had proved themselves a decade of climax for the extravagantly fat meat animal. Consumers had tended to assume that any meat animal short of waddling fat was either sick, undernourished, or "tough," or perhaps all three. The so-called "quality meat" trades had nurtured that myth and continued disparaging the "grass-fed" and extolling the "grainfed" with almost imbecilic disregard of the facts that all our grains are indeed grasses and that hundreds of species of forage grasses, along with clovers and various other companion legumes, if given a reasonable chance are magnificently capable of providing the ingredients of lean meat and fat in desirable ratio.

But the already world-leading U.S. meat production had gravitated toward the grain storages and feeding lots, leaving the attainable pasture of range land merely to supplement or "live storage" for the fattening pens. The grass-blessed U.S. West was among the bigger losers. Mormon "colonizers," or, more literally, recolonizers, had once more taken a way-showing role by restoring Western "graze power" and developing more suitable grazing animals. Their work seemed to me to have profound and virtually worldwide significance, and it was showing a definitely hopeful way of redemption for larger and ever important areas of the U.S. West.

In the Deer Lodge Valley of Montana, during 1936 I studied a valiant attempt to restore to productive solvency what had once been the largest open-range beef-raising enterprise in the United States.

Back in 1865 Conrad Kohrs, a German-speaking butcher from Schleswigz-Holstein, bought a 60,000-acre ranch near what is now Deer Lodge, in Western Montana. The fact that the former wagon-train cook and more recently meat supplier for Montana gold rush followers paid the price of $19,500 in gold dust proved his competence as a trader. Within a third-century the Kohrs' spread was home base for the Pioneer Cattle Company, which had operated as many as a million head of open-range cattle, thereby establishing Kohrs as the Cattle King of Montana.

Now, after another third-century, Con Kohrs' favorite grandson, Con Kohrs Warren, son of the then departed Cattle King's daughter Katherine and a pioneer Virginia psychiatrist, had taken over the remnant, about 6,200 acres of the once tremendous cattle base, and set out to make it live again. During his heyday, Con Kohrs and scores of other bigtime operators had ranged their herds on the public domain lands, where free, or almost free, grass waited by the tens of millions of acres—bluestems, buffalo grass, and scores of others of the grand old forage standbys. The old-time cattlemen moved their herds to the grass and with comparable expedience adjudged cattle as low-cost meat.

A longhand page from a Kohrs Company 1881 range book read:

No. of cattle as shown by the books	9,226
less small lot in Judith basin	47
estimated loss on road last summer	50
butchered at Fort and at ranch	68
last year's calves killed by wolves	128
losses during winter	750
killed by Indians	1,300

Even so, his open-range cattle ventures thrived. In 1883, as the railroads began pushing in, Kohrs bought a two-thirds interest in the DHS Ranch in Central Montana and turned to ranging herds on superb public grasslands. As early as 1872 the American Abraham of public domains effected a first big-scale purchase of Texas cattle. This raised his holdings to an eventual half-million head. Con Kohrs was delighted with an additional bovine cornucopia. He was no less delighted by his opportunity to serve as guardian and godfather of his youngest grandson and namesake, whose father had died two months after the child's birth.

While the ranch-prone grandson was in high school at Helena, and directly before Con Kohrs' death in 1920, the Pioneer Cattle Company was abruptly liquidated. Con Warren finished high school, worked a spell as an intinerant ranch hand, then packed off to the University of Virginia to study medicine. After an unhappy year there Con Kohrs Warren came home in 1924 and took over the withered remnants of what had once been the proud Kohrs home ranch, which had dwindled to 6,200 acres. The available irrigation water was adequate for about only 500 acres of field crops. The remaining high-yielding native pastures had shrunk to a single square mile, with the Deer Lodge mountains, lavender and blue, still standing alluringly in the background.

Though long indoctrinated as a cattleman, Con Warren promptly became a practical farmer and a capable irrigation engineer. He was obliged to supplement the surviving remnants of range with planted grasses and legumes, and to limit the size of the herds to the attainable supply of feed. He shaped his irrigation system to snow water supplied by two mountain creeks. The nearby Clark Fork River still provides irrigation water. Warren began planting about two hundred acres of the irrigated land in feed grains—barley, oats, and wheat; about one hundred in mangel-wurzel, a root crop similar to sugar beets; the rest to timothy, clover, and native hay for feeding horses, steers, and bulls, and to alfalfa for feeding cows and calves.

It followed that the old ranch soon became dotted with fattening pens, haystacks, sheds, granaries, and small barns. Trucks and tractor-drawn trailers came puttering over the landscape, driven by cowboys who had learned to double as dirt farmers, engine handlers, veterinarians, and nursemaids to mothering cows. In the old ranching days, nature was left to take its course with calving livestock. The "get" either survived or it didn't, and for a big range herd the natural loss of a few hundred calves was to be expected. But with inevitable reduction of herd numbers and immensely higher unit values, knowledge of bovine obstetrics was a working prerequisite for the cowpuncher on what was once the nation's largest cattle ranch.

A new era of dungareed cowboys had come to Montana. The Con Warren force began at wages averaging a bit higher than the prevailing salaries of local high-school teachers. They were living in bunkhouses that had been used for three previous generations of cowboys, sleeping on army cots, eating at a splendidly set table, quite frequently with vases of flowers gracing the nearby window sills.

Old Con Kohrs hired three cowboys for every thousand head of cattle. Modern ranching requires six or seven men for a thousand head. But where Con Kohrs raised cattle to be butchered, his grandson was raising them to become parents and grandparents of cattle to be butchered. In the main, Warren was selling herd bulls instead of steers, breeding heifers instead of beef cows. All the bulls and about half the cows were purebreds with registry papers waiting the buyers. The rest of the females were grades bred for range use.

Nobody knew better than Con Warren that registry papers alone do not assure successful cattle growing. The payoff remains a matter of developing types of young cattle that can endure on sparse range and carry more pounds of good beef on the same bone structure. Rainfall is still the wild face-card in the deck. If a rancher uses his herd bulls to breed all the cows that are fertile and the next year is one of drought, it is just too bad. Lacking the free grass that cushioned the old school of ranching, the contemporary cattlemen, Con Warren among them, were obliged to take careful inventory of the carrying power of their lands. Con had open-range grass and enough irrigated land to carry about 800 head of cattle dependably. When good seasons came, his laboriously built feed power could sustain about 3,000 head of cattle; even that was a subdued, penny-whistle shadow of the once momentous Kohrs herds.

But Montana, like about two-fifths of the United States and somewhat more than three-eighths of the food-producing world at large, is semi-arid country, and seasons for abundant grass are but handouts of fate. So, like most other Far West cattlemen, Con Warren was keeping his herds close to proved minimum, never more than 25 percent above it, and seeking survival by better feeding, breeding, and management. Above all, he was building for hardier stock better suited to what remains of the Far West range lands.

As I continued to travel the West during the drought-seared 1930s, I observed that both the leavings and restorations of Western grass were providing a steadily increasing argosy of beef. No less significantly, the beef bearers were acquiring a renewed hardiness engendered in principal part by a turning back to more rugged and basic types of range cattle. Here again were meaningful shapes of international applicability, a reiteration that most sizable and populated areas of Planet Earth have at least the memorable remnants of indigenous food plants and food animals that invite and reward attention and persistent efforts to re-establish them.

A century or more earlier, in the 1830s, unowned, open-ranging, and otherwise wild longhorns (there are formalists who insist that the longhorn, which lacks formal registry, is not truly a breed but rather a utility type, or forebear) had been the self-adapted and best-adapted cattle breed of the lower American West and Southwest. As of 1850 or thereabouts, the open-ranging longhorn herds had been estimated as no fewer than forty million head, somewhere near the present total of beef cattle west of the Mississippi. Fairly reliable railroad records indicate that during the 1870s no fewer than twelve million open-range longhorns were shipped to

Eastern markets. But by 1920 the amazing breed that Indians had called rainbow cattle (because they come in most of the colors of the rainbow) was far along toward total extinction.

During the 1930s longhorns were being brought back by one valiant old-school Western cattleman: as this is written William Earl Drummond, Jr., is eighty-six and still hustling cattle in the rough drylands around Cache, Oklahoma, where he devoted his best years to reviving the American longhorn.

When I first met Earl Drummond he was a youthful fifty-two, and head ranger for the Wichita Mountains Wildlife Refuge, which adjoins Fort Sill artillery ranges in far southwestern Oklahoma. There this soft-spoken, wiry man, five-feet nine, sun-browned to about the color of an oak leaf in midwinter, and impressively bow-legged from a lifetime in the saddle, was beginning to triumph as reviver of the rainbow cattle. Earl had spent most of his first thirty years as one of the last drivers and "recruiters," or buyers, of open-range cattle; not all of them were true longhorns, but practically all were self-fending "open rangers."

Earl's father, Bill (William Earl) Drummond, Sr., had been a partner of Jesse Chisholm and a fellow opener of the two-pronged Chisholm Trail. The elder Drummond was a cowman with a liking for history and a talent for memorializing historic occasions when he met them. Accordingly, on May 20, 1891, while moving a herd into railroad corrals at Dodge City, Kansas, Bill Drummond halted his forces and sent for a photographer. When the latter arrived, the great drover of longhorns lined up his seventeen helpers, six of whom were Negroes, then dismounted, pushed back his doe-skin sombrero, and squatted on the heels of his fancy-figured, sharp-toed, and highly polished cowboy boots. Appropriately, Bill's then eight-year-old son, who had ridden the outfit's chuck wagon more than two hundred miles, pushed back his little doe-skin sombrero, dusted off his fancy-stitched little boots, and squatted beside his father.

It made a memorable "pitcher," all but reeking with historic significance. The elder Drummond and his rangers had recruited the herd all the way from the tall-grass prairies near Galveston, completing it while driving through the Cherokee Strip and the Wichita prairies. On arrival at Lamson's pastures near Dodge City, buyers had begun converging to view the stock and offer bids. Among these were two notable personages, Conrad Kohrs, cattle king of Montana and president of the Pioneer Cattle Company, and his half-brother and partner, John Bielenberger. After viewing the herd the two big-timers assembled their accompanying cowhands, and after a prolonged conversation in Dutch-German Con Kohrs bid $30.17 each for his pick of 1,300 head. That left Drummond with a remainder of about 2,000 to drive on to the greening grainlands of Iowa and Minnesota, where farmers waited to buy the lean range stuff, which they would "feed out" to market-attracting plumpness.

But before moving the cattle again, dehorning was necessary. Many of the steers had horn spreads of around five feet, and occasionally more; as Earl Drummond recalled, something in the grass down Galveston way growed wicked big horns. Taking off the horns called for roping, hog-tying, and manual sawing. On cows and calves, and on bulls with buffalo-style horns, Bill Drummond left the head cutlery intact; to dehorn the steers he divided his work force into roping crews of three or four men and assigned a saw man to each crew. They sawed off the big horns and smeared the bloody stubs with warm tar. Day after day the pile of horns grew. By the end of the week it was almost as big as the Dodge City Baptist Church.

When the big and bloody job was completed, Bill Drummond was in a mood for what he termed "memorializing." With his entire work force and several buyers as a captive audience and his son as straight man, he opened, "This here's not by no means the biggest herd I ever droved. Plenty of times I've contracted herds of better'n five thousand to railheads up to a thousand miles from first buyin' places." Nobody could deny that. Outbound drives of longhorns began during the 1840s, long before the railroads "got West." One of the first and longest cattle drives was the McInerny brothers' "push" from Galveston across the Rockies to Sacramento, California, during the Great Gold Rush of 1849. As a young man (late in 1861) the senior Drummond had participated in one of the more daring of the Civil War drives; he and five partners succeeded in swimming a sizable herd of longhorns across the Mississippi to already beleaguered Confederates at Vicksburg.

But the real push began after the war ended, when bulging industries in the East and North catapulted demands for beef. During that era, Texans took the lead in rounding up and branding the "wild" cattle and recruiting the big long drives to railheads and river ports. Perhaps never before in history had wild lands given so much good beef to so many consumers.

After the big exoduses over the Chisholm and other major cattle trails, which in great part began as open routes on which the rainbow cattle grazed their way, Bill Drummond, along with most of his colleagues, changed to a free-lance cattle buyer. The "big gush" was fading. Bill spent most of the 1890s recruiting longhorns for the audaciously long drives to Minnesota, where homesteaders with big grain crops were eager to buy "feeders." Drummond and his helpers searched far and wide, buying longhorns by fives and tens, or as need be by ones and twos, collected them in "muster pens," then, with several hundred in tow, headed the long drive north. Over a route where "modern" cattle would probably perish of thirst and hunger, the longhorns not only got to the feeder pens but, with expert herding, even gained weight en route.

The driving was never easy and without hazards. The longhorns were wild, ready to stampede at the drop of a hat, a loud sneeze, the shadow of a buzzard, or a plunk on a banjo. Most fortunately, the adversity of singing cowboys had not yet materialized. But the real ruiner of the longhorns was barbed wire. The damned stuff was being popularized about the time Earl Drummond was born; by 1891, when he first went longhorning, it was being shipped West by the trainload. It had begun cutting the guts out of the Great Plains ranges and thereby doing more to strangle the longhorn than all the ropes or lariats ever thrown.

When the elder Drummond insisted that the era of the longhorn was finished, Earl, who usually agreed with all his father thought and said, respectfully took issue. "There will always be longhorns," he said, "on account of longhorns is the best damn cattle that walks! And I aim to keep with 'em!"

Earl Drummond did keep with 'em. About twenty years after stating his resolve, the old-timer's trailin' son found employment as custodian of longhorn cattle and buffalo on the Indian lands that were presently to comprise one of the first and most effective of the federally owned wildlife refuges. This Wichita Refuge is haven for some of the best native prairies remaining in the Americas; experts contend that its deep-rooted grasses have been growing for many centuries. Earl Drummond first became acquainted with the 69,000-acre spread back in the '90s, when it was part of the Apache-Kiowa-Comanche Reservation. As the reservation's head ranger from 1917 through 1953, Earl worked to permit the great indigenous grasses to bring themselves back on the bare flats, in gulches and on mountainsides, at the bases of the natural rock piles (called wild-turkey altars), and on the high mesas where antelope still run and elk still thrive.

Before Earl Drummond came along, the reservation's most steadfast enthusiast had been Vice President Theodore Roosevelt, Rough Rider, former New York Governor, and presently the youngest President of the United States. While Vice President and ardent follower of customarily tumultuous Rough Rider conventions (most of the Rough Riders were from either Indian Territory or Oklahoma Territory), T.R. had spent considerable time at wolf hunting on the Wichita lands. After his induction as President, one of his first moves was to have about twenty of the rougher square miles of the land fenced off as a wildlife refuge. Around that time Earl Drummond was in the area, buying and selling cattle among his good friends the Kiowas.

In this pursuit and on rough and dry ranges where the fancypants breeds could not conceivably endure, Earl Drummond continued to recruit the sparsening longhorns. On medium grass they kept butter-fat, even where water holes averaged twenty miles apart; for good measure, the rainbow cattle remained free from tick fever and other contagions that afflicted the purebreds.

Late in 1914, after he had "cattled" his way back to southwestern Oklahoma, a government job as "buffalo ranger" sort of settled down on Drummond. As the first and last of the U.S. Civil Service buffalo rangers, he mapped the grass, painstakingly located and counted the bison—at the time thirty-seven head—and determinedly began herding them to hillside grasses, thereby giving the valley ranges a chance to recover. All the while he kept thinking and making plans in terms of longhorn cattle. Early in 1917 another great Paleface Chief, named Woodrow Wilson, ordered what had been known as the Wichita Mountains National Forest changed to the Wichita Mountains Wildlife Refuge and abruptly canceled all existing grazing leases.

Two longhorn steers were left on the refuge, as "too wild to ketch." The manager instructed Ranger Drummond to go out and rope them. Earl tried, but every time he got within a quarter-mile of the mavericks they tore out like shot cats and took refuge in a jungle of wild sunflowers. "Shoot 'em!" the bureau boss commanded. Earl hated to do it. But orders are orders, and the regretted results only whetted the Drummond determination to bring back the wildland breed.

The episode of the martyred longhorn mavericks catalyzed Drummond's resolve to bring back the longhorns. He was interrupted by the First World War, during which he served two years as mule driver for the AEF. On his return to buffalo ranging, he began writing letters to seek support of his one-man crusade on behalf of the vanishing breed. One of his first answers came from a New York congressman who asked what was meant by "longhorn cattle." Earl replied:

Dear Mister Congressman:

Longhorn is the original Western American breed of cattle. It is generally rangy stock with fairly big bones. Average weight for cows is 700 to 800 pounds; for young steers around 1200; ton-weight steers generally take seven to eight years to get there. . . . Longhorns have fairly shallow heart girth; and long legs which take off fast on a sprint. Eyes are wide apart and appear more so because of the long face. Horns are sizable; a five-foot spread with ten-inch butt circumference is average for a five-year-old steer, though the horns frequently grow a lot longer.

Colors of longhorns come all the way from white, or cream, or dim pale blue, to solid black, though the cattle is apt to be speckled, roan, brindled, or faun colored, with light reds very common. Black points, including black muzzles, black circles around the eyes, or on forelegs or tail brushes, are good signs. So is color lines, in red, black, or brown, down the backbone.

Longhorns made theirselves a true cattle breed. They are thought to be descended from Spanish cattle first brought to the Mexico ranges by a Spaniard named Gregorio de Vallabobo. I happen to know the north Mexico ranges right well, but wasn't around while Mr. Vallabobo was there and so never got to look at his cattle. I do know that longhorns are the best and hardiest cattle that walks.

Earl Drummond confided that, next to roping a buffalo, writing letters was the hardest job he ever did. Nevertheless, he wrote hundreds. After about three years he struck pay dirt in the person of John B. Kendrick, then a United States Senator from Wyoming, also then the nation's biggest independent sheep grower, and a perennial authority on open ranges.

The Senator maneuvered a Congressional appropriation for "establishing a breeding herd of at least twenty true American longhorn cattle." Earl Drummond was assigned its implementation as an addition to his regular duties. The Forest Service assigned him two "junior" foresters as would-be assistants. Earl tried to tell the tree men about longhorns. After a tour of the Louisiana Everglades the foresters returned with voluminous notes on Everglades sylvan life and a scrub bull calf. Earl Drummond took over as searcher—on horseback. As a first play he worked the lower Mississippi Delta lands. Swamp angels, sharecroppers, town marshals, village drunks, and other preponderantly good people showed the way to hundreds of mongrel cattle that they described as longhorns. But none was.

Next he tried the Galveston marshes, again without success. "I had buffaloes, elks, antelopes, wild turkeys, quail, deer, scissortail flycatchers and fattail straw bosses, but nary a longhorn." But he kept right on searching. In the Houston-Galveston marshes and the Pecos lands of West Texas he found some promising facsimiles. While riding open-range country in Mexico's Sonora, he located and purchased eighteen longhorn "types," and after extensive foraging he located a dozen more in the Rio Grande back flats. The first gathering of might-be longhorns—twenty cows, three bulls, three yearlings, and four calves—arrived in slatted railroad cars at the Cache, Oklahoma, railyards, bellowing and battling. After thoughtful re-examination, Earl listed twelve of the group—one bull, eight cows, and two calves—as "true-breeder" longhorns.

He next escorted the founding dozen to the refuge and the green pastures he had been grooming for them. The cattle, so he admitted, were wild as a beer-soused baseball pitcher on a hot night in St. Louis. Earl Drummond set out to tame them by means of prudent handouts of his wife's butter-pecan cookies, and fascinated them by cupping his hands to his mouth and crooning "soo-ooo-ook" in a reassuring baritone.

During 1928, after three weeks of diligent rousting on Chihuahua ranges, Earl located and brought back alive two well-pointed longhorn bulls, both light red with good shoulders and back lines; the following year eight longhorn calves were born on the refuge, five of them with impressively good markings. Drummond's next acquisition was a "lot" of three half-starved Mexican steers. The three weighed in for a total of 1,501 pounds. After one year on good bluestem grass and without other feeding or shelter, the same three weighed out at 3,006 pounds. "Real longhorns!" Earl mused.

The need for additional recruiting remained. In Juarez he acquired two more bulls, which he named Old Broad and Old Brown. On arrival both looked and acted most gentle. In the slatted freight car they just stood and kissed each other. Taken to the refuge pastures, they nodded respectfully to the senior bulls, kissed several of the cows, and gave slobbery hairdos to some of the young calves. Earl fed them a pocketful of his wife's cookies. But the instant that another range-hand came in sight, both the Juarez bulls took after him. The range-hand jumped to his saddle, spurred his horse, and took the corral fence in the nick of time. The two bulls hit the fence head on, flattening the entire panel, then regained footing and chased the fleeing range-hand for another half-mile.

"Real longhorns!" Earl mused. He repeated the observation when a longhorn cow with tooth marks indicating an age of about twenty-five gave birth to a healthy calf with excellent longhorn markings. And again when two six-year-old longhorn steers weighed out at 2,035 and 2,045 pounds. Ton-weight steers are almost unknown in present-day cattle-raising. A longhorn steer does not come prime until five to seven years old, but it carries rich-flavored and chewable steaks at least a decade longer than most beef cattle pure-breds.

Late in 1940 Earl Drummond was told of a herd of four hundred Mexican range cattle that were being held for the required ten days of quarantine at El Paso. He hopped the next train and viewed the herd in the customs corral. To his surprise and delight, he was able to pick out another ten excellent specimens of longhorns. He loaded them into two cattle cars and quite personally escorted the cars to the railhead next the Wichita Refuge. There he named one of the new bulls "Young Spots" (to differentiate from "Old Spots") and placed him directly with the cow herd.

It was a muggy summer day, with black clouds piling in front of the sun. Earl slipped the poncho out of his saddle pack and began driving for a sheltered valley. At the end of the valley he spotted an ominous wind funnel. So did the new bull. Abruptly, Young Spots left the cows and headed down the valley toward the forming tornado, which was already beginning to lift green leaves. Young Spots went galloping along toward the forming storm. Lightning struck a juniper within a rod of him. The young bull staggered, then got to his feet and charged the tornado funnel head-on. A split second later a lightning bolt struck the animal. Young Spots skidded to the earth and died, head up and horns gleaming, a knight defender to the end. Longhorns are like that.

Earl Drummond spent twelve years recruiting the breeding herd to a strength of 150 head; at that point he was in a position to practice selective breeding. He instituted yearly roundups at which he supervised the branding, selection and discarding of breeding stock. Following each roundup, as decreed by Bureau regulations, he instituted a yearly auction of surplus breeding stock. The first public auction of longhorns was held in September 1945, when the longhorn herd totaled 700. Ranchers and farmers waited in line to bid on the "rainbows." Several of the buyers expressed interest in developing private longhorn herds. Still more bought the bulls or calves for cross-breeding to develop more rugged range animals for rough-land and dry-land pastures. That, too, pleased Earl Drummond.

This is a continuing story; it could be one of the more encompassing and heartening of animal stories. The gist is that the best hope for maintaining meat supplies for principal numbers of people is in better uses of poorer lands by means of better adapted and hardier livestock. The "wild" cattle of the U.S. West and Southwest have counterparts in other countries and continents. There are many other basic or forebear breeds of cattle, sheep, swine, goats, and other valid meat animals which wait selective restoration. Thus the rainbow cattle of an earlier American West continue to symbolize the hope and promise of a better-fed earth.

Going
Global

SUGAR BOWL

DURING THE course of a single week early in 1937, I received letters from two exceptionally perceptive Americans, letters with substantially the same text. Theodore Dreiser, the preeminent American novelist of the period, and Howard Odum, the most gifted rural sociologist, shared the belief that the American era of nationalism was fading, like a morning fog being "burned off" by a strengthening sun. Both pointed out with emphatic eloquence that the American scene was taking its place in what Odum termed a "much more nearly total global mural." "We can no longer get away with pragmatic isolation," Dreiser declared. "The world is catching up with us. 'Nationalism' is no longer a dirty word, it's getting to be a silly word."

Dreiser, who had befriended me during one of my dingier years in New York, was in the vigorous throes of getting out of Greater New York, which he had begun to designate as God's Number One Spittoon. He was then getting himself resettled in Sante Fe, New Mexico, where he reported finding himself "momentously intrigued" by both the Indian and Spanish American farmers. He declared that both are world citizens—not by retreat to tourism or migrancy, but because, more successfully than any other Americans he knew, both the farming Indians and the *arroyo*-tenanting descendants of a nobler Spain have succeeded in shaping a sustaining companionship with the lands they till and love.

Howard Odum wrote that in the course of a summer spent in the impoverished and generally typical community of Farmington, in the Arkansas Ozarks, he was gaining what he termed his best comprehension of the "living sociology" of Italy and lower Eastern Europe. In their confused ways, my own prevailing ventures in earning a livelihood were shaping comparable findings for me.

I had shifted from magazine deck-handing and free-lance writing to a short-lived post as "listener coordinator" for would-be farm entertainment then being perpetrated by the National Broadcasting Company. My almost instant finding was that there was nothing to coordinate. The network concept of farm programs seemed to have no particular appeal to farmers as a professional group, who appeared to react most favorably to local news broadcasts, weather reports and forecasts, market quotations, and similarly mundane interests. The so-called "good" programs, such as they were, seemed to interest farm people much as they did (or didn't) interest the town or city listeners. "Regional farm interests" ranged from the dimly peripheral to the wholly unprovable. When I continued to conjecture that the American farmer could get along without network radio, NBC, at the time vigorously promoting its tenth anniversary as a network, revealed the brave premise that it could somehow survive without me.

Even so, my obdurate interval with the "pioneer national network" whetted my interest in several phases of food production with which I had no previous acquaintance. One of these was farm operation by corporations or corporate management. Among my befuddled radio chores was "arranging" for a network broadcast dealing with a British-owned plantation company that operated several large cotton plantations. This stirred my interest in the general subject, on which the Soviet Union's state farms and various other international farming companies seemed to have considerable bearing. Was there a place for corporation farming in the United States?

A frequently delightful Russian immigrant and political renegade who called himself Alex Gumberg was then the ingenious director of public relations for the Atlas Corporation. Alex suggested that I beat NBC to the firing play, resign and join Atlas as coordinator of its farm operations. Floyd Odlum, then head of Atlas, explained that his company was in temporary possession of a divergency of farm properties that included, in California, an apricot orchard, a lemon grove, and an English-walnut orchard; in Utah and Idaho, a mixup of sugar-beet farms; and here and there, some rather deplorable chicken and egg farms. Mr. Odlum genially suggested that I visit the properties and report frankly on my estimate of their worth and future, if any. After about three months of looking and listening, my estimate was that none seemed to require corporate ownership, that all except a circus-animal farm in Florida, which I had not visited, would appear more effective as privately owned and managed farm properties.

Odlum smiled pleasantly and said that he had arrived at the same line of thought; he had decided to sell the establishments as soon as even faintly solvent buyers could be found. He next suggested that I might care to have a look at an international farming company that he regarded as "interesting." This was the United Fruit Company, in which Odlum had lately taken the posts of director and vice-president. He added that I might enjoy a visit with Samuel Zemurray, the "oddball," Russian-born president of United Fruit, who was sometimes findable in Boston. The Atlas magnate added cautioningly, "I doubt if he has any job to offer, but I ask, as a personal favor, that you call on him."

The following noon, after a very baffling encounter with the cow-trail geography of downtown Boston, I located the general offices of United Fruit. An elderly lady receptionist favored me with a tremendously large and warming smile and skillfully minimized exposition: "I am Gertie, you are Wilson, and Mr. Zemurray wishes to see you now."

In a sparsely furnished, almost auditorium-size office, I saw a conspicuously tall, hard-featured man who stood before a large window, munching a banana and frowning dourly as he peered out on what appeared to be a virtual infinity of tar-smeared Boston roofs. He motioned me to a chair and, still frowning, finished off the big yellow banana. Having deposited the peel in a large and obviously hand-carved mahogany waste basket, he began striding the immense floor and speaking with a heavy, profoundly baffling accent.

"I don't veel much like talking," he glowered. "Vot I got to zay is you vent on pay roll dis morning, for the zame lousy pay Atlas giffs." He sighed loudly. "Go find Hatch and he vill vix you ship's pessage to Cuba. I vant virst you should go find out vot goes wrong there vid the zugar cane."

"I really don't know anything about sugar operations."

His big hands pantomimed impatience. "Vid zugar, people who don't know nuddings about it vork out best." He retreated to an oversize chair. "I vant you should go and vind oud vot goes wrong. Ven you find out, zend me a letter in caze I zend you vun."

The interview was ended. Two days later I was aboard the S.S. *Musa* bound for Santiago de Cuba, with everything to learn and little time in which to learn it. Cuban sugar was in its usual condition—crisis. United Fruit, as owner-operator of a hundred thousand acres of cane plantings and contract purchaser of cane privately grown on about fifty thousand acres, was operating two *centrales*, each with a major railroad, an oversize grinding mill, and fourteen thousand quasi-unemployed workers. The two centers comprised what was then the world's largest integrated sugar property and for fifteen consecutive years it had been losing money.

One principal reason was the severe limitations of milling quotas. As of 1937 the 153 cane mills then functioning on the island were limited by government quota to operating only 9 weeks of the year. For the other 43 weeks the sheet-iron-armored grinding mills, which rose out of the blue-green cane fields like colossal exclamation points, were gently rusting away.

Yet, economically sugar had remained the one proven hope for the largest of the Caribbean islands. Despite the severely restricted harvests and apparently deplorable records of the elaborately incorporated sugar companies, Cuba had kept on pouring out eight million tons of refinery sugar plus a million tons of commercial molasses each year.

At less than one-third of its known capacity, Cuba in 1937 was producing more than half of all sugar in international trade. Soviet Russia was in second place, with about one-third of Cuba's sugar production; the United States was in third place, with slightly more than a fourth of Cuba's output; while India, France, Puerto Rico, Germany, and the Philippines tagged along in that order. Cuba's very special distinction was one of environmental aptitude; the comparatively small island of about forty-four thousand square miles—not as big as Pennsylvania and less than half the size of Oregon—had already proved its capabilities for supplying every ton and pound of sugar in international trade. Quite

regardless of appallingly greedy and incompetent management and government, Cuba was already sugar bowl to the
world.

The lesson there was in support of particular crops for
particular places. For at least two centuries sugar had remained the dominant commercial crop of Cuba. Shackled
as it was in 1937, it still comprised four-fifths of the island's
foreign trade. But the sweetness of the *azucar* was literal,
not figurative. Cuban sugar had grown and endured by the
toil, sweat, and suffering of people who were, and alas still
are, enslaved.

More than three centuries earlier this Pearl of the Antilles
had emerged almost simultaneously as a slave island and an
international sugar source. The shackles of outright slavery
had been replaced by those of outside ownership. By 1915
U.S. investment capital owned outright about 40 percent of
all the island's sugar facilities; other alien investors or specu-
lators owned about 20 percent. Too literally for anyone's
comfort or good conscience, Cuba's incomparable sugar
crop again had been taken into bondage from abroad. Like
other procedures of enslavement, the overtures were on the
giving side. The First World War hugely increased world demands for sugar, particularly cane sugar. Combat armies
wheeled and trampled under much of the beet-sugar crops
of Europe. Beet-sugar lands of the U.S. West, already pap-
ping on political subsidies, turned to the greater profits ob-
tainable from the booming international demand for grains.
Cuba was deluged with the sweet juice of almost fabulous
prosperity.

With an unrivaled leadership in the international food
trade, Cuba's millside price of raw sugar cane spurted to
$400 a ton or higher, and mill-run cane lands began netting
an average of better than $800 per acre yearly. The biggest
and most instant winners, of course, were the alien owners.

United Fruit, the largest of these, took out immense profits throughout the war years and several more that followed. Cubans and their lands and climate produced the sugar; outside corporations took out the lion's share of the profits— practically all the sweet pap from about 8 million acres of cane plantings.

The "waltz of the butterflies" continued strong for at least five fabulous money-grabbing years. But the rural Cuban was the man (or woman) who made it possible. And the *buen hombre* and his *mujer* remained preponderantly hard-working, kindly, easy-smiling, and poor. Particularly in Oriente, the sugar state, sugar cane was their life; in lean times or fat, they met resurrection with each cane season.

Cockfighting was the symbol extraordinary. When mill stacks began to belch flames, the cockpits came alive again. Rural Cuba, I began learning, is a completely unscientific haven for all manner of freely roaming chickens; among these are the outrageously ugly, reptilian-like throwbacks called fighting cocks, which serve as magnets for the cock trainers who come and go with the cocks. I was assured that the trainer's first function is to make the birds *want* to fight, but I soon became convinced that a Cuban game cock never knows a conscious moment when he does not want to fight in the very worst way.

Even so, and weeks before the sugar pay-days begin, the trainers take their pens into deep and mysterious seclusion. Whatever the warlike meditations, any fighting cock may win, and any rooster may lose. With unpredictable randomness touted champions flutter to the dust and unknown scrubs march away victorious, while winners and losers of bets arise and cheer and pat shoulders. Rural Cuban life and sugar were like that.

But by 1937 the sugar-cane cock had been fluttering in

blindness for half a generation. Millside prices for "brown"
—the raw, unrefined sugar—were averaging about 20 percent of that twenty years before. As an added penalty, tariffs
on Cuban sugar ranged from the United States' "swat" of
$18 per ton to France's $33. Yet the Cuban sugar crop endured; in its darkest years it could survive the tariff
bludgeonings because it was vastly more efficient than any
other source. Thus sugar stayed the definitive life of Cuba.
A *Cubanero* was still appraised by the tons of cane he could
knife and strip during a field day, or his fleetness in the face
of a cane fire, or his prowess at manhandling those 330-
pound bags of raw sugar. Perhaps never before had a single
crop and its particularly demanding harvest so completely
dominated the lives and viewpoint of a great agrarian nation.

During my first week at the Banes *centrale*, I met the
island's then perennial strong man, Fulgencio Batista Zal-
divar, a sugar man to his twitchy eyebrows. Batista had been
born of a cane-cutting family and raised in a succession of
palm shacks on the wrong side of the railroad tracks at
Banes. He began his earning career as a cane cutter, then got
employment as a switchman on United Fruit's sugar railroad, then enlisted in the army as a common soldier. He
earned a sergeancy and, ultimately, by revolutionary coup
and deft help of U.S. sugar companies, a seemingly inter-
minable dictatorship. But first and last Batista was a sugar
hombre.

As a railroad switchman Fulgencio worked "under"
Chico Gonzales, a sugar-train engineer who was then closing
out his wheeling years as chauffeur for the manager of a
sugar mill. When Batista made a triumphant visit to his old
home town, his twenty-coach train pulled into the station
encircled by a cheering and flag-waving crowd. Old Chico
strolled up to the *Presidente*. Batista viewed his former boss
with a tremendous smile, cried out his name, then delivered
the authentic Cuban embrace—*slap, slap, slap* on the right

shoulder, *slap, slap, slap* on the left, followed by an impulsive hug. The crowd cheered again; Chico wept and Batista also wept.

Later Chico told me, 'That Batista was likable as a sugar *hombre*. As the *gran politico, Señor*, he smells. As dictator he is no longer a *Cuba libre*, but only a *Yanqui* hireling. Even so, *Señor*, like myself, that Fulgencio is still at heart a real Cuban. What is real Cuban? Ah, *Señor*, it is having the blood and breath of the islander, a splash of Indian, a stronger pouring of Negro, and maybe a drop or two of the Spaniards. But not enough to cause one to pretend he is a Spanish *don* with a bit of dark complexion, and a tattered black cloak of pride that is the always-showing inferiority complex of so many otherwise good mestizos."

My own interests were centered in the sustenance of people. Anybody could see that the sugar people were not well fed. I wondered why. My first glimpse of the island indicated that about half of it was still in forest. Principal provinces, including Oriente, Pinar del Rio, and Las Villas, are at the verge of being mountainous. But there were fertile green plains, such as those of Camaguey and Matanza, and the island's climate, with annual temperature averages in the low 70s (Fahrenheit) and rainfall of about 40 inches, is exceptionally well suited to a great many food crops. For Cuba as a whole, these were not being developed.

On arrival I indulged in a rather deliberate tour of the island by bus and railroad train, with some turns at cross-country walking. The potentials for subsistence agriculture were magnificent. For the most part they were not developed or apparently even perceived. The general farming was most needlessly inadequate. Never before had I met such likable agrarian people. Yet a majority of these people was enslaved by the sugar crop. With unrelenting finality, Cuba was sugar and vice versa.

The price of sugar was the fact or direct threat of food

shortage, and the dogging menace of malnutrition. Anyone could see even by a passing glance that great numbers of the sugar workers were not eating anywhere near well enough. My first look at United Fruit's sugar *centrales*, at the new sugar town called Preston and the drowsing old Oriente port of Banes, included hungry children and deeply disturbed breadwinners. I could not contradict Jesse Trinler's (the manager of the Preston division) assertion that United Fruit's sugar laborers were less hungry than the average and housed very much better. Nor that the feat of assuring adequate food and other necessities for 20,000 workers and their families during the yearly work waits of nine or ten months was indeed "one hell of a job."

But nobody could deny that United Fruit, like, even if less outrageously than, other principal sugar operators, had been needlessly lax in terms of readily establishable food crops. The company's employee houses were far above U.S. averages, the best I have ever seen in any tropical or subtropical place. The company stores and bakeries were well managed, with products fairly priced. There was accessible abundance of company-owned lands. Why not apportion some of these lands as home gardens or subsistence food plots for the benefit of employees who wished to grow at least some part of their needed foodstuffs for the cruelly long waits between cane harvests?

"It's an academic question," the two managers assured me, almost in chorus. "Naturally we've thought of that. But we are certain that no more than a trivial handful of our sugar workers can be sold the idea of growing their own *frijoles*. You must remember that these are sugar people, not dirt-scratchers. Maybe a few, one or two in a hundred, might eventually generate some interest in subsistence farming. But there's a heck of a long time drag involved."

But the mill engineer, a hard-working, patiently observing Irishman from South Boston, took a contrary view. He volunteered to discuss the idea personally with some of his mill workers who had been wondering aloud how they and their dependents would eat during the customary prolonged layoff just ahead. He presently extended the confidential canvass to twenty; all but one indicated they would like to have a try at making a garden. By the year's end a total of 1,256, about two-thirds of the resident employees of the Preston *centrale*, had expressed interest in having a try, for most of them a first try, at making a garden.

We marked off the lands, about an acre a family, and had it plowed and harrowed at company expense. At that point the difficulties began raising their stubborn heads. There was no "appropriation" from Boston; the only available source of the necessary costs was from the maintenance fund. We did not have the right kinds of seeds, fertilizers, or spray materials for garden making. The tools were limited to what the company stores had in stock, which included only hoes and hand-rakes, and not enough of those.

The available seed supplies were mostly of shell beans, and about fifty bushels of seed potatoes that a company clerk managed to procure in Havana. An accommodating florist in Santiago succeeded in producing about a hundred trays of tomato plants and a like number of green peppers, for transplanting. A company sugar chemist arranged for air-freight shipments of melon seeds supposedly adapted to subtropics use, while a resident Haitian farmer supplied several bushels of lima bean seeds. With the expert aid of a cane ranger, I searched for some tropics-adapted sweet corn, a venture that enabled me to become acquainted with the parents of Fidel Castro; they had lately emigrated from Spain and were toilsomely developing a sugar-cane acreage near Cedro Alto. Fidel was then about eleven, a solemn, rather handsome and almost worrisomely polite youngster who spent much of his time playing with dolls with his younger sisters. The Castros had been experimenting with vegetable growing, and very generously shared with us their homegrown supply of sweet corn.

The February garden plantings met with exceptionally unfavorable growing weather, but fortunately this was off-set at least in some part by a marked improvement in leadership. The resident superintendent of agriculture, an old-line county agricultural agent from New Hampshire, took over what he called "urging along the home gardening enterprises" when I was moved on to mainland Central America. Bill's report at the end of the season was a cryptic, "Made out pretty good."

During the following year a much more competent encore met with much greater success when two thousand of the family subsistence *milpas* were proved winners. Though by then long gone from Cuba, I tried to summarize the significance; at that stage of my life practically everything had to have significance. On the negative side, of course, the company's failure to have provided food-growing facilities several decades earlier was deplorable as well as stupid. The affirmative entries included the self-evident fact that Cuban sugar workers, long divorced from subsistence farming or gardening, possessed ready restorable talents for diversified food growing, as did their wives and children. All had been weaned away from self-sustenance by a pointless potpourri of neglect, evasion, and careless inference, and, more tangibly, a lack or failure to provide suitable seeds, fertilizers, spray materials, hand tools, and land—even though the latter was at hand in great abundance.

The acceptance that "sugar people are not dirt-scratchers" was obviously quite unrealistic. By the following late winter the communities of both sugar *centrales* had displays of home gardens of which any farming realm could be proud. The sugar workers were well acquainted with the fact that nobody can subsist on sugar, and they were actually quite eager, as they put it, to grow their own groceries. The fact that so many succeeded so readily doubly demonstrated that the "world's best sugar land" is capable of producing effectively a huge range of food crops. What was more, the readily improvised home gardens proved better agronomic competence than the master crop, sugar cane.

Actually, sugar cane, including that grown in Cuba, when measured by practical farming standards as already attained with other crops, was far short of being competently grown. Though the decisive story of Cuba was still being written on the scrolls of blue-green cane fields, it was not being written well enough. Although a great deal of varietal and other genetic improvements of sugar cane had been effected in Eastern Tropics research centers, particularly in Java, most Cuban sugar was still "scrub cane." Some improvements had been made in sugar refining, but the procedures of planting, harvesting, and grinding-mill operations showed only very belated advances, or none at all.

The real point, it seemed to me, was one of profound international significance. Cuba epitomized both graphically and humanly the gifted spheres or dabs of earth with preeminent ability to grow a particular crop with such outstanding effectiveness that by sound economic measure it deserves the privilege and advantage of serving as an international supplier of that crop. It is conceivable that tomorrow's world will necessarily be fed by the development and intelligent correlations of superior aptitudes for superior production of many or most of our basic food crops.

But this demands responsible and continuing improvements in planting materials, harvesting and processing techniques, and related agronomics. Cuban sugar was not receiving or being permitted these improvements. The attainment of these required enlightened government leadership at home and enlightened acceptance abroad. Cuban sugar was not receiving these. There was basic need for general and interrelated advances in domestic agriculture adequate for sustaining the principal population that would produce the "world crop." Here again, Cuba was left lacking.

CENTRO-AMERICANO

SAMUEL ZEMURRAY, president of United Fruit, replaced his upper plate and looked down on me despairingly. "So far you get by vid not knowing nuddings from nuddings about nudding you are doing."

His large hands scooped up a desktop collection of unopened mail, which he shoved remorselessly into the oversize wastebasket. "Like, for instance, dat silly banana train wreck you managed out of in Guatemala the day after you got there. I've been noticing for longer times than you've been crackering around on earth that in railroading the only sensible answers come from peoples like you vot don't know a ga-damn t'ing about railroading. Likevise, about zugar." He sighed loudly. "But starting now I vant you should begin to learn more about Middle America—by dat I mean from Cuba and Gutemala down through Ecuador and Columbia—about all such places I vant you should get to know more than any vun man liffing. I vant you should begin by forgetting all such hokum-bunkum that tropics come different from elsevare. Land is land, farming is farming, beople is beople vareffer they hoppen."

I began my ventures in confirmation in the subcontinent called Central America, a vivid conglomerate of doorway lands to the too often unreasonably hungry tropics. Comparatively speaking, the subcontinent is not big. In area Nicaragua, the largest member country, is about the size of New York State. Both Guatemala and Honduras are roughly the size of Pennsylvania. El Salvador is approximately as big as Maryland, and vies with Haiti, Belgium, and the Netherlands for dubious first place as the most densely populated of sovereign nations. Costa Rica is about half the size of Virginia; Panama is a little bigger than West Virginia.

It is almost equally easy to learn that Central America remains a miniature world of contrasts, a frequently engaging conglomerate of Indian nations, disintegrated or partially surviving; of fascinating geography of old and new frontiers, of wet jungles and dry highlands, grassy mesas and giant forests, and bare-topped mountains that overlook fertile valleys where the magnificent vegetation seems too preoccupied with birth and growth to allow time or space for death. The range and variety of vegetation are second to none of any like-sized area on earth; at very fewest Central America is the home of at least 250 species of edible plants.

The diversity of the people is at least comparable to the potential diversity of crops. I reflected on this and on the unending, ever-sustaining dependence on the age-old providers—earth, soil, rain, and sun—at the invincibly colorful depot at Barrios, one of Guatemala's older port towns. When I boarded the daily train, affably misnamed *El Rapido*, I found a seat beside a cheerful young man in blue dungarees and a gaily beaded, oversized sombrero. After a gracious exchange of greetings in almost verbless Spanish, *El Señor* shoved open an outrageously dirty window, then reached down to take a freshly peeled pineapple and a napkinful of *arroz con pollo* from the head-basket of a black-clad Indian woman who peddled homemade edibles to the *pasajeros*. Having paid generously for his purchase, the affable young man invited me to join him for a post-breakfast snack. When he inquired where I was bound, I explained that I was going to an inland village to visit with an interesting *patrón*. He asked if by any chance the village were Santa Rosa and the *patrón* were Tony Ramirez. When I answered affirmatively, he revealed that he had the same destination. "I work there," he explained. His smile revealed a double line of well-tended white teeth and one highly noticeable gold-plated incisor.

As we left the train together at the adobe depot booth, my companion graciously offered to lead the way to the Finca Ramirez. After we had walked a couple of kilometers and leaped across a series of newly built irrigation canals, we came upon a group of obviously amateur bridge-builders who shouted *"Buenos dias"* and waved broadaxes, mallets, and miscellaneous building tools in confirming salutes.

"I gather you are a very popular *mandador*." I hazarded the textbook word for "manager" with uncertainty. He smiled and painstakingly replaced his hat. "We are friends, *Señor*. They are my people, and I am their man."

I suggested that if he would show me the way to the owner's house I would not take more of his morning. He smiled and pointed to a circling gravel road. "The *patrón* lives at the second bend, *Señor*."

I thanked him and strolled ahead between neatly kept fields of corn and rank citronella grass with borders of young oil palms. Then, on a high ground at the second bend of the road I saw a modest white stucco farmhouse with intensely blue trimmings. When I knocked, a voice called out in English, asking that I enter and be seated. For a minute or so the contrast between the rather ornately curtained living-room and the intense sunlight outside impaired my eyesight. In due time I made out the person of my English-speaking host, who looked remarkably like my Spanish-speaking travel companion; except for the neatly combed black hair and the freshly laundered jacket, he was practically the spitting image. Even the voice qualities were remarkably similar.

I proceeded to indicate my surprise and befuddlement. "So you are Don Antonio Ramirez. Your English is—"

He interrupted happily, "My English is American self-harvested, beginning in Philadelphia." As he smiled I noticed that he had splendid white teeth with one lone incisor plated with gold.

The smile persisted. "I read your mind, *Señor*. You are asking yourself 'How much can look-alikes look alike?' Well, *Señor*, the answer is you are tiring your eyes by looking at the same *hombre* you met earlier today on the *rapido*. I am the same Tony Ramirez as previously. This is a silly little act I enjoy putting on in my own silly way. I have a back pathway to this house. Like now, when guests arrive, I meet them as a *laboro*, or as you say, *mandador*. Then I sneak in the back door, comb my hair and put on a clean jacket. That makes me Antonio, the *patrón*. A very silly game, but a sensible reminder that we *centroamericanos* are most really all the same—earth people."

He began to tell me his decidedly revealing story. His farm is what remains of an "ancestral estate." When Tony was fifteen, his father, then seriously ill, made final plans for financing his son's post-Rio Grande education to include high-school in Philadelphia, then four glorious years at Cornell University. Tony gratefully received his "heritage" of money and proceeded to Philadelphia. There he deposited his inheritance in a savings bank and took on a job as a bell-boy in a downtown hotel. He found that one of the better ways of learning English, sustaining his study at night school. After about a year in Philadelphia, Tony ventured to the Detroit area, where he found employment on a Ford assembly line. The following year he worked his way to an assistant foremanship at Chevrolet's plant at Flint, and next transferred to a General Motors plant in the San Francisco area. There the young immigrant looked to sea.

In successive night schools, Tony had been applying his talents as a linguist. This led to his next adventure in *Yanqui* job-holding, a secretaryship in a fruit and vegetable growers' cooperative down in the Modesto area. That opened the way to still another horizon-broadening employment, this time as a ship's purser—in the beginning, an assistant purser—for a British-owned cargo ship. In the course of about two years at sea Tony gained at least a portside view of many tropical places. He gained passing acquaintance with Java, where forty million farmers and twenty million other residents were sardined into a space about the size of Pennsylvania.

By contrast he found that New Guinea, the earth's second largest island (only Greenland is bigger), with a land area about the size of Texas, had barely one and a half million people, and major areas with around two people a square mile. He presently came to glimpse Madagascar, another Texas-sized island, describable as being about four-fifths unsettled. He therefore drastically revised his earlier concept of the tropics as hot places more or less swarming with people. This revision was further motivated by passing acquaintance with the coastlands of West Africa and various Western Hemisphere promontories, beginning with Mexico's generally dry and extremely sparsely peopled Pacific peninsula called Lower California. Subsequently he came to know the extremely sparsely-settled coastlines of northern South America and the vast coastal rinds of Brazil.

From his hard-scruffed shipboard retreat Tony Ramirez

had lengthy and varied opportunities to ponder man's use and misuse of tropical earth. As a reading man as well as an attentive listener, he grew aware that many of the limitations were in greatest part political and arbitrary. In those times (the middle 1930s) a majority of all tropical and subtropical lands were still colonies of old-line powers that willfully and often unwisely discouraged the development of colonial industries and, usually unwisely, maneuvered to favor so-called "trade crops." In great part these were poorly chosen in terms of the best interests of residents, and in too many instances they were not expertly or even competently grown.

From seaports and ship's cargo listing Tony Ramirez noted many other chronic problems that beset the basic economies of the warmer places. Most tropical harvests are bulky, heavy, and require railroad and ocean transportation. Quite outrageously, good tropical seaports are excessively scarce; at least three-fourths of tropical cargoes still require ferrying or have to be lightered to ships that are unable to dock directly in established harbors. Tropical railroads are notoriously difficult to build and operate. Back of their shorelands, most tropical countries are afflicted with impediments, including troublesome rivers, antisocial swamps, rugged mountains, and other barriers generally related to the persisting truth that although fragments of the tropical earth are regrettably overpopulated, more than two-thirds of it remains chronically underpopulated.

In the course of reading, for which the multilingual freighter purser had plenty of time, he became converted to William Crawford Gorgas' thesis that a given measure of human energy applied to a given resource is usually more productive in the tropics than anywhere else. Dr. Gorgas, like other wise appraisers, stressed the favorable fact that freedom from killing winter provides great advantages in terms of producing foods and incidental harvests from perennial crops. Rather oddly, the great sanitarian for the Panama Canal building project did not stress that freedom from winter kill also adds mightily to disease hazards and to the damages of other natural enemies, particularly insects and fungi.

From perceptive experience, Tony could add to the list of what he termed the human "down-pushers." For one, through the ages tropical people have lacked the disciplines required for making ready for and enduring long winters. For another, at least in principal part, tropical peoples have been by-passed by the pastoral ages, which in the temperate zones have done so much to enable pastoral man to change himself to a settled farmer and eventually to a merchant or craftsman or an industrial or professional worker. Another unbalancer is the fact that in the tropics mortal strength is ever slight in comparison with the might and lustiness of tropical vegetation, which is ever crowding itself against the man-made clearing, making it less and less possible for man by himself to realize tropical abundance with his own two hands plus his brawn. His productive work requires mechanical power and technical advantage.

Back in the 1930s, much was being made of a conquering era of synthetics. More and more creations that originated in the tropics were being produced under factory or laboratory roofs. But the meditative purser began to observe that more and more of the starting materials for synthetics originate in the tropics. Tropical sun power still comes free, as do great portionings of fertile soils and generous rainfalls. Any compiler of cargo lading could note a persisting increase of harvests. By 1935 the ship tonnages of tropical products were about six times those that had obtained a quarter-century earlier. Correspondingly, human population increases were shifting in tropical zones.

All too evidently the nineteenth-century concept of tropical colonies was no longer maintainable or even desirable. The pompous expedient of keeping the natives in their place had succeeded only in crowding the too many natives into untenable places.

Señor Ramirez grew more certain that tropics and temperate lands can endure only by increasing trade and interdependence. Quite aside from bulky freight cargoes such as timbers, mineral ores, copra and palm oils, jutes, and a hundred other entries, he was deeply impressed and gratified by what are sometimes termed tropical penetrations. American-made gadgets had long since invaded practically the whole of the populated earth. In reasonable or unreasonable return, the United States and the Temperate Zone world beyond had latched on to many elements of tropical culture: great spirituals from Africa, distinguished styles and apparels from Mexico, Guatemala, the West Indies, Java, Brazil, Siam, and other places; dance forms and music from as many more. Artists such as Picasso had derived inspiration from African primitive art.

The traveler from Guatemala was less favorably impressed by the little he saw and the much he heard regarding extreme tropical poverty. He was gaining acquaintance with now common phrases such as "underdeveloped" and "developing" countries. He noted that a preponderance of these were already of the tropics or subtropics and that, again speaking generally, tropical populations were increasing more rapidly than others.

After seven years of job-holding, with related and perceptive travels, young *Señor* Ramirez had a compelling urge to return to Central America, to which region or state, he was not sure. During his earlier years he had at least glimpsed most of the states of Central America. He fondly remembered beautiful Costa Rica, with her surprising abundance of unused and unoccupied lands that are more than half of the area of the little country. He correctly remembered Honduras as a sparsely settled and ever engaging frontier. He remembered British Honduras, a fertile, enticing, and largely unpeopled frontier, and the impressively fertile David area of Panama, with its magnificent farm lands still untouched by cultivation.

But he saw no compelling reason for not returning to Guatemala, his homeland. After all, he owned a midland *finca* there of two hundred hectares, or almost five hundred acres, for the most part restorable as crop land. He had his going-to-college inheritance intact with interest, and a dab of savings from more recent earnings to expand it.

The prodigal's homecoming was without boasts or fanfare. As Tony had anticipated, the family *finca* had suffered a great encroachment of jungle growths. Only one tenant remained; all the livestock had been sold to meet taxes.

The homecomer had expected to begin from scratch. To aid with the scratching he boldly invested in a light tractor and several plow and disk attachments. His first planting was grass, a well-studied attempt to establish a pasture for milk and beef cattle. His first building ventures included a screened milking barn and poultry house. He promptly abandoned the hillside coffee plantings that his grandfather had established more than half a century before, set and tilled according to his interpretation of moon phases.

"I hold no grudges against the moon," the cogent grandson told me. "I just can't believe she has much to do with farming. Anybody could see that the old coffee bush was badly diseased and yielding poorly. This land is not high enough to grow fine coffee, and there's no merit in growing bad coffee." He noted with a quick turn of revelation that even good coffee makes poor eating.

Tony had decided in advance that food growing was of

first essence: he would require helpers, and good helpers require good food. He was therefore determined to try growing beef and milk cattle, breeding native cows with purebred bulls. With due caution he also launched an experiment in chicken and egg growing according to *Yanqui* rule books. It wasn't so easy or so simple as represented, but after three discouraging failures he succeeded in developing a first flock of about forty laying leghorns. By the end of his first year he had built a powerline to his farm, purchased a *Yanqui* refrigerator and deep freezer; he had also very personally made a trial crop of sweet potatoes and lima beans and sweet corn.

"By then I had country neighbors calling me crazy, making whirling gestures about their hats when they saw me passing by. What I was trying for was to prove that a man in the tropics can feed himself adequately without leaving the limits of his farm. Without that, I simply couldn't see any chance of succeeding. My forefathers were all enslaved to the store or public market—forever buying what they ate, much of it grown and milled abroad, like milled rice and canned beans and salt fish, and *Yanqui* flour and meal, never really tasty or sufficiently nourishing. So I swore to break free from that *Yanqui*-style enslavement."

He did not seek to establish a model farm as such. But he regarded the attainment of self-sufficiency as imperative. About four-fifths of all Central Americans are rural people. Many, perhaps most, have never been adequately fed. "It is preposterous, *Señor*. God made this Central America a world seedbed for food plants. Man must keep it so. By natural ways our crop growing here compares with that in the United States like cooking with a well-made pressure cooker compares with frying in a big open skillet. Tropics are God's pressure cookers, but they must be used as such, and that correctly."

Tony's father had employed about eighty laborers, who

lived in hillside manacca shacks that they built themselves. His father issued his *mozos* rations of store-bought rice and beans, and sometimes salt fish and flour. When they were good, he patted their heads; when they were bad, he whipped them. When the *mozos* grew sick, the earlier Ramirez doctored them with home-brewed medicines; when they died, Don Hector called in the priest and went searching for replacements.

Tony had never approved of those procedures. Instead, and with greatest care, he first set about locating and employing six families of farm workers. For housing he recruited local carpenters, who worked with inexpensive lumber bought from a local sawmill. Though compact and inexpensive, the helpers' cottages were made clean, well screened, and otherwise comfortable. Each was provided with about a hectare (2.47 acres) of garden land, and a pig pen and a small, pole-built barn. The first work assignment was that each family grow enough food for itself.

As he worked to gain helpers, the younger Ramirez set about establishing cash crops. He chose to plant fifty acres to bananas, for direct sale to one or both of the banana companies that then operated in the area. The first planting grossed about $10,000 but required a formidable amount of work. The self-revised *patrón* next moved to develop more advantageous cash crops. "I just couldn't feel too much confidence in money trees, peso bushes, or *Yanqui* banana chasers," he explained.

In the course of his years as a recorder of freight ship cargoes from tropical places Tony had gained what he termed a speaking and smelling acquaintance with many marketable harvests. Among these were the so-called tropical grasses. Citronella and lemon grass are the most-used, though there are others, including the fine perfumes base— oils distilled from a tropical grass called vetiver. During the course of a look-and-see journey through the West Indies, Tony located a first planting stock of both lemon grass and citronella, and from the Imperial College of Tropical Agriculture he obtained a bagful of vetiver roots.

The grass introductions were successful. Within a year the test plantings covered about three acres; in another year they totalled about one hundred acres. Meanwhile, the enterprising *patrón* put together a grass-oil still, using materials acquired mostly from a Guatemala junkyard. By the following year his earnings from the essential oils (the first commercial planting in Central America) almost doubled his take from bananas. "A better money crop than bananas," the entrepeneur summarized. "Better for the soil; better in cost of shipping to markets; a lot less middleman's profits. But it's only one of the answers. If these tropics are ever to grow ahead, they'll have to have many more export crops, also many more and a lot better food crops. My own belief is that food crops and industrial crops are meant to grow and go together. Also, in the tropics it is particularly important to keep on trying out and developing new crops."

Antonio Ramirez has continued to practice what he preaches. From Arkansas he procured seed and planted a wilt-resistant rice preadapted to tropics use. It succeeded. He next tried peanuts and Irish potatoes, supposedly adapted to tropical planting; both failed. He tried tropical castor beans as a source of machine oil. Because of unanticipated blights, that venture also failed. His subsequent tries with tropics-adapted vegetables, particularly sweet corn, tomatoes, and green beans, were partly successful. His workers are producing both for their home needs and sale to local markets; "incentive bonus" is the *Yanqui* term for this. The same goes for ventures in growing pineapples, papayas, and avocados.

In the course of his freight ship service and incidental

shore rambles, Ramirez had grown favorably acquainted with one of the great upcoming crops of the presentday tropical earth—the African oil palm, which Tony had first observed not in Africa but in Malaya, back of Singapore. The "Africano" is a hardy palm, one of hundreds of the known but still underdeveloped multitudes of palm harvests. Its heavy nut clusters supply a superior food oil and margarine base, both chronically needed in prevailing tropical fares. With some auspicious borrowings and swappings, Ramirez managed to establish a sideyard nursery that presently supplied planting stock for ten acres of oil-palm groves. As soon as the young roots were securely established, the *patrón* double-planted the groves with pasture grasses and followed with an assignment of grazing cattle. He then began devising and building a pressing mill for extracting the palm oil. From the beginning, the combination of palm oil and cattle-grazed pasture proved successful.

Antonio Ramirez had expected that; he explained that he anticipates losing battles while remaining completely certain of winning the productive, people-benefitting war. "We *tropicos* can feed ourselves; given time and work, we can feed the world. And while doing those things, we can work upright in the sun and rest in the shade."

CHIQUITA

🌿 BY HIS own perceptive choice Antonio Ramirez had come back to his homeland to establish himself as a proprietary neighbors-employing farmer in a region chronically in need of more of the same. He was succeeding in both restoring an ancestral farm and standing against the ever-encroaching jungle. He was successfully diversifying crops, employing citizen-neighbors, and otherwise proving the potentials of a substantially new caliber of tropical farmer.

Tony believed and still believes that the native-born proprietary farmer is the best hope for making the tropics, still far and away the most extensive of earth's frontiers and in greater part the least developed, agriculturally self-sufficient. He knew the implicit difficulties in that course. He appreciates the ever basic fact that in the tropics as a whole, even in most subtropics, a lone man without money or credit or mechanical equipment has little chance of fighting the jungle and winning. The easier strategy is by way of the company, as a rule the international farming company.

Particularly during the eighteenth and nineteenth centuries the term "plantation company" had foaled a special and somewhat formidable meaning. Its first function had been that of helping an empire establish colonies abroad. In return for royal grants of lands and various related privileges, an officially chartered company agreed to actively help with founding colonies and to assist in, or direct, the development of commercial exports and domestic food supplies.

In colonial North America the plantation companies veered away from commercial food production to more immediately profitable lines, including furs, tobacco, naval stores, ship and mast timbers, and, in time, cotton. By contrast, colonizing grants in tropics and subtropics, both East and West, were predicated in more and more instances on producing exportable foodstuffs—sugar, spices, palm oils, coconut, and dryable fruits beginning with such world trade staples as figs and dates, and copra or coconut "meat." In time, and particularly with the progress of the Industrial Revolution, plantation agriculture shifted to a greater variety of nonedible industrial matériel, including natural rubber, tropics-grown fibers, distilled volatile oils, and special-use tropical timbers.

Despite this trend the beginning of the present century found plantation agriculture shifting back to tropical food crops. But American participation was long delayed because, prior to the Spanish-American War, the United States had no overseas possessions and a seemingly inexhaustible abundance of food producers within its boundaries. Except for coffee, cane sugar, spices, tea, cocoa, a variety of medicinal crops, and a very few fruits, food imports were few and slight.

But as the world at large presently had reason to note, the Spanish-American War marked the debut of the United States as an empire and accordingly opened the way to government-favored postboundary enterprises, sometimes labeled "dollar diplomacy." The first wobbly steps toward U.S. entry into postboundary plantation agriculture were principally by would-be producers of cane sugar, one of the easiest harvests to distribute internationally, and sweet bananas, thus far the most difficult to sustain in international trade. Ironically, of literally hundreds of available tropical fruits, only the sweet banana (*Musa sapientum*), which most tropical people regard as inferior to the plantain or cooking banana (*Musa paradisica*), attracted sufficient U.S. demand to justify even modest and cautious investment in the lands, cultivations, ships, and resident colonies required by this most difficult and erratic of tropical harvests.

For the most part, U.S.-developed sugar-cane properties began as mediocre and gradually sloughed downward. The plantation agriculture of bananas began as little more than a primitive jungle-edge grab-bag, lacking capable agronomy or shipping and the confidence of conservative investors. Between 1854 and 1899 more than three hundred U.S.

firms had attempted to grow bananas in various parts and places of the American tropics and/or market them in the United States. More than two-thirds had failed immediately. Early in 1899 the most successful of the banana firms, the Boston Fruit Company, and the most extensive one, the Minor Keith Company, led in establishing a "banana confederation" of fourteen banana companies, shortly increased to twenty-eight.

After a staggery beginning, United Fruit had prospered and multiplied as an international tropical operation for growing, shipping, and selling bananas—with sugar "on the side." By the late 1930s the company was supplying about two-thirds of the multiplying North American banana trade and about one-third of the world trade.

My own first estimate was that the most regrettable fault of United Fruit was its unnecessary tardiness in correlating and supplementing banana farming with more capable efforts to grow food crops, or at least help its workers build a better, certainly an attainable, subsistence agriculture. About 100,000 banana plantation workers, and several times that number of dependents, were being fed principally or entirely on imported foods. This was outrageously extravagant; much more seriously, it was frustrating the broader agricultural development of what could and should be one of the great food reservoirs of the hemisphere.

The principal banana company had not completely bypassed the needs for developing a valid agriculture for the expanding banana strongholds. A dozen years earlier, in 1925, its then new leadership had established at Lancetilla, Honduras, the first competent crop experiment station ever founded in the American tropics. From this bold and worthwhile beginning, and with the help of several able tropical agronomists, Victor Cutter, a market gardener's son from Draycut, Massachusetts, and United Fruit's first progressive president, set out to develop supplementary commercial crops and to reinforce the banana plantations with food crops.

For a conspiracy of reasons this had not been attained. Victor Cutter was heaved out of the presidency of the largest plantation company in 1934, another Depression casualty. In most of the banana-producing countries politicians, including reigning dictators, opposed any agricultural changes that would reduce the excises and other taxes that the banana crops showered down so generously. The most effective opposition to crop diversification in the banana centers were company employees. Great power was relegated to the resident managers of the respective banana divisions. They were accustomed to being paid and promoted in keeping with their proved records for producing the largest attainable quantity of marketable bananas at the lowest cost per ton.

Shareholders with itchy palms and headquarters stuffed-shirts with convictions of being clairvoyant could and frequently did recall that the company's experiences with crops other than bananas had not turned out at all well. The off-and-on exception was sugar cane, which had intermittently profited lushly and, if one would believe the dividends-grabbing dilettantes, balanced off by producing more red ink than cane juice. The tropical division managers had their own grounds for opposing crop diversification in their realms; they decried its diversion of work forces, repeated that their assigned budgets did not permit providing land for subsistence crops, and echoed that the banana workers were simply not interested in "bothering" with lesser crops.

The last was very largely buncombe. But the company's experience with exportable crops other than bananas or "good times" sugar had bordered on disaster. Earlier, in lowland Costa Rica United Fruit had set up a group of pine-apple farms. The resulting *piñas* were of superb flavor, but the very fertile soil and the warm wet climate joined in making the pineapples too big for efficient canning and too soft for the long sea-haul to markets.

Attempts to develop commercial export of Central American mahogany collided with complex transportation and milling problems. More prolonged efforts to establish cacao (chocolate and cocoa) as a long-time major crop clashed with already glutted world markets. Though the dapple-barked and otherwise beautiful little fruit tree is indigenous to Middle America, cacao had been adapted as a major export crop of Equatorial West Africa, where multiple-wife labor comes almost free. Earlier ventures in producing minor tropical fruits such as papaya, avocado, and mangosteen, were spurned by U.S. importers and jobbers. Efforts to introduce beef and dairy cattle in the "deep tropics" also began badly, owing primarily to failure to develop first-grade pastures and effective crosses of cattle; Temperate Zone purebred livestock rarely thrives on direct transfer to lowland tropics.

Meanwhile, even as the world Depression settled, North American and European demands for bananas continued to boom. The strong Temperate Zone demand for bananas is ever a source of bewilderment to the tropical people who actually grow the "monkey feed." I recall a night spent in company with a migrant group of Nicaraguan woodsmen who had been employed to fell big timber for new banana farms in Guatemala. On being roused by uproarious laugh-ter, I strolled out of my tent to find out what was so very funny. An Indian squad boss, who was munching moldy boiled beans from his shoulder pack, explained in oddly drawled Spanish: "It is truly very funny, *Señor*. My men and I got to thinking how very greatly funny. We do not ex-

actly say *you* are silly, *Señor*. We are only laughing because
so many *other* white-skins are so silly as to eat this goddamned monkey feed called bananas. Oh, haw, haw, haw!"

Granting, if one would, that the merry woodsman had a
point, the fact remains that demand for bananas keeps
growing like the fabulously fast-growing banana plant itself.
At the time the same did not hold for other possible or
more probable exports from Latin America. By 1938 an average of 91 percent of the dollar value of all tropical harvests imported in the United States was from the Pacific
tropics. The catapulting demands for plantation-grown rubber, palm oils, copra, spices, and tea kept adding to the imbalance. U.S. imports from vast Africa remained negligible.
Coffee, though an indigenous African shrub, kept its place
as the largest import from Latin America as a whole; Cuban
sugar was the big Caribbean entry. But the banana, which
many scholars still list as a pod vegetable, continued to domi-
nate the international fruit trade. Grapes remained the
world's foremost fruit crop, with oranges in second place
and apples in third. But in the international fruit trade the
banana had taken over first place and, not without cause,
the foremost banana company was holding with its best bet
of a money crop. And to revive the prevailing cliché, *Why
not?*

From my own station as a kind of mud-splattered bellwether of bananadom, I struggled to replace the *Why not?*
with *Why?* Anyone could sense the magnificent versatility
of the verdant subcontinent called Central America. It had
already given scores of great food crops to the world, from
kidney beans and common squashes to sweet peppers and
cultivable tomatoes. Even a nonbotanist could see that the
entire area had immense resources in native edible plants.
The whole concept of centering all major farm developments on lowland bananas and highland coffee seemed

ludicrous folly, particularly when banana workers and most of their deplorably underpaid coffee-picking brethren were being fed extravagantly and badly on imported foodstuffs. I pleaded loudly the cause and case for feeding tropical workers better from tropical sources. I exhorted and pestered United Fruit to establish test or pilot plantings of alternative export crops—certainly including plantains (baking bananas) and oil palms—and to reintroduce beef and dairy cattle and poultry for supplying employees (without profit).

In these urgings and proddings I was joined by a far more competent student, then head of tropical crop research, Dr. Vining C. Dunlap, with whom I shared bachelor quarters at La Lima, Honduras. As unwed male freeloaders, we were learning a great deal about the restrictions and expensiveness of imported foodstuffs, and the almost fabulous abundance of free-growing edibles. In this realm of first-hand research we had an exceptionally effective ally: Joe, a most engaging Oriental, an erstwise rice-ship stowaway whom Doc had extricated from an Ecuadorian jail where Joe had been settled for unlawful entry. At least, we called him Joe; more than a few company-employed neighbors called him a one-man crime wave.

That, of course, was a regrettable lapse of understanding related to the fact that our Joe was an all-time great food rustler. He knew, collected, cooked, and served a truly wonderful menu of wild-growing food plants gathered from nearby countrysides—greens, berries, fruits, roots, and God alone knew what else. For good measure, at twilight our friend and provider was wont to stroll the neighborhood with a large empty burlap bag draped over his left shoulder.

The bag was only temporarily empty. Petty gossip represented that the very day a neighbor's best pineapple or papaya cluster ripened, or his adolescent chickens reached broiler size, or the hickory-cured ham arrived by ship's post from Paducah or wherever, the coveted food item somehow entered the ever convenient burlap bag. Joe's gently smiling reply was that at least we were not obliged to fill up on those horrible bananas or the deplorable rice and weevilly beans sold at the commissaries.

Matters reached a sort of climax when a drainage engineer from Kentucky vowed that beginning the following night after his return from a surveying assignment he would start guarding his two sugar-cured Paducah hams with his eight-gauge alligator shotgun. However, on his return the Blue-grasser discovered that he could bisect his intended diligence—by then he had only one ham to guard.

A week or so later, when the kind-hearted but highly vocal son of Paducah gave a very informal dinner party of peace and forgiveness, he invited Doc Dunlap and me, and yielded to Joe's neighborly offer to cook and serve the dinner. In time, all present found their plates bulging with great slices of the oddly vanished ham and, for good measure, generous servings of a smoked turkey that my housemate had stealthily cached in dry ice for the oncoming holidays. Thanks also to our friend Joe, the feast of forgiveness included other tidbits recognizably lifted from the refrigerators of at least four other guests present. It was epicurean larceny, but it was also revealing symbolism.

The most extensive and productive show of American plantation agriculture indicated these general shapes:

United Fruit was then taking about 92 percent of its gross agricultural earnings from about 190,000 acres of banana plantings in eleven American countries, the Canary Islands, and the African Cameroons. Almost 85 percent of its American tropics banana lands had been salvaged from quagmire, untenable jungles, or very sparsely settled valleys. The feat of land salvage was truly outstanding. So were the ensuing harvests. Annual banana yields of the late '30s, though less than half of the present averages, were about 400 bunches or "stems"—17 to 18 tons—per acre. Fruit was being reaped throughout the year. By prevailing contrast a good average annual corn harvest was about 3 tons of ear grain per acre; average wheat yields were about .75 ton; a superior apple yield was around 4 tons; a good potato yield 9 to 12 tons. Thus, when measured in edible prolificness or, as nutritionists say, digestible calories, the banana crop was already a marker of extraordinary abundance.

But, like the more experienced *bananeros*, I could not feel awe-stricken by the banana yields. There was good reason to believe that they could be at least doubled (this actually has been accomplished as this is written), and that the working agronomy of the crop was actually much less than competent.

The cultivation—mostly by machete swinging—was appallingly primitive, as were the harvesting techniques. At the time only one division (Tiquisate, in west Guatemala) was using tractors and insulated carts to draw out the harvested fruit. Most of the rest were still using pack mules equipped with clumsy, fruit-bruising stave saddles, to tote the newly reaped fruit to railside, farm tramlines, or other loading "spots." In the company's West Indies (Jamaican) division the ever bruisable green stems (all bananas must be harvested while green) were still being head-toted (or drawn in in springless and uninsulated bull carts). In the Colombia divisions, also, bull carts still prevailed as first carriers.

What was being called the mechanization of banana agriculture was primarily concerned with spraying the crop, principally for protection against a windblown roundspore foliage disease, *Cercospora musae* Zimm., or "Sigatoka"—presumably from the Sigatoka, banana center in the Fiji Islands, where the ruining wilt had first been identified—and providing overhead irrigation, which made for more uniform harvests throughout the year.

As the 1930s neared an end United Fruit had about 80,000 acres of its Central American banana plantings under both "permanent spray" and overhead irrigation. Standard Fruit, the principal competitor, was installing similar spraying systems on about 25,000 acres of its own. In developing two new banana divisions in the areas of Golfito and Quepos, in Pacific Coast Costa Rica, United Fruit had demonstrated that the total costs of clearing and planting; building two required seaports and a railroad, first-class housing, schools and hospitals; and miscellaneous colonization costs hoisted the investment to around $4,000 per fruit-bearing acre. At the time this was probably a world record for developmental costs of any extensive openfield crop.

Here as elsewhere the mechanization, though momentous in weight, bulk, and capital cost, did not really modernize the living, bearing farms. These remained, in working essence, quite primitive, and the elaborate gadgetries remained tangential to the continuing use of manual labor and animal draft power. The formidably oversize mechanical spraying installations were not realistically conceived; they succeeded mostly in setting up a metal-happy maze apparently devised by a congregation of hyperthyroid Rube Goldbergs presumably descended on Boston. Besides being too big and too heavy, the "new workin's" were outrageously difficult to repair and maintain.

There was the no-less-conspicuous truth that we were growing the wrong kind of bananas. The then predominant Gros Michel—the big yellow fruit that most consumers had come to accept as the "standard"—is only one of twenty-seven principal varieties of the sweet banana, and is nowhere near the best. The plant is excessively tall and usually stem-brittle, and therefore extremely vulnerable to wind damage. The variety is medium yielding, but very difficult to harvest; when grown in rich soils the fruit stems are too heavy for most workers to handle with competence. And the

Gros Michel is an excessively easy prey to the more destructive banana diseases. The self-evident first need, to which United Fruit and the banana trade at large began waking after another twenty years, was the adoption of a better variety of commercial fruit; a smaller, heavier-bearing plant with greater resistance to wind, foul weather, and ruining diseases.

But certainly the principal American adventure in international plantation agriculture was not without merits. As already noted, United Fruit had established productiveness where none had existed before. It had built livable colonies for its tropical workers—less than utopian, but far above average for the time. It was paying native workers far more generously than any other principal farming enterprise in the American tropics; United Fruit in the late '30s was paying out about seven times as much in wages and about twice as much in taxes as in corporate dividends. By 1938 its average farm wage in Central America was better than that prevailing in the United States.

United Fruit had also built, staffed, and kept at work (at rapidly growing deficit) a twelve-nation chain of tropical hospitals, public clinics, and field sanitation enterprises. As a very direct result, and granting errors and limitations, banana workers had ceased being a sick man's society; their health levels were climbing, their death rates, although still too high, were down to levels then prevalent in the United States. The principal banana company had pioneered in providing elementary schools for employees' children. Though nowhere near good enough, they were definitely superior to the prevailing public schools. United Fruit's commercial fleet, or "banana navy," was the largest working unit in U.S. merchant shipping, a crucial need of the struggling economies of these Caribbean Americas.

These and related merits were deserving of recognition. But so was the dogging and largely inexcusable fault: the company's failure to develop or, better still, help the citizen farmers develop a more capable balance and profoundly needed variety of useful crops—both for export and for sustaining the home population.

Two facts were clear as any tropical dawn: United Fruit could effectively plan and surely attain the all-necessary diversity of crops; the reward for such an attainment could and would support the case for a valid revival of international plantation agriculture.

The significance here, of course, was not and is not merely of more bananas. Ironically, and in great part avoidably, the tropics and much of the subtropics had been permitted to emerge or remain not meccas of abundance but reservoirs of malnutrition and never distant famine. Plantation agriculture has tremendous potentials for standing successfully against the ever greedy jungle. It has survived and prospered in numerous tropical areas that remain obdurate to the best and most valiant efforts of the small farmer. United Fruit, in a recognizably Yankee métier, had proved that despite formidable investment costs, attainable yields can economically justify the great investment—even though there was still cause to doubt that entire nations or other vast numbers of people can be fed completely or principally from distant tropical regions.

STONE-AGE LARDER

❧ DURING MY up-and-down adventures as a tropics trouble-shooter with plenty of tropics and more than plenty of troubles, I found my compensation principally in revealing side glances.

Early in 1940 a bumper harvest of the latter began to

materialize when United Fruit's executive committee was seized with a revival of the company's intermittent sponsorship of Middle American archeology. Dr. Paul Saunders, a maverick financier who had served time as professor of Greek and Latin at the University of Mississippi, had almost simultaneously taken over as the financial vice-president of United Fruit and layman sponsor for a revival of the company's financing of archeological "projects" in various of the Maya lands of Middle America.

Paul Saunders suggested that along with my other somewhat vague assignments I take over the management of a company grant of "$50,000 plus" for the continuation of what the befreckled Mississippian termed "definitive archeology." When I explained that I knew regrettably little about Mayas and nothing about archeology, he simultaneously shook my hand and whacked my shoulders. "Son, I know you are an ignoramus; you keep on confirming it, amusingly and commendably. This archeology project will be in keeping with your perennial qualifications of self-admitted ignorance. Take it, Son, and do your ignorant best."

I began by seeking the advice of one whom I knew to be an eminently capable archeologist, Dr. Alfred V. Kidder, then the director of the historical division of the Carnegie Institution of Washington, D.C. Alfred Kidder agreed to supervise the as yet extremely foggy "project," and also to provide for expert counsel from his Guatemalan assistant and to seek the "good offices" of the staff of the Peabody Museum at Harvard and Kidder's revered Cambridge University protégé, J. Eric S. Thompson. The latter had come to Peabody and Harvard following a long tenure as field assistant to Sylvanus Morley and as acquisitions officer for the Field Museum, and he was unquestionably one of the most able Maya-delvers in action.

Thompson was warmly interested, and imparted his

enthusiasm to his exceptionally able colleague and hard-working associate, Gustav Stromsvik, another of the better-proved working archeologists of the era. Thompson and Stromsvik agreed with Dr. Kidder that there were good possibilities for coming up with a consequential "dig" in either anchor lands or known centers of the major Empire periods of the Mayas, possibly in the less probed frontiers of British Honduras or Guatemala's Peten territory, or perhaps in the backwoods area of Mexico's great Indian state, Chiapas. All saw advantages in seeking the hoped-for find with the help of contemporary Mayan descendants. There are great numbers of such Indians who live between the Tapajos and Ulua valleys. My able advisors agreed that the best attainable contacts with Mayan peoples would be the Lacandones, or White Robes, who survive in the comparative wilds of Chiapas and the Peten.

The scholars confirmed that the land of the living Mayas is reachable, though at the time the reaching was far from easy. This realm is called the Lacanja country. As I was shortly able to confirm, their miniature though somewhat less than literally lost world is about thirty miles long and averages somewhat less than a mile wide. Densely forested mountains shield the Lacanja Valley from east and west. The north end of the trough-like valley is strewn with swamps and blotches of dense jungle growth interspersed with treacherous mires and quicksand beds. Entry from the south, though possible, is markedly impeded by a great littering of swamps and shallow ponds, and directly beyond these the imperiling rapids of the Lacanja River.

Some historians believe that following the conquest of Yucatan by Spanish forces under Alvarado and Cortez a group of Mayan survivors took refuge in the lost valley of Lacanja and there rejoined the Stone Age. Another theory is that these white-robed people of the miniature lost world have lived apart there for the past dozen centuries or longer, as country cousins of the "great Mayas," i.e., as codescendants of common ancestors.

The rather reasonable consensus was that the best way to get back into the much wondered-about Middle American Stone Age was to try going forward into its less touted contemporary survival. The thesis here is that although the term "Stone Age" becomes less literal as total isolation grows less attainable, significant vestiges of the Mayan Stone Age people are not willfully established as such; they are not hermits or arbitrary returnees to the so-called simple primitive society—which, even if truly primitive, is very far from being simple.

Back in 1905, the Harvard-Tozzer expedition had counted about six hundred of these Lacandones in the backwoods of Guatemala's Peten territory and directly across the boundary in the Miramar area of Chiapas. By 1940, the census had apparently declined to somewhere near two hundred; the decline was generally attributed to severe religious tenets that permit marriage or matings only in or among particular totems or clans of these Mayan-speaking contemporaries. There were dependable reports, affirmed by Franz Blum, then of the Middle America Institute of Tulane at New Orleans, that most of the surviving White Robes are in the Lacanja River Valley in Chiapas. The Lacandones, Blum stated from cogent and firsthand acquaintance, still speak the Mayan language, keep with the ornate Mayan religion (but do not practice human sacrifice), worship in the ruins of Mayan temples, and live at least in definable part like the Maya commoners of the sixth to the ninth centuries of Christian times.

I shortly learned that the Lacandones are a generally intelligent, markedly kindly forest people who excel at subsisting off their homelands. Like most other residents of Mexico's incomparable Indian state, the White Robes (men, women, and children alike still wear the same free-flowing, night-gown-like cotton robes that Maya commoners wore a dozen centuries ago) are listable as agrarians.

The typical family—a husband, one or at most two wives, and usually one to four children—is pivoted to a *milpa*, or garden-sized field, a land plot rarely larger than one acre. As a rule, every second or third year the head of the house-hold stakes a plot of new land and clears it, principally by fire. He banks coals around and so burns down the larger trees, using a broadax or heavy machete for felling the smaller trees and underbrush. Except for his ax (in most instances, of antique manufacture) and hoe (which is fre-quently homemade with stone cutting-heads lashed to a pole handle), he has little interest in farming tools. Usually he punches seed holes with a sharpened pole or stick and covers the plantings with his bare feet. He weeds and har-vests by hand, never plows, and depends entirely on home-grown or locally traded seeds.

His first food crop is corn, obviously of very old strains, apparently self-hybridized, and with varicolored kernels, for the most part intermixed red, blue, and white. The corn ears are extremely slender and heavily husked; measured by the acre, which is not easily done because the *milpas* rarely include more than a small fraction of an acre of corn, the yields probably average less than forty bushels a *milpa*. But the *milpa* soils are dependably fertile; the cornstalks, in-cluding those that serve to screen off the open-sided palm-thatched huts, are frequently twelve to fifteen feet tall. The ancient cotton, with fiber bolls that presently turn gray or gray-brown, further attests to either soil fertility or genetic trends toward giantism, perhaps some of both. In any case, the Lacandon cotton picker reaches up instead of down.

The other vegetable crops are similarly antiquated. The

squashes resemble the roundish summer squashes commonly grown in the United States; the beans, principally black or red, are heavily padded shell beans, similar to the "Lazy Wife" varieties still grown in U.S. gardens. They grow a great variety of gourds, including calabashes, that are edible; also yams, seeded from home-saved roots; tall-growing varieties of capsicum, or sweet peppers, both green and red; and on the non-edible side, giant broad-leafed tobacco plants.

There is no sugar cane or other sugar-bearing crop; so far as I could identify, the only source of sweet is the very plentiful wild honey. They have no livestock for food use; the animal possessions are revered pets, such as wild pigs, wild turkeys, crows, or deer, in each instance, the sacred or quasisacred symbol animal of the various clans. The local abundance of game, abetted by Lacandon hunting skills, makes livestock-raising superfluous.

The subsistence agriculture is profoundly interwoven with the Lacondon's religion, a deep and strongly traditional pantheism. He worships at the temples of his forefathers; his special holy place is the ruins of Yaxchilan; the full moons of April and May direct his annual religious pilgrimage. The fact that the Lacondones use the ruins of Mayan temples as worship places led to the archeological finds at Bonampak and elsewhere.

The Lacandon has at least one special god for every crop, and he "feeds" the first harvest to its respective god or gods. In worshiping he stands or kneels before the prescribed pot or row of pots, home-fashioned of clay. Always present is the corn pot, symbolizing the staff of life for all Mayas. The Lacandon also feeds his god pots with a very special home-brewed liquor called *balche,* made from the bark of a tree by that name, fermented with wild honey and corn. The Lacandon drinks only to establish better communications with his gods; otherwise, at least so far as

I know, he is a teetotaler. He lives as completely as possible with and from food crops. Squash and gourd rinds provide most of his cooking utensils, food bowls, and miscellaneous containers. He preserves his harvests (including, of course, tobacco) by drying. Men, women, and elder children alike shape and smoke oversize loosely rolled cigars of profound potency.

The exaltation of subsistence is all prevailing. The family home belongs to the family; the land is communally claimed by the clan, of which at least a dozen endure. Home building is a community responsibility. Duly aided by kin and neighbors, a man expects to build his home in a couple of days. Armed with axes and machetes the builders hew and drive down corner posts and wall sticks, raise center poles and rafters taken directly from nearby forests. They lash together the crude framework with bark strips or leather thongs; women usually join in providing the thatch roof. Such, one gathers, were housing procedures of the Mayans of old. Split-log tables comprise the solid furniture. All beds are hammocks, woven of native fibers and swung several feet above the bare earthen floor.

The men do most of the house building and all of the land clearing and burning; boys join their fathers at hunting and fishing. Girls and women prepare the food, beginning with pounding or grinding the meal for tortillas, which by an odd hallmark are invariably square or rectangular, never round. The women do the spinning and weaving from the homegrown cotton (they still use the ancient hip looms) and make the generally unimpressive pottery, including the god pots and strongly conventionalized clay dolls. They are experts at creating hair-braid ornaments of highly colored feathers (men, women, and children alike wear their hair long and quite frequently ornamented). The women have a special penchant for making necklaces of riverside shells or animal teeth; more than any other outside merchandise except salt, which the children eagerly gulp in lieu of candy, they covet beads. Frequently they walk great distances to swap tobacco, their steadfast barter crop, for glass beads. This attraction, apparently, comprises the principal lust for luxury.

The procedures of subsistence from an abundant nature are moderate to a point of intensive traditional frugality. The Lacandon takes at least half, in some instances two-thirds, of his subsistence from hunting and fishing, carefully directed toward food stuffs immediately consumable. Hunting and fishing are the particular chores for men and boys. Though some have acquired the white man's firearms, the most favored of which is the muzzle-loading shotgun, bows and arrows are still the principal hunting weapons. Both are deftly made. The Lacondon's preferred bow is the long bow, as long as he is tall (a man's height averages about five-foot six) and strung with native fiber, such as agave, or tightly braided deer tendon. He still heat-chips arrowheads of flint or, when available, sets on iron tips. He is not necessarily a surpassing archer, though his marksmanship probably excels that prevailing in archery deer seasons in the States. But lifelong practice (the boys literally grow up with bow and arrows) plus the self-perpetuated abundance of game—particularly red deer, free-roaming peccaries, or wild pigs (the boars sometimes weigh 200 pounds, though the far more vicious sows are considerably smaller), the loudly abundant howler monkeys, and the marsh-roaming green turtles—preassure abundant meat supplies.

Lacandon fishing is mostly by gigging in shallow water or from home-hewn log dugouts; a javelin headed with sharpened flint or a piece of sharp metal is the oftenest-used fishing implement. Carp, crappies, and bullfrogs are the preferred water quarries.

The total fare is unquestionably good. The Lacandones are an outstandingly healthy people, well bodied and from all appearances longer lived than most Latin Americans. The fact that they are fading away is certainly not attributable to malnutrition; the White Robes are exceptionally well nourished and apparently completely free from pestilence. Though still quite really of the Stone Age, they seem to be above-averagely happy people who eat well, sleep well, smile easily, and think clearly. Their significance, I submit, is of today and tomorrow as well as yesterday. Their gentle reminder is that man can still take sustenance at least in substantial part from the lap and teats of nature—to what extent, is yet another subject for thought and inquiry. Man is not removed inalienably from the common mother. And he never will be.

The Lacandones showed the way to what Eric Thompson and his Carnegie colleagues subsequently recorded as the most revealing finding of Mayan color art yet attained. This included the Bonampak (Mayan for "painted walls") clustering of eleven temples or pyramids and two major murals of well-preserved frescoes showing rituals and processionals of the Mayas *circa* A.D. 400. As a non-archeologist and fascinated onlooker, I rejoiced in the finding of Bonampak. As a student of food and people, I remain most grateful to the living Lacandon and his reassuring revelation of man's unending ability to take sustenance from the wilderness.

THE HUNGRY JUNGLE

MY ADVENTURES and misadventures with the international plantation agriculture that United Fruit had already effected were diversely revealing and in some part extremely tantalizing. One self-perpetuating reason was the company's continuing status as an outfit of jungle-busters. Because of its particular needs for soils that are exceptionally rich in organic materials and its affinity for high-rainfall areas, banana growing strongly encourages the direct and frontal conquest of jungles. By expedient contrast the Lacandones and others of the surviving race of Mayan descendants have survived by expediently plucking from jungle edges. Obviously, both procedures are of widespread significance in terms of utilizing the most far-reaching of undeveloped frontiers that remain.

To list one example, in Central America United Fruit once owned or leased land areas that totaled about five thousand square miles. Of these no more than 6 percent had ever been developed as crop lands; the preponderance had remained undeveloped. With reasonable cause some commentators severely criticized this "arbitrary perpetuation of jungle." In his tinier and more aboriginal way the Lacandon followed the same general course. The procedure of nibbling at edges or selecting minikin plots of jungle wastes for highly specialized development still holds for easily a third part of the earth's land surface. Central America and the vast bulk of South America continue as a far-flung repetition of dribbles and dots of used lands interspersed with larger areas of untenable mountains and the persisting verdant wastes called jungles. The same status holds for land masses from lesser islands to mighty continents.

A typical desk dictionary definition of jungle reads:

jungle: 1. A dense tropical thicket of high grass, reeds, vines, brush, or trees, choked with undergrowth; hence any similar tangled growth.

The truth—ever relevant to man's food supplies—is that by no means all jungles are tropical; a great many are forests so tall and otherwise dominant that they cannot be "choked with undergrowth" or even "tangled growth." Stated even more broadly, and, alas, paradoxically, most lands called jungles remain heavily populated vegetatively and unpopulated, or at most very sparsely tenanted by people, and yet are still substantially or completely lacking in food production. Practically stated, the preponderance of so-called "jungle," when measured in terms of people feeding, remains a dense green liability.

Early in 1940 I began to meet with the opportunity for venturing into one of the largest concentrations of true jungles, the baffling Amazon Basin. By then the explosive spread of World War II was making natural rubber one of the most coveted items of war matériel. By 1940 the United States was as good (or as bad) as gone to war, and waging war demanded much more rubber. As any schoolchild knows, the Amazon Basin is the homeland of the Hevea tree, still the principal source of natural rubber. We would therefore go to Amazonia for rubber, even while going to du Pont or Dow for explosives, or Madison Avenue for war-compelling propaganda techniques. Whatever else the word "jungle" meant, it was to the U.S. war planner where one goes to grab off the bloody rubber wherever it grows or otherwise occurs.

One of my first counselors on the very far-reaching subject of Amazonia was a good gray Brazilian Indian, Juan Fialho, who then lived in a palm-thatched shack about a day's walk from Belem-Para, the Amazon River port that has been termed the jungle capital of the world. To Señor Fialho "jungle" meant 2 million square miles of the dark, wet, and less-than-adequately explored Amazon Basin, which he knew perhaps as well as any man then living. I had met Juan Fialho in a pleasantly disreputable beer garden in the humid river port on the lower Amazon. At the time the

United States, by way of an entanglement of federal corporations, was seeking to bestir a revival of wild-rubber procurement in the great homeland of the best of the rubber trees, *Hevea brasiliensis*. Fialho was in heroic minority; he was one of the very few Rooseveltian rubber recruiters who knew anything at all about natural rubber.

Juan had spent his best years, beginning in his early teens, as a *seringueiro*, a taker of wild rubber from the mighty tree-darkened Amazon area. In graying middle age, he was game to try it again—even at the onset of another malaria-ridden *zafra*, or less wet season (the other is the damned wet).

When he chose to talk, Juan's usual conversation was of random nouns mumbled in Portugese. As became an old man—at the time he was crowding age forty, mature old age for a jungle prowler—he spoke mostly of the remembered past. When Juan was born, circa 1907, the Amazon era of wild-rubber snatching was at or approaching climax, from the far-flung state of Para through the great dark wetness of Tocanta, Jurua, lowland Madeira, and the even more remote valley of the Purus. From his very early childhood Juan remembered the man-hunting *patrãos* who stalked the Indian villages, including his own Juilotos, making recruitments of all available men or boys, frequently offering advances of coveted materials such as firearms, ammunition, sewing machines, musical instruments, and other alluring merchandises, for repayment in smoke-blackened rubber, and blood.

It was a tragic story; perhaps no other harvest was ever more depraved, corrupt, or costly in lives. The world, particularly the United States, required rubber, but even when the *pelles* were bringing a dollar a pound at Belém-Para and twice that in New York or London, the *seringueiro* was lucky to get one *milreis*—then equivalent to a nickel a pound. That was, and still is, part of the jungle story. Another typical entry was that transportation, even to the nearest market port, usually ate away at least 40 percent of the prevailing world price of crude rubber.

But Juan Fialho took the rubber and the jungle as they came. He presently maneuvered north to the Tapajos country, where the dapple-barked Hevea trees grew tall and numerous—by averages as many as two or even three to the acre. At high-water time he rafted his accumulation of *pelles*, or smoked balls of rubber, down the Tapajos to the now demised river port at Don Rajo. There he sold and bartered the rubber as best he could, and with the money strapped around his belly and salt fish and farinha flour swung over his shoulder he would tramp overland to his own selection of an *estrado*, or tree site, and begin again. That continued through twelve rubber-snatching years that saw Juan leave the great jungle as he had entered it: without money and with few certainties.

By around 1915, when the auto tire began treading most of the earth, the Hevea tree was being shifted from the open, wet wilds of the Amazon to man-planted and -tended groves almost completely around the globe from its homeland. By 1920 or before, plantation-grown rubber was powerfully established in Malaya, Ceylon, Java, and presently Sumatra, and a prolonged list of "hot" lands, including the rain-forest fringes of Equatorial Africa. As plantation rubber advanced, wild rubber continued to retreat. Then, because of what Juan Fialho could imagine as another marathon of anti-Christian deeds by piously professing white Christians, wild rubber was again in demand.

Money-jangling *hombres* were again recruiting "compatriots" to tramp and wade back into the great jungles for another turn at wild-rubber snatching. The *politicos* gave assurance that their *presidente*, Getulio Vargas, had broken the hold of the rapaciously greedy "rubber barons," and that it was once more extremely patriotic for good Indians to clamor forth into the death swamps so that noble white allies might continue to have rubber-tired trucks, planes, cannon, and other gismoes to help them again blast the living hell out of ignoble white foes.

It was magnificent oratory and Juan Fialho was deeply touched by it. Accordingly, as one among a first group of nineteen thousand re-recruited *seringueiros*, Fialho returned to the wet, dark jungle lands. This time, so he thoughtfully recalled, he went with God and a revised attitude. This time the Brazilian government, with *Yanqui* money dribbling freely, sent along workmen to build riverside warehouses and commissaries for the tree bleeders. The rubber snatchers, no longer taken as stupid *brutos*, were being given backpacks filled with such delectables as grain flour, salt fish, pinto beans, and tins of beef, along with advances of real jingling pocket-money—as much as a fifth part of what their rubber takes would bring from Washington.

Juan served out a twilight stint of twenty months, then bowed out as gracefully as could be expected of one grown partly lame from jungle rheumatism. Once more he was thankful to have come out of the jungles alive and more or less whole. He added, with a *seringueiro's* occupational cough and squint, that if he had children they might very well live to see a time when this most tremendous of jungle lands would be dotted with harvest bearing fields, gardens, palm groves, and pastures stocked with fine cattle munching brave new grass. Even when under the grim shadows of giant swordgrass or sky-punching ironwood trees a man has a right to his visions.

I, for one, wholeheartedly agreed. But by then, intimate though less extensive experience had taught me that most jungles are still hungry places. And experience would confirm that hungry jungles continue to cover millions of square miles of developable but not yet arable farm lands.

But I was also beginning to learn that not all jungles are hungry. At various points in South and Southeast Asia they had been changed to some of the most prolific food producing lands in all the world. Superior tropical agronomy had changed the people-swarming island of Java to the most provident concentration of food production then existent. Nearby the more recent jungle stronghold of Sumatra was emerging as perhaps the world's best showground of a major tropical jungle land transformed to a most impressive exhibit for plantation agriculture.

The changeover from jungle to indisputable food-producing lands was surely and clearly being attained in tropics and subtropics of both hemispheres. On all continents, and no doubt on many islands, people were standing against jungles and demonstrating that the nonproductive vegetative anarchies (or commanding ecologies) can be changed to food-producing wonderlands.

But in measurable acres of square miles these gains were proportionately small, and the techniques of conversion were very far from adequate. Self-evidently, the mere felling of trees and underbrush, whether by ax or machete or oversize power machinery, and the setting up of superficial drainage are not necessarily enough. The felling of the forests and underbrush too often opens the tropic soil to violent erosion. The correct techniques of primary drainage were and still are nowhere near adequate. The same holds for procedures for anchoring soils and recovering silts from rapacious streams and rivers. Man has learned to fear or dread the jungle. He has barely begun to appreciate it.

As one who feared the jungle even while he lived from its erratic bounties, Juan Fialho sensed astutely and predicted boldly a time when man at large would survive not by conquering jungles but rather by befriending them. He had never heard of the theory that back in Paleozoic or Rock Age times, the first epoch of predominant land vegetation, most or practically all lands of the earth were tropical jungles; from that vast womb of vegetative abundance emerged the principal sources of animal food, including man's. One after another of the great food crops, beginning, one gathers, with the ancient fruits or vegetables such as bananas and plantains and the still uncounted edible harvests from palms, through the thousands of species of grasses, including the large-seeded ones called grains, and so on to and through the great people-sustaining vegetables, the roots, tubers, and groundnuts, the decisive food sources have evolved in and come forth from the jungles.

Juan Fialho favored finding or deriving many more and much better food crops for returning to the jungle. He had no specific idea of how this could be accomplished by people. He believed that in His mercy and wisdom God would show the way. Or, come to think of it, maybe He has already shown it.

MOTHER AFRICA

IN MY early boyhood I acquired a firm if somewhat temporary reliance on a particular trade sign that boldly advertised: ARKANSAS NATIONAL BANK: DEPOSITS $800,000 AND GROWING. At the time (*circa* 1911) I had no comprehension of $800,000; my own share of the deposits was below $8. But my father was a very minor shareholder in the great and growing Arkansas National Bank of Fayetteville, Arkansas: he owned four shares. Early in 1930, when the bank tumbled before the first impact of Depression plus some regrettable hanky-panky on the part of local financiers, reputedly with molasses on their hands, my father didn't exactly lose his shirt. He merely went the rest of his life without buying any new shirts.

By the 1940s my general feeling toward Africa, though I had never actually seen any part of the second-largest continent, were generally comparable to my first feeling about the trade sign of the long-closed Arkansas National Bank; they were of confidence in, and noncogent acceptance of, great strength.

For Africa, too, is big. Any reasonably competent map indicates that it has six and a half million square miles of potentially arable lands, more than the entire land area of the waste-strewn continent of North America. At least theoretically one could drop the entire United States into Africa and not be able to find it for years and years. Africa remains the oversize crossroads to the peopled world; whoever or whatever leads Africa is all but inevitably a world leader. The continent's resources, in great part not yet capably explored, are too stupendous for ready comprehension—timbers, metals and minerals, water and fertile soils in all but fabulous abundance, yet in great part with people in hard-to-believe scarcity. Africa, the routes of the seeds and roots peddlers; the confluence of the great civilizations of man, his great religions, languages, and cultures; Africa, the sleeping giantess, ever at the verge of awakening, ever stirring, but as yet never actually arising.

My own resurgence of interest in Africa was arising from the fact that I was being sent there. The cause was again related to rubber. The background was again in the realm of common knowledge. Following Japan's accelerated conquest of more than a million square miles of the better-developed

South Pacific lands, certain dabs and fringes of West Equatorial Africa had come to hold most of the in-tree rubber supplies then left available to the Allies. More specifically, a wildly improbable series of military conquests and power politics plays in great part as inept as they were venal had made Liberia, though a tiny fleck from the green vastness of the second largest continent, temporarily the "Free World's" principal source of natural rubber.

Though anyone who ever glanced through a geography text gathers that the continent's rain forests are by far the largest remaining, the concept of Africa as a prime source of international supply of rubber was indeed a bizarre twist. My own World War II contribution, such as it was, had been concerned with natural rubber supply. As a most trivial layman I had chosen to defend the case for natural rubber, not merely as a wartime need but as a way-opener for more general developments, particularly food production.

This was another instance of an insignificant mouse pondering alone amidst the mightiest of elephant herds. The newly arisen Pentagon had blared: "Get the rubber! Never mind how, where, or how much it costs!" Prior to 1943, chiefs of staffs had discussed seriously, if insanely, stratagems for recapturing Indonesia and Malaya in order to retake the rubber groves. Once that were attained, one gathered, draft notices that would give forth greetings of the President of the United States on order of General Hershey would be delivered individually to the Hevea trees. At the time the Allies had no available forces for blasting into the rubber groves. Later in 1943, when the nascent industry of synthetic rubber making began to show promise, the high brass grew entirely willing to totally bypass natural rubber, wackily disregarding the facts that both natural and synthetic rubber were and would remain prime industrial needs for decades and generations to come, and that decisive improvements of both were attainable, indeed, were being attained.

My bold little move to proselytize for refraining from the total abandonment of natural rubber disgusted the self-admitted military experts, but to my profound surprise several factions of the commercial rubber industry chose to support my mouse-size stand. Indeed, the so-called Rubber Roundtable out in Akron, Ohio, issued a fiat statement to that effect. By sheerest coincidence, on V-J Day I received an invitation to report immediately to Liberia and there undertake some vaguely suggested works, such as performing liaison with African proprietors of rubber groves, devising or at least recommending ways for locally producing foodstuffs for the requisite throngs of rubber tappers, and somehow "correlating" with Liberian and nearby colonial governments. As a tropical tramp for United Fruit I had gone my frequently arbitrary way with a most exceptional lack of directives or restraints. Here there seemed to be none at all. And here was my chance to see at least something of great Africa.

On reporting at the La Guardia hydroplane base in New York I found myself the only unsaved member of a planeload of missionaries bound for stations in the Congo. The aircraft was a hard-used Boeing hydroplane, lifted in the nick of time from the "China Clipper run." At best the battle- and Bible-scarred flying boat pushed along at about a hundred miles an hour; at worst it could not even rise from the waves. The latter became evident when rough waters left us stranded for a day in Trinidad and a week in the Azores, and after a painful and bruising night of bouncing in the Lisboa River off Lisbon and another week at the Portugese capital for repairs.

Throughout the ordeal of port waits and wakes I listened

to the testimonies of the veteran missionaries, who tended toward unanimity in deploring the food of Equatorial Africa, praising its cause, and commiserating on its weather. One obese elder took exception to the latter, insisting that the African climate is at very least *salubrious;* he seemed to have a fanatical attachment to the word. He repeated it even when the plane's air conditioner broke down while we were a few thousand feet above the Sahara. After many more oven-hot hours the old hydroplane bumbled above Fisherman's Lake on the Liberian shoreline. There it descended with all the directness of an oversize watermelon accidentally dropped. As we took leave of the airborne hotbox, the fierce breath of tropical Africa struck like a pouncing leopard. Once more I heard the fat minister puffing, "salubrious." At almost the same instant he collapsed and tumbled face downward in the seaside mud.

After we had carried the limp, lead-heavy form to the medical "rest hut," the entire male passenger list joined in sweating out the night in a thatch-roofed compound that seemed to be a hunting spa for scorpions. Then, following a predawn breakfast of acrid black coffee and subtly spoiling sardines, I answered the honking of a decrepit pickup truck. The rusty vehicle was driven by a severely sunburned young man who explained that he was a Firestone "rubber planter." The manager had earlier set out to meet me, but his limousine was "sunken out of sight in mud."

A couple of miles up the gummy red road my receptionist managed with remarkable dexterity and Ohio-style profanity to bypass the manager's deeply mired Lincoln. Directly beyond, a rescue crew of seven natives clad in the prevailing fashion of mini-shorts and flimsy cotton undershirts was taking a recess from probing and pulling while the manager struggled to place a fulcrum log in still deeper mud back of the rear wheels. I noticed that one of the younger

men was deftly kindling a candlesized flame beneath a
wigwam of dead twigs. Another was standing by with a recently slain field, or perhaps forest, mouse. With great skill
he tied the mouse's extremely long tail into the top of the
wigwam, where the carcass was by then being rather effectively barbecued.

When I asked what was going on, the fire-builder explained with pleasant matter-of-factness: "Small beef,
Missa. Small beef."

As I immediately learned, "beef" in the prevailing near-
pidgin meant any kind of edible flesh, from mouse or snake
or roaming rat to elephant—in all instances eaten eagerly.
When the cooking was completed, one of the natives rescued the mouse carcass, laid it on a rock, took a jackknife
from his solitary back pocket, and began carving the mouse
into seven pieces, one for each member of the work crew.

It was a meaningful act; I had never seen people eat
mouse before; certainly I had never imagined a barbecued
mouse being so expertly and democratically divided among
seven hungry people. I remarked with my flair for the obvious that the meat ration appeared to be running short.

"Hell, Mister, in these parts, it never runs no other way,"
the young rubber planter assured me. The manager, who was
diligently probing for a disappearing rear fender, remarked
that the overall food situation was then somewhat worse
than usual. The big war had cut off local supplies of ammunition. Tribe hunters, even the most expert, had nothing
to take meat with except homemade bows and arrows, or
traps made of roots and leaves.

To worsen matters, the native rice crops had been faring
badly for the past two years, and the big war had practically
shut off imports of rice from Ceylon and other Asian
sources. Throughout the entire area, elephant hunting had
fallen casualty to the war. Practically no hunting licenses

were being issued; particularly in the nearby French-African veldts, there had been an elephant population explosion; rogue herds were dealing wholesale ruin to tribal rice farms. Tribes-people were going hungry or eating roots all the way from hell to breakfast.

The young planter took issue with the figure of speech. "Who the hell ever heard of the natives eating breakfast in these parts? The best they ever had is a once-a-day afternoon meal. Once, and I mean just once, I got silly and tried feeding my rubber tappers breakfast. The lousy rice-burners all went out into the shade, picked theirselves soft spots, and went to sleep. The old bastard who bossed here before you came told me to try it out. Man, you shoulda heard what I told him."

"What did you feed them for breakfast?" I asked.

"Canned dog food shipped over from the States. It was one of the cheaper brands. Even so, the boss raised hell because it was too expensive to feed rubber tappers. Besides, he figgered they'd get more meat from eating the usual weeviled rice."

"I'm learning," I murmured.

"Charlie-boy, just troupe these bloody jungles awhile and you'll be learning a hell of a lot more."

He was so right. When the manager's Lincoln was finally hoisted free of the mud we continued on a roundabout tour by way of a hinterland outpost where the young planter made his headquarters. By noontime we were in tribe country. I noted a tribe village of about thirty extremely uniform huts, all built of mud with windowless rounded bases, each about nine feet in diameter and with a conical thatched roof.

I noted a footbridge, steeply arched and built of small barkless poles bound in place with vines. I noted a native postman, who carried several folded papers on his head weighted down with a flat rock. A particularly beautiful Negro girl wearing a dangling blue cape and carrying a kerosene lantern on her head followed a tall man garbed in a white robe and a blood-red fez; he carried a blue prayer rug on his left shoulder.

This Africa, one learns, is profoundly religious, but the basic religion is pantheistic, finding the "God spirit" in all things. Like so much of African living, the religious life is quite basically tribal; of the more formal and alien creeds, Mohammedanism is vastly more widespread than Christianity. But the spiritual essence is deeply, meditatively African. At a tribal village a few miles farther up the outrageously muddy road I observed a living example. A graying man in a worn and faded chief's robe was sitting alone on the bare, packed earth beside his hut. He was not reading, or whittling, or doodling, or fidgeting. His posture told of appreciative acceptance; his rain-stained blue robe draped toga-like from his narrow shoulders. His eyes were closed. His expression was one of exquisite peace.

"This is only one small spot in Africa," the Firestone manager was reflecting. "But after twenty-five years of roaming the bloody dark continent I'm convinced it's typical—like one squirt of blood is typical of what's sloshing about in the entire body. Sure, this Liberia is little. But it's real Africa; some say the most tellingly African place, with twenty-seven old-line tribes still stashed out in a space no bigger than Maryland. The point being that Africa is, above all else, a tribal continent; to understand it, you've got to understand about tribes and the funny deep ways of tribes —which still live, breed, and act a mighty lot like their ancestors did centuries before white men began lousing up the Dark Continent."

He suggested that as a first lesson in "real Africa" we

might call on a village chief who doubled as a district com-
missioner for the so-called government down in Monrovia.
Chances were we could freeload a "country chop"; any
damn fool knows that the best way to learn about food
supply is to try eating some of what goes. The conspiracy
was pleasantly successful; it included sampling a higher-
status country chop prepared and served by two somewhat
overweight first wives.

One begins by smearing his or her plate with shredded
pepper—oily green pepper that is violently hot. One next
fills his or her plate with tender, well-cooked native rice
(with the husks intact). Over the mound of rice one pours
palm-nut gravy, dark brown, richly flavored, and formidably
fattening. Next one sprinkles on the meat—if there is any;
in this instance there was plenty—shredded roast chicken,
forest buffalo, and smoked fish. Finally, the ample mound
is topped with shredded coconut, roasted peanuts, and
slices or chunks of the unmatchably sweet pineapple of
warm wet Africa. One reaches for a fork and spoon, and
eats, then refills the plate and eats again. Then one looks
about for a cool, airy place suitable for taking a long nap.

Before night leaped down I had begun liking Africa tremendously. With time and exposure I would learn to like
the less credible resources such as the fast-walking snails; the
oversized salamanders with protruding stubs of eyes; the
stilt-legged sheep without wool; the forest birds with wings
that go *phlopp-phlopp-phlopp* as they fly; the black crows
with "formal" white bands about their necks. And the engaging "bush money"—twisted strips of iron about a foot
long and shaped like slender T's. (The iron is locally mined
and smelted, then "drawn" into money by local blacksmiths
who leave it readily convertible to knives or hoes or other

useful tools.) I liked Africa enormously, and through the ensuing months and years I found it most engagingly confusing.

As one roaming onlooker, I came to appreciate the sheer yet subtle magnificence of Africa, of its hundreds of tribes that are neither precisely alike nor convincingly unlike, yet are the first measure of the fabulously vast, deplorably unappreciated resources of the least-known continent.

Africa is a potential food basket to the world, yet a continent of abject hunger. However far scattered and inadequately known, its rich-soiled areas are unquestionably the largest highly fertile lands remaining on earth. For purposes of people-feeding, the availables are neither used nor completely measured. As recently as the 1940s there was no competent census of Africa's people, much less of its lands. The prevailing standards and usages of agriculture were and still are almost unbelievably bad. There are myriads of jungles; in general, the larger they are, the hungrier they remain. The colonial governments, those that I personally encountered, were almost uniformly slothful and incompetent. There may have been exceptions; I speak only of British, French, Portuguese and Spanish African colonies that I actually encountered. The native governments, such as they were, seemed oddly disjointed from the indigenous and crucially important tribes.

With a few rather heroic exceptions the tribes-people were very poor farmers; their poor-to-mediocre crops were being grown mostly by ill-directioned wives living apart from their owner husbands. In greatest part the tribal man power, in its masculine majority, was not anchored to the land, or anything else save the frequently intangible affiliations with, and feeling of belonging to, the tribe. Yet the ancient communism of tribal land ownership was far from adequate for minimal food production.

Trivial as they were, the Firestone Plantation Company's efforts to produce beans, bananas, okra, sweet potatoes, and various other food crops for helping feed their tappers and other plantation workers proved at least some measure of the productive potentials—even of the newly cleared rain-forest boundary lands. But at most and best these experimental efforts were a great deal like filling a trailer tank by using a sewing thimble as dipper.

My best, if far-less-than-good, appraisal of the prevailing African agriculture was, "Bafflingly bad and not easily correctible."

CROP CONCENTRATION

ONE WIDELY applicable characteristic of African food growing is its concentration on comparatively small and for the most part widely scattered pockets of land. During 1949 the British Colonial Office, as an overture to Britain's African Development "Scheme," compiled what it termed a "master survey" of the still too dark continent. The survey estimated that about seven-eighths of Africa's food supplies were being grown on about 1.5 percent of the continent's land mass—exclusive of the Sahara.

At that time about 8 percent of the habitable land surface of the earth was being listed as actual or operable farming lands; the current percentage is apparently closer to 7. When I returned to the United States late in 1949, I came with the awareness that the shrinkage of tilled acreages was in keeping with a more and more global trend. During the earlier 1940s I had observed evidences in fourteen other countries in which I had worked or traveled, and on return to my homeland I began noticing even more impressive instances.

For the most part the concentration of higher-yielding food crops on fewer acres was encouraging and in many instances corrective of some part of the formidable damages that World War II had dealt to agricultural food production all the way from France to Indonesia and far beyond. In both hemispheres the global war had destroyed or impeded all kinds of agricultures, by violent combat on or near consequential food-growing centers, by upsetting or literally driving away established farming populations, by forcing hundreds of millions of acres of unsuitable or unreadied lands into duress cultivations, and by mass destruction of important reservoirs of livestock, to name but a few causes.

The last-named injury had included the outright destruction of an estimated 90 percent of the livestock of Western Europe, and severe reduction or total destruction of so-called "shrines" of purebred livestock had increased the damage. I recalled, for example, that most—about 80 percent of all our dairy products—are from three Old World breeds of milk cattle: Jersey, Guernsey, and Holstein-Friesian. As of D-Day the Isle of Jersey, original home of the world's leading dairy breed, was a German-held prisoner-of-war colony; Guernsey Isle was also seized, as were the island birthplaces of the world-important Holstein-Friesian breed. All were without cows.

Almost innumerable aftermaths of deplorable precedences in wrongful uses of land had lingered from World War I; moss banks and sand dunes misguidedly torn open by plow and hoe; swamps and marshes ruinously drained; hillsides opened to ravaging erosion; tired fields left irreparably gullied. In great part the altogether too permanent Dust Bowl of the U.S. West had been begun by the duress

planting of "war wheat" on lands far too dry for field cultivation, though highly valid as short-grass prairies.

World War II had demonstrated even more extravagantly
that war is indeed hell on crops as well as people. For bad
measure, it had served to delay or erase a great deal of valuable agricultural research and destructively invaded many
important food-growing centers in the subtropics and tropics where altogether too many of the imperiling food deficits
still hold. Even more distant strongholds of tropical food
production suffered grievously for lack of maintenance when
rationing of war matériel shut off their supplies of copper
sulfate and other crucially needed spray materials. Others
were put out of production by shipping priorities that re-
fused ocean transportation to fruits and various other important foods. The permanent destruction of several
extremely valuable research centers for tropical agriculture,
such as the still irreplaceable Dutch-founded Proefstation
Oost-Java, had dealt irreparable losses.

By a mixture of chance and motivated expedience the
close of the biggest and cruelest of wars marked the beginning of a continuing new era of more provident selection
of crop lands. In this the United States again took its place
as a kind of bellwether. During the middle and latter 1930s
the United States had served as an international show
ground for land retirement plans. By 1940 about 160 million acres, almost a sixth of the U.S. farm plant of 1930,
had been withdrawn from cultivation through the controversial functioning of the Soil Conservation Administration.
By 1945 another 65 million acres were in processes of being
changed from field or row crops to grass lands or similar
partial retirement. A like area had already been purchased
from private owners by federal or state governments for
publicly owned forests. A comparable total of one-time crop

lands had been withdrawn from farm use to provide sites for suburbs and residential communities, airports, military reservations, water reservoirs, wildlife refuges, and other uses.

These and other withdrawals are continuing; about two-thirds of the land mass of the United States can now be listed as definitely out of food production. Even so, and while U.S. farm acreage per citizen diminished from about twelve acres in 1905 to about five acres at present, yields per acre are steadily increasing; the overall average gain in cultivated harvests is about 73 percent since 1920 and is rapidly upbound.

There are many specific causes, but the total development is rapidly changing the map of agricultural food production in the United States to a more and more impressive scattering of high-yielding oases of food crops. Barely one-fourth of its field lands keeps Kansas the powerful "wheat capital of the world." Barely 400 square miles now produce most of the nation's rice crop; about 100 square miles grow most of our commercial grape crops; the decisive tonnages of our citrus fruits are from about 200 square miles; and most of our commercial apple crop is grown on about 100 square miles of even more widely scattered lands.

All this is attained by increasing yields and multiplying overheads, not to mention the continuing genetic improvements of crops. The gain in intensive and concentrated food-crop production is complemented by more and more substantial increases of grazing and range lands, as well as forests. But for the United States and several other countries the most effective yardstick for measuring the progress in effecting more food production on fewer acres is the congregation of vegetable crops.

By 1950 the vegetable crops were outgaining all other groups of food yielders. Between 1920 and 1950 U.S. per capita consumption of vegetables had doubled. By 1968 the average consumption of vegetables had gained another 100 pounds per capita yearly, to reach a completely unprecedented total of about 285 pounds.

That, too, is a widely typical statistic. The vegetable-growing renaissance that followed the Second World War actually began in Europe, in response to commanding needs and by means of bits and parcels of available lands, in great part in cities, suburbs, towns, and villages. News files show that the great vegetable revival began largely in Germany prior to V-J Day. From Germany it spread rapidly throughout Europe and beyond.

By mid-year 1946 Western Europe was quite literally gardening its way back into business, while proving again that people do not starve or suffer serious malnutrition so long as they have fresh vegetables at hand or in gardens. For good measure, the largely homegrown harvests of potatoes, turnips, cabbages, snap beans, peas, and other garden staples proved themselves the first really effective restorers of war-paralyzed inter-European trade.

That the United States shortly began participating in, and in some areas actually leading, the vegetable revival was doubly appropriate; it fitted the materializing patterns of more intensive farming of fewer acres and it was in keeping with rudiments of formative American history. With the exception of its key grain, maize or Indian corn, American farming before Columbus was preponderantly vegetable growing: squashes, including pumpkins, beans and peas, calabashes (edible gourds), roots suitable for bread making, and capsicum (food peppers) were among its principal staples.

European colonists quickly adopted most of the Indian's crops and supplemented them with wild-growing edible plants and with vegetables and grains already developed as food crops in Western Europe, Scandinavia, the British

Isles, and various countries of the Mediterranean and Eastern Europe. Back of the numerous details was the enduring general truth that the vegetable garden is ever an international enterprise and an unending saga of food crop adaptations.

While planting the seeds of the "European" vegetables, for the most part herbaceous aborigines of the Middle East, India, and upper Africa, the early European settlers turned to the available abundance of indigenous edible plants, which included the beginnings of dozens of food crops of world importance, including potatoes from the Andean lands, peanuts from what is now Brazil, tomatoes from upper Central America, kidney beans, sweet potatoes, and sweet peppers from Central America and so on and on. The U.S. census for 1830 recorded sixty-eight already developed vegetable crops, actually only a majority of a very extensive crop list.

Vegetable growing is a big subject, the more so because it is the very special stronghold and mecca of superior plant breeding and other scientific devices for improving and increasing food yields. I found an exceptionally revealing demonstration of the foregoing at the century-old, four-generation Seabrook garden farms, headquartered at Seabrook, New Jersey. This is an impressively internationalized enterprise predicated on growing at least two marketable crops on the same land during the same season.

Arthur Seabrook and his wife, Ruth, founded the garden farm during the Civil War years when they set themselves to earning a living growing and selling vegetables on their thin-soiled twenty-acre farm. The couple eventually succeeded, but only by eating a great many of their own vegetables and by encouraging the diligent help of their young son, Charles Franklin, who accommodatingly dropped out of school in the sixth grade in order to work full time on the farm.

In 1901, when he was 19, Charles Seabrook happened to read about a Danish farmer who had effected "tailor-made rain" by trellising lines of punctured iron pipes across his fields, then plugging the far ends and pumping pond water into the near ends.

Accordingly, Charlie took time off from the snap beans, dammed the pasture brook, raised a much-punctured pipe over his celery bed, and waited for the expected dry spell. When the drought struck he acquired a slightly used hand pump and began producing the tailor-made rain. It may have been the first overhead irrigation contrived in the United States. By means of it Charles Seabrook succeeded in growing and marketing the only "fancy" celery grown in the area that year.

He invested all his earnings and all he could borrow in extending the overhead watering device. As a direct result, some ten years later when Arthur Seabrook decided to quit truck farming and take up something easier (like salt mining) Charlie was able to purchase his parents' farm and carry on with what he termed "upbuilding it."

That included the eventual purchase or long-time leasing of about six square miles of farm lands in three New Jersey counties and the letting of contracts for purchasing vegetables grown on some twenty thousand acres by some twelve hundred suppliers. By 1948, when Charles Seabrook's three sons, all college-trained engineers or chemists with at least one graduate degree, took over the operation, Seabrook Farms was producing, processing by quick freezing, and selling throughout the United States about thirty vegetable harvests totaling well over one hundred million pounds a year. Prevailing yields had increased from five-fold to twenty-fold during Charles Seabrook's lifespan. Back in the 1890s, three hundred pounds of green peas per acre was considered a good market yield. Now, six thousand pounds of shelled peas per acre is the Seabrook average. Once boasted-about sweet corn yields of a thousand pounds an acre are replaced with routine averages of eight thousand pounds. Productive gardening operations cover nine months or more every year, and the multiplied yields show far better nutrient contents than those prevailing when Charlie Seabrook took to picking snap beans at a nickel a bushel.

What intrigued me most was the profoundly international character of the seven-state vegetable growing enterprise. Currently the Seabrook Farms, which make no pretense of being the country's biggest, plant about two million pounds of vegetable seeds each year. The accompanying work includes test planting about two thousand new varieties, acquired from or developed in forty different countries. Directly or indirectly the breeding stocks are from at least seventy countries and include such genetic curios as sky-blue tomatoes and deep purple cauliflower.

The Seabrook work force is one of the most impressively international I have ever encountered. Back in 1920 an immigrant group of about three hundred rural Italians settled down on the expanding homestead. During the early years of World War II, about fourteen hundred additional displaced Europeans, mostly Estonians, made Seabrook Farms their first American home and job base; about half of them have stayed on. During 1945 about nine hundred interned Japanese-Americans came to the farms to work and live; they and their children are exceptionally effective gardeners. At a youthful eighty-one, Charles Seabrook reflected that vegetable growing is properly a world business dedicated to getting maximum food yields from minimum space with the greatest continuousness attainable. His grandson, Charles

Seabrook II, senior member of the fourth generation of gardening Seabrooks, reminded me that commercial gardening, like all other procedures in intensive farming, survives and gains only with the help of "soil improvers."

In the course of various rambles I was encountering a great deal of confirmation of this reminder, and more or less inevitably, both as a scratch farmer and a perennial farm reporter, I had been giving more and more study to the multitude of concoctions, compounds, and contraptions that share the designation of soil improvers, a term which in general does not include fertilizers or plant foods.

From its American beginnings back in the 1930s the principal sponsors of soil improvers have been petroleum and other chemical companies seeking new uses and, admittedly, greater profits from their primary resource or products. The effective helpers include thousands of plant scientists, for the most part employed by state and national governments as well as by industrial concerns, and, as always, practical farmers and gardeners.

The first echelons of specific products, in greatest part chemical compounds, include both stimulants and retardants of vegetative growth; germination stimulants for seeds and bulbs; defoliants, which cause premature leaf-shed and thereby advance or retard harvests; and great numbers of nontoxic compounds that destroy weeds and other vegetative pests by altering their respective metabolisms, to the end of causing unwanted vegetation rather literally to grow itself to death. The common goal is the increase and improvement of crop yields.

Two taproots of the multipliers of attained food harvests came to life in the 1930s. One of these was the isolation of vegetative hormones by Dr. P. W. Zimmerman, of the still too little honored Boyce Thompson Institute for Plant Research (of Yonkers, New York), and ensuing synthesizing of chemical equivalents of plant hormones. The other, first effected by the Hawaiian Pineapple Research Institute (Honolulu), is a means of delaying pineapple ripening so that the crop may be harvested and canned without excessive wastage.

By 1950, plant scientists at Washington State College and the University of California Citrus Experiment Station began independently to develop and apply specific compounds that serve to expedite fruit harvests or delay blossoming (in order to avoid frosts or freezing) or to stimulate blossom shed in order to effect more favorable fruit settings. Interestingly, the commercial fruit crops share the limelight of soil-improving goals with the vegetable crops.

Also at mid-century soil chemists and other scientists began developing and proving techniques for treating seeds and bulbs with a most impressive growth stimulant, gibberellic acid, which is derived from the earth fungus *Gibberella fuikoiros*. Though the growth stimulant has admitted disadvantages, its uses for such divergent goals as causing seeds to germinate in cold soils and as growth stimulant for winter pastures are being proved impressively.

Though still in its very early chapters the story of the soil improvers holds impressive promise and supports a severe pragmatic discipline. It is already axiomatic that no soil improver has even a fair survival chance unless its use can repay the food grower at least five and preferably seven or eight dollars for every dollar it costs him. It is almost requisite, too, that the compound improve the appearance, flavor, or nutritional worth of the harvest, preferably all three.

Since the mid-century mark the nonpoisonous weed killers have scored the greatest gains among the soil improvers. Currently they are leading with specialized compounds that kill grasses as well as weeds and so protect sown crops as well as row crops. Increased yields are practically inevitable, but the more epochal results relate to diminishing the extravagances and injuries incident to the long-prevailing and usually excessive cultivation of vegetables and most other row crops. The distinctly tragic story of the Plow that Broke the Plains, and dang near ruint 'em, dates back to the invention of the iron or steel moldboard, said to have been invented by John Deere, a strapping, solemn-featured blacksmith, originally of Middlebury, Vermont.

Nobody can say surely how much injury has resulted from deep plowing. Many experts believe it has been the most costly nemesis to food production throughout most of the Western World. Opinion now is against it and against the use of the plow or mechanical cultivator for weed killing.

R. E. Bryan, a farm-implement engineer for the International Harvester Company, told me, "The goal in cultivation nowadays is reducing the number of trips over a field. We are therefore developing and pioneering machines that in a single operation till the soil, apply fertilizers or weed killers or other treatment compounds, and plant the seed. The least damage to root systems and the lowest hazards of wind or water erosion are getting to be buckled up with the other absolute need of present and future farming: One has to get a lot more crop with a lot less cultivation."

R. R. Poyner, one of the better known career designers and testers of farm machinery, agreed with Bryan's view: "While I was growing up on a farm in Wisconsin, my father and uncles invariably plowed every corn row at least five times, whether it needed it or not. The remarkable thing is that enough roots were left to bear anything at all. The important thing is that the age of the deep plow is over. What I'd really like to do is to stencil on the flank of every tractor in big letters, 'Is This Trip Really Necessary?' We'll never feed the world or even ourselves merely by plowing the living daylights out of all the farm lands."

When I quoted that to the design engineer for Allis-Chalmers, he smiled wearily. "Tell Mr. Poyner he needn't worry too much. The way I see and find it is that, nowadays, as soon as a new farm machine goes into a field or truck patch, it's obsolete. If it digs any deeper than two inches, it's precondemned."

The revolt against deep plowing is spreading farther and farther. What used to be called organic gardening or, as some prefer to designate it, compost farming is gaining a great new measure of acceptance. There are varying interpretations and disagreements as to specifics. But the gist is substantially unchanging and in generally common agreement. The first reliance is on vegetative manure supplemented as required by chemically compounded plant foods. Unused plant tops and harvest wastes should be returned to the producing soil so that its "bank" of organic material may not fall below 1.8 percent or preferably 2 percent of the total bulk of the topsoil. Crop lands endowed with organic life produce bigger harvests of more nourishing foods with less need of cultivation and minimized need of rainfall or irrigation.

The 1950s were proving to be years of increasing yields from more selectively chosen lands. In the United States particularly, but perceptibly also in other agricultural nations, the development and expanding use of soil improvers were helping to attain bigger yields and more competent selection of crop lands, and providing attainable vistas of much greater food yields. For good measure, there were flashes and tangible promises of still more impressive advances in genetic improvement of food crops and more fundamental, some would say more natural, methods for attaining still better and more varied yields.

New techniques of so-called "thermal" farming were also rising to view. In Australia and New Zealand the use of steam for reducing bacterial or fungal infections of soils was being proved quite effectively. Soviet Union crop scientists were stabilizing methods for the storage of seeds at favorable preplanting temperatures. In Holland, where forty thousand acres of greenhouse vegetable plantings were bearing prodigiously "under glass," and in Denmark and Sweden, where thermal destruction of root diseases was being proved in impressive detail, the food-producing merits of thermal farming were being demonstrated with unprecedented brilliance.

In the United States one could observe, as I did, an impressive preview of soil surface mulching with plastic films, such as polyethylene, which in one application provide a soil warmer, a weed eradicant, and a moisture retainer. Research workers at Michigan State University were among the first to demonstrate the capacity of plastic mulches to effect tremendous increase of yields, such as marketable harvests of open-cultivation tomatoes from 507 to 1,180 bushels per acre and green peppers from 905 to 1,285 bushels. Self-evidently, and like other soil improvers, the development and use of plastic mulches was proving capabilities for helping move the practical range of vegetable growing northward by several hundred miles. In terms of future food supplies this, too, is noteworthy.

All in all the 1950s were building together what was then an all-time high of worldwide food production. Significantly, this was the decade of the great vegetable revival, the advent of the soil improvers, the multiplication of higher-yielding concentrations of crop lands, and in many nations the improving use of rangelands for livestock raising. Though there were still lapses and digressions and conspicuous flaws in agriculture, and though world population drifts were still toward or into towns and cities, food production was preponderantly on the upgrade. Throughout most of the decade for the world at large, with the imperiling exception of India, the figurative race between stork and plow was beak-to-share with breath-straining acceleration. The hope for a victory by food production was growing more and more dependent on the more productive use of better chosen farm lands, improved crops, better working agronomy, and, ever incidentally, better use of grazing lands.

HUNGRY EARTH

IN TERMS of food supplies the 1960s began with firmly drawn lines and already deepened shadows. About five-eighths of the populated earth was haunted by hunger, or was, as described by Dr. Addeke H. Boerma, director-general of the United Nations' Food and Agriculture Organization, "already beyond the nutritional danger line." The chronicles of food supply and population increase were permanently merged. According to United Nations' estimate, world population had increased from about 2.5 billion in 1950 to 3.16 billion in 1962. Of the last-named total about five-eighths, or 1.85 billion, were in food-deficit countries; two-eighths in food-sufficient countries; a bare one-eighth in food-surplus countries.

Again, by world averages population increases were ahead of the gains in food production. Pestilence, famine, and excessive infant mortality had ceased to be dependable retarders of human increase; the so-called "historical" human increase of somewhere near one-tenth of one percent per year had multiplied tenfold during the first four decades of the twentieth century. By the beginning 1960s it had catapulted to the wholly unprecedented growth of two percent yearly. By global averages food production had been drowsing along at from one-half to one percent. Thus, the early 1960s found more than 100 food-deficit countries; the U.S. AID (Agency for International Development) count was 111. This included most of the "new" nations, i.e., those established subsequent to World War II, and, far more surprising, an actual majority of all tropic and subtropic countries of Asia, Africa, the Caribbean, and Latin America.

Regardless of continent, country, or region, the human young remained the prime losers to hunger. By 1966 there was forehead-wrinkling evidence that about 70 percent of the world's population under six years of age, in all at least 350 million babies and young children, was malnourished. For the world at large food demands had already played havoc with supplies. Certainly, by the hundreds of millions, man, the most numerous of the higher animal species, had already arrived at what Mahatma Gandhi used to term the perpetual involuntary fast.

Birth rates meanwhile had begun establishing durable patterns. Equatorial Africa was leading all principal geographical regions, with 50 to 60 births a year for each 1,000 residents. In the persisting hunger lands of Asia, the Middle East, and Latin America, the prevailing annual birth rates were ranging from 40 to 50 for each 1,000 people—about twice that of "medium prolific" countries such as the United Kingdom, Canada, Australia, New Zealand, Israel, and the Soviet Union, and nearly three times those of the European averages, which ranged from 13 to 19 for each 1,000. Thus, by the later 1960s, Hungary, with a birth rate of 13 and a death rate of 9 for each 1,000, had taken position as the world's slowest growing country, while Costa Rica, with about 50 births and only 8 deaths for the same base is at least momentarily the fastest growing sovereign nation.

The correlation or lack of it between population increases and available food-producing lands had earned what seems to be a status of paradox. Anthropologist Michael La Hood suggests that in Stone Age times, when man foraged his living from the wilds, the indigenous food supplies, both animal and vegetable, from 2 square miles, or 1,280 acres, were minimal for supporting one adult human. Human multiplication inevitably reduces the ratios of both total land surfaces and arable lands to people. Yet, as recently as 1960 at least 45 percent of the arable lands of the earth (according to the U.S. Soil Conservation Service) were not yet in cultivation. Even so, the calamitous 1960s were bringing proof that neither population density nor rate of population increase is an absolute criterion of food needs or production potentials.

Africa, South America, and the Middle East had long been demonstrating that comparatively sparsely settled countries are among the hungriest. Other premier facts already proven were that no nation can successfully "feed the world" by extravagant shipments of foods to distant seaports, and that chronic hunger problems cannot be solved merely by largess, or by spur-of-the-moment philanthropy, or by emptying warehouses of remotely edible flotsam.

Improved food crops are quite essential, and they cannot be just wished into being or picked up like somebody's lost quarter. Expert research and testing are prerequisite for crop improvements; so are competent harvest and distribution. And, sometimes most difficult of all to accommodate, good food must be within the buying range of the majority publics that require it.

The gist is, of course, that food is an enormously human facility. Food is people, including at least a billion contemporary people whose principal business is growing and/or processing and selling food. Food supply—past, present, and, almost certainly, future—is also of soil, sun, rain, and air, and of people making use of them to sustain themselves.

But above all the scholar of food must be a student of people, the growers, handlers, preparers, sellers, and consumers of foods. The foregoing is the thoughtful assertion of an exceptionally perceptive citizen of the world's second largest, and perhaps first hungriest, nation.

Naomi Mahu is a forty-eight-year-old grandmother and career homemaker of Visag, India. Having borne, fed, and otherwise helped six younger citizens grow up, Naomi now encores by feeding and otherwise raising five of her nineteen grandchildren—with a budget fixed permanently at about fifty rupees, or ten dollars, a month. With that background, Naomi describes herself as a warrior against hunger, which, as she knows so well, continues to lurk and stalk and strike down like a marauding, ever deadly tiger.

Naomi's father was a food merchant who began as a melon peddler and worked and bartered his way to the proprietorship of a food stall in a local public market. Customarily, girls were not expected to work as helpers to their fathers, but as an only child Naomi had no alternative. Accordingly, from her ninth year to her fifteenth (when she married) she helped her father with his food stand.

Naomi clearly remembers five great famines during the seven years she helped her father. She recalls vividly the children come to market to beg or, the instant a back was turned, to snitch, and the grown-ups who swarmed in, crying and clamoring for any remotely edible throwaway. She learned that wasting even a spoonful or pinch of food is practically synonymous with murder; now that India has 12 million additional mouths to feed each year, this rudiment cannot be expected to change. Good food handling can mean only economical food handling. In turn, that must tie in with economical food production. Here the big decider is what her father termed the always human responses.

India has a very old proverb that politics, sociology, and

economics come together in the pantry. When Naomi was a girl a dependably big part of all foods, including grains, found their ways from the farms and rural areas to towns and cities. In those times most of India's farmers were tenants or sharecroppers. The landlords collected their rentals in grains or other readily salable harvests and marketed them directly to towns and cities. That is now quite substantially changed. Like most other contemporary nations India has agrarian laws that greatly increase the percentage of landowning farmers. Although two-thirds of India's people are still rural, and although her towns and cities are now growing very rapidly, the emergence of a vast new public of small landowners is not always compatible with urban growth.

Nowadays India's farmers, as a vast group, are no longer obliged to do what their landlords wish. They are disposed to sell only as much of their harvests as they choose, and to eat much more of what they grow at home. Yet oddly—as a devout Christian convert Naomi believes, miraculously— most town markets have recently become better supplied with foods than they were back in her childhood four decades ago. Can such a miracle be perpetuated?

Partly by faith, partly from reading and occasional travel, Naomi Mahu believes that the answer is "yes." The farmers of India are a vast legion; they far outnumber the entire census of the United States. As she learned from her market-keeping father, great numbers of India's farmers, including millions on millions of small-croppers and tenants, have very real talents as food growers. India's distinguished food administrator Shri Jagjivan Ram, who bears the formidable title of Minister of Agriculture, Community Development and Cooperation, points out that India's food production climbed from a stagnant decade-average increase of .5 percent yearly for the 1950s to what promises to be a decade's average annual increase of 3.9 percent in all field harvests for the 1960s. The 17-fold multiplication of chemical fertilizers used on India's farms and the feat of placing about 50 million additional acres (22 million hectares) under irrigation have had much to do with upping India's total food production by about 70 percent between 1955 and 1969, and in justifying the current "drive" for making India self-sufficient in food production by 1971. This great hope is supported by Minister Ram's explanation that, "For the first time an effort has been made to bring the scientist, the extension worker and the cultivator together for a practical demonstration, on a farmer's field, of the achievements of research for better land management and productivity."

By the middle 1960s, and despite two widely damaging droughts, India's case for eventual self-sufficiency in food growing were being supported by the beginning of a series of exceptionally brilliant "breakthroughs" in the improved upbreeding of food grains. Included here are two "jowar" or grain sorghum hybrids, already in widespread cultivation, that are currently raising the yields of that grain by better than 50 percent. At least nine new maize hybrids, also in widespread cultivation, are increasing corn yield levels as much as 400 percent over those of the "scrub" corn commonly grown a few years ago. Newly developed varieties of "bajra," or spiked millet, have succeeded in doubling yields of that especially protein-rich grain. Adaptations of more hardy and higher-yielding strains of wheat from Mexico, Canada, and several other countries are adding to harvests of the great flour grain, while the Indian development by citizen plant scientists of hardier rice species is currently doubling rice yields in Madras and neighboring rice-growing states.

By 1964–65 India's total grain production had reached what the government agronomists term a base potential of

90 million tons a year. That was nowhere near enough for meeting even minimal human diet. Even if attained, the goal for 1970–71—120 million tons of food grains—is still quite skimpy. For even if the hoped-for 107 million tons can be used as human food, leaving barely 13 million tons for all livestock, the per capita daily consumption of cereals could be no more than 16 ounces (as against 14.5 ounces attained in 1965). The total of "pulses," i.e., field-grown foodstuffs such as beans, peas, lentils, soybeans, etc., the principal grain-supplement diet, averaged only 2.2 ounces per capita daily in 1965 but is now headed for a hoped-for 2.5 ounces.

Thus, India's chances for fending off continued mass hunger and famine must be built on not only the most effective birth control yet attained or clearly envisaged but also by the continuation of large increases of food production—increases averaging near 7 percent yearly. In turn, such can be attained only by "multiple cropping"—two or more harvests a year—on at least thirty million acres; effecting irrigation for an additional thirty-three million acres; and continued development of higher yielding and hardier varieties of food crops, along with momentous advances in pest control and soil improvement.

Can all this be attained? Naomi Mahu believes it can be. She grants that there are perils and tremendous labor involved, but the survival of half a billion people depends on effecting this, the most ambitious food-growing plan yet specifically envisaged by man. Nobody can overlook the hazards of droughts, monsoons, and other weather calamities. But Naomi points out that her India now demonstrates a great surging spirit of determination. At long last the national government is showing by tangible deeds its will to help the multitudes of India. To cite only a few specifics: the irrigation works are more far-reaching and provident than any previous undertakings by any government of man. The Indian Council of Agricultural Research is gaining stature and accreditation by means of its attainments in agronomic fundamentals. As a career student, handler, and preparer of foods, Naomi Mahu believes that the survival of her beloved India is an absolute test of the survival of mankind in foreseeable times.

She recalls from childhood experiences that the best foodstuffs usually came from the better-run small farms. The new government at New Delhi now tends to share that view. It is seeking to "restore" Great India, not by politicians' handouts but rather by area developments that permit the "small cultivators" to share as fully as possible in the coordinated development. Laws to protect all the remaining tenant farmers are strongly in incubation as "self-sufficiency" takes on a greater reach of meaning.

Meanwhile, as Naomi Mahu repeats in modest eloquence, the small-plot peasants remain the first line of food supplies and therefore the prime deciders of India's destiny, and quite probably the world's. For the song and the suffering of India are the saga of all man.

Maria Cristina Galvandes, of near Cartago, Costa Rica, would not deny the foregoing. But on the basis of experience and known geography she could not confirm it. Like Naomi Mahu, Maria Cristina is a mother, grandmother, and career homemaker, but she is also a career farmer.

By comparison with India her own Costa Rica is microscopically tiny; it is one of the smallest nations to have survived for more than a century. Clearly, if Maria Cristina's country fails to survive for another century this will not be due to any breakdown in human propagation. At least for the time, and as already noted, Costa Rica has the highest birth rate and one of the lowest death rates in the present-day world. The least militant and, as some believe, the most beautiful as well as the most democratic of American republics is located between Nicaragua and Panama. Costa Rica's area is somewhat less than West Virginia's. The majority of its people (about a million of the total census of 1.6 million) is rural; farming seems permanently fixed as the majority occupation. Even so, the engaging little rainbow country has never attained total self-sufficiency in terms of food supply.

Beginning very early in her childhood Maria Cristina chose food production as not only a career occupation but also a crusading mission. She was born and raised on the 50-hectare (124-acre) farm she now owns. Her father was a capable market-gardener. Her husband was a milk farmer who helped introduce purebred cattle (Jersey and Holstein-Friesian) into Costa Rica. While bearing, feeding, and otherwise tending their five children Maria Cristina found time and energy to work along closely with her husband. Following his death she took over active management of the farm, with her eldest son, her youngest daughter, and her brother as working partners.

The very busy partners keep with what they regard as the more valid new trends in food production. They "operate" and improve the purebred milk herd. Most of the milk now goes to market in San José, the capital, by daily plane shipments. In the local airport, as in many others throughout Latin America, one now sees milk cans waiting on the loading spots. The Galvandes family believes and helps prove their belief that air transportation is one of the brighter hopes for better food production. Besides marketing dairy products by plane, Maria and her partners grow and sell produce, including potatoes, vine-ripened tomatoes, melons, and salad vegetables especially prepared for provisioning the airliners. These and similar enterprises make the Gal-

vandes family a sort of *avant-garde* in the crusade for growing more and better food for more elite markets. "Aiming
high is always the better way," Maria explains, as a beginning for a succession of her own sustained maxims.

Speaking as a farmer, a food caterer, and a homemaker,
Maria Cristina believes that the first half of food producing
is in the heart and the other half is rather evenly divided
between the farmer's land and his mind. She is further convinced that food good enough for yesterday is not necessarily good enough for today and rarely good enough for tomorrow. In this connection the Costa Rican woman farmer
makes no pretense of being a dietician, but relies on the expert counsel of a physician cousin who is a distinguished
nutritionist. Her doctor cousin assures her, among other
items, that although a daily intake of about eighty-five
grams of protein—around three and a third ounces—is the
minimum for maintaining adequate health, the present
world average is less than sixty grams; even in Costa Rica it
is only seventy grams, still below the safety line.

How are food standards improved? Maria Cristina answers, "First grow the better food." She has learned from
long experience that as people are able to earn more they
invariably spend more for better food; when they spend
more for better food, usually in time people earn more.
Her priest, a very wise man, assures her that according to
responsible statistics the developed countries spend about
four times as much per capita for food as the developing
countries, and about six times as much for food imports.
The *padre* also notes that until the First World War almost
half the human race lived in colonies. All too often these
were hungry lands, in no small part because their imperial
masters required them to produce "merchantable" goods
that were advantageous to the motherland. Too often the
less-than-spontaneous compliance did not take account of

such trivialities as feeding the territorials or allowing the benighted blighters to feed themselves.

But the era of colonies has faded away. Twenty-three independent nations emerged from the First World War; thus far fifty-nine additional independent nations have come into being since the close of the Second World War. Most of the new nations are (or are hoping to be) sovereign; most call themselves republic; most are poor and precariously short of food. If the new countries are to endure they cannot and will not endure as starvelings. The good priest says all this. As a believing Catholic and a dutiful food producer and user, Maria Cristina agrees with her priest. From her own experience she believes no less devotedly that food is the staff of life, that producing and supplying it is a calling of supreme importance, and that the ways to and from food markets are the best ways to peace.

Like Naomi Mahu, Maria Cristina also believes that the many blessings of food are best purveyed by women. She, too, is wholly convinced that, just as bearing children and helping them grow to adulthood is a woman's very special privilege, nurturing people is her very special duty. Now more clearly than ever before, she reflects, this ever-growing family of man cries out to the woman, "Mother, we are hungry!"

For that timeless plaint there is but one capable answer: Get to the fields and gardens, the barns and orchards, the fishing fronts, the livestock pens and pastures, and the food-growing wilds. And get back to the kitchen and the mixing bowl.

ERA OF THE NEW MOSES

BY EARLY 1966 I had resumed my rovings in the American tropics, this time as a sort of planner emeritus and reporter inevitable.

Inevitably, too, I was encountering a new generation of *tropicos*, in great part sons and grandsons of those I had met as a novice banana chaser. I had liked their parents and grandparents enormously, but now I found this new generation *del Sur* even more engaging, even more deeply inspiring. As a word handler, I should and do respect the fact that "inspire" and its related noun, adjective, and adverbs require handling with care. As my desk dictionary reiterates, the root meaning of "inspire" is to breathe, or blow into or on. The ensuing meaning is to affect so as to enliven or animate. This leads to the mission of impelling to creativeness or at very least infusing into the mind. All these build up the connotation of filling with a supernatural power or energy.

For one, I believe that the feat of feeding a hungry world demands a total muster of the meaning of "inspire," and that the living breath must come from God and living prophets and the leaders of people. In a world that must be better fed if it is to endure, the prophet, the shaper of goals or shower of ways, rises again as the indispensable Moses of today and tomorrow.

In a broader sense these new Moseses can be envisaged as nations—Mexico, India, Israel, Denmark, Pakistan, Australia, Taiwan, the United States, Canada—to cite only part of the first echelon. More literally, the new Moseses are individuals, for the most part little known and too little appreciated beyond the peripheries of their specific works and devotions.

Recently I located a fairly typical contemporary Moses in the jungle-strewn littorals of lower Central America. A generation earlier I had met his parents and some of his less close kin, all very poor farmers who managed to subsist from a ribboning of tiny fields beside the Ulua, directly below the old Honduran banana town of La Lima.

The Herreras had named their first son Salvador; at his christening the local padre had termed him without excessive imagining a big *niño* predestined by grace of his namesake to better the earth with big and useful deeds.

During his exceptionally robust childhood Salvador had chosen Moses as his special hero of the Old Testament; appropriately, he envisaged leading his people to a better land. The resolve was eminently rational. The Ulua is an evil river, perennially browned by fertile upland soils that it relentlessly lifts away and tumbles down to its farspread, swampy flood-plains and littorals. The Herreras and kin were among the harder used of Ulua victims; at least once a year by averages their farm lands were ravaged and mucked by ruining floods. Salvador's father vowed that if ever he could harvest one good sequence of crops, he would pay off his debts and move somewhere far away. But Vertugio Herrera never succeeded; he only died trying.

Salvador was about sixteen when I first met him, and a fledgling employee of a nearby banana plantation. He had again rescued his mother and younger brothers from the recurrent floods and found temporary quarters for them in the workers' quarters of the banana plantation. But the Herreras presently resettled themselves at the riverside, leaving the family's prophet to his self-chosen role as Moses—for others to follow. After about twenty years of laboring on banana farms the big, easy-smiling machete man arose very early one morning and of his own volition set out to find a promised land somewhere in Central America.

Following due wandering and pondering Salvador found his way into what has long been known as Squatter's Hell.

This is the *Atlantica* region of Costa Rica, back of gently decaying Puerto Limon. There, in a jungle-fringed community rather outrageously named Siberia, the devout wanderer found himself confronted with a chance to homestead a twenty-acre plot of jungle that was dimly scattered with comely, dapple-barked cacao trees.

Salvador had understood that cacao "bush" requires protective shade, but here the shade was excessive; as anyone could see, the jungle was taking over and snuffing out all man-planted competitors. When he inquired about gaining ownership of the land a local onlooker exclaimed, "Mistah, whoever heard of *owning* chocolate bush?"

The newcomer tramped on to Siquirres, the nearest town, and there sought legal advice. The lawyer grinned resignedly. "Don't give it any worry, man—it'll give you more than plenty to worry about. At least nine-tenths of these bush plots without roads are occupied by squatters, mostly starvelings. It's a jungle hell-hole and why in God's name you want in it is a complete mystery to me. But if what you wish is to descend into this inferno, all you have to do is build yourself a shack, hack down some of those smelly jungles, establish Costa Rican citizenship, and in time, if you should live that long, you might even gain lawful ownership, God forbid!"

Salvador so wished and God did not forbid. But, though born and raised in poverty, the man destined to be known as the Chocolate Moses had never encountered or even imagined such poverty as he found in the flotsam jungle. For most of a century Squatter's Hell had been afflicted with one calamitous turn of hard luck after another. Most of Costa Rica's twenty-two thousand Negro citizens and perhaps half of its four thousand native Indians live in or near the long-lost realm.

At the time of Herrera's arrival there, late in 1946, his

companions in misery included about a dozen cacao buyers who couldn't make an honest living because of the deplorable quality of the available cacao crop, and about twice that number of stranded Chinese storekeepers who could fend against tiny volume and near-destitute customers only by seeking excessive profits. The principal recreation of the distressed was blaming their numerous adversities on those devils incarnated as cacao buyers and storekeepers.

That, of course, symbolized the history of Atlantica, which had been one wretched mess after the next. The first settlers had arrived back in 1870, when an oddly romantic erstwise Brooklyn lumberyard worker, Minor Cooper Keith, set out to build a railroad from the swampy, yellow-fevered littoral to the beautiful and at the time badly lost Costa Rican capital, San José. Keith's most effective workers were West Indian Negroes, of whom about two thousand were rewarded by being left stranded in the odorous jungles that subsequently emerged as Squatter's Hell.

Construction of the Panama Canal presently brought in another wave of no-longer-wanted laborers, for the most part West Indians. Some 1,600 of them moved into the nearby Costa Rican squatter lands.

Following the First World War United Fruit undertook planting to bananas and to cacao about twenty-five square miles of the backshore lands that it then owned. For reasons of both economy and pathology, the company abandoned both attempts. The bananas died of "root rot," or Panama disease; the squatters took over the cacao, such as it was.

At the time of Salvador's somewhat hard-to-explain arrival most of his ill-faring neighbors were second- or third-generation squatters. But this dubious seniority had not made them competent farmers. Most of them lacked even the simplest hand tools for pruning the trees or whacking open the melon-shaped seedpods for minimal drying. Almost none could afford the necessary sprays and fertilizers. Though thousands continued to snatch-grab their livings from an acre or two of remorselessly bad cacao, many were earning less than twenty dollars a year. At least four families out of every five were living beyond reach of roads; they were obliged to shoulder- or head-tote their naggingly small harvests to the despised middlemen, who could drive their donkey carts only so far as the cleared trails reached. Herrera met oversize families that had never owned a pair of shoes or a store-bought mattress or a wardrobe of more than one or at most two garments per person. Still more had never tasted cow's milk, or encountered a bona fide doctor or dentist.

Salvador built himself a thatched shack, cleared and planted a garden field, and managed to restore about twenty acres of his homesteaded and otherwise unused cacao bush to marketable bearing. Having learned the hard way how to grow and market the whimsical chocolate crop, the big man from the Ulua moved discreetly to help his neighbors learn what he was learning. "I had never stopped wishing to be a poor man's Moses," he told me. "My first move was to make myself a sort of what you *Yanquis* call an agricultural agent. I didn't expect any pay; all I asked were the invitations, and those I got. I began with the certainty that if these cacao squatters were ever to win, they would have to meet the minimum market standards. But I next learned that the best hope for doing that is to qualify for premium-grade harvests, which usually bring a market bonus of two or three cents a pound."

As a first bold step Salvador organized a buying-and-selling "pool," which he named El Cooperativo de Productores de Cacao del Atlantica. It is not a cooperative in the textbook sense; rather, it is a self-help club. The current membership of 233 cacao growers pay no dues and make no absolute commitments regarding sale of their harvests. The average-size "grove" is still less than 6 acres. Even so, by 1965 the group was actually marketing about 10,000 tons of valid cacao, about a third of it qualifying for price premiums. In 1966 the COOPAR met its goal of 11,000 tons, about half sold at market premiums averaging about three cents a pound above so-called "world price." The production and marketing stories are steadily, if slowly, improving.

As the unsalaried head of the club, Herrera seeks or accepts no government grants in aid. He abhors Moscow's "assistance," and recalls that not long ago a handout of five million United States "aid" dollars for establishing rice as a citizen crop for nearby Panama found that near neighbor with about two hundred rice growers. The duly stated goal was to at least double that number. Following the munificence from Washington, Panama had only eight rice growers, most of them big, at least for Panama. Last year, three planters produced about 80 percent of all rice grown in the Isthmus Republic. Not incidentally, the rice-eating Panamanian neighbors are again importing much of their rice. "Government money is for making things bigger, Señor." Salvador further assured me, "We can grow big only by staying little."

As usual, "staying little" didn't come easily. Salvador made a one-man pilgrimage to San José, pleaded the case and cause of his followers, and maneuvered a two-digit loan for hand tools, sprayers and spray materials, and fertilizers. He very personally pledged the payment of the loan. Within a year every member had repaid his indebtedness. On that basis Salvador at least managed to keep up his own credit. When his group agreed it was necessary to buy a collecting truck and the least expensive drying rig available (a kerosene-burning "Sumatra dryer"), and set up a storage shed at a ships' pier at Puerto Limon, Salvador again journeyed to the Banco Nacional at San José, asked for another short-term loan, and offered all he owned as collateral.

The bank manager told him that Costa Rican banking laws forbid making loans to squatters. However, the regulations might permit the loan, provided the bank had its own representative on the *cooperativo's* board of directors. When Salvador agreed to this, the bank manager smiled, as bank managers have been known to do: "Very well, *Señor*, I'll assign an accountant to attend to the bookkeeping, and I will name you the bank's official representative."

That proved to be the point of upturn for the cacao "fringers." With his membership assured of means for self-reward, Salvador moved to effect what he terms the era of good feelings. One step was to subscribe to *The New York Times* and to post the daily world price of cacao for the enlightenment of both local growers and buyers. He next maneuvered to permit any of the Chinese storekeepers or the middlemen who so wished to join the growers' club and try their own hands at raising the crop. Most of them joined gladly.

By 1960 the cooperative was free of debt, and its members were no longer starvelings. But there remained forty thousand other residents of Squatter's Hell who didn't have any cacao to work. Inevitably, their poverty was contagious. Salvador knew there were four remaining centers of excessive and imperiling poverty. He felt certain that each of these could benefit from a self-help club of its own, dedicated to developing salable and edible crops for lands unsuited to cacao. Perhaps pigs or rabbits; or spices such as nutmeg or ginger root; or vine pepper; or tea trees, or plantains or rice; or several of these. In order to attain this, both individual effort and group work would have to be bestirred.

The Chocolate Moses realized the need for other leaders, including church leaders. There are members of twenty-

two denominations in or within walking distance of
Squatter's Hell. Salvador is a Catholic, one of the hardly more
than a dozen in the area, which has no priest. Salvador took
his foaling idea to a Church of England minister and resident missionary, Timothy Farley.

He proposed founding a self-help club or *cooperativo* for
each of the poverty centers. Each would be self-governing,
providing its own constitution and by-laws. All who chose
to join would be admitted without prejudice of race or
creed, and without fees. As the memberships saw fit, they
could authorize their respective associations to sponsor new
crops or other enterprises they deemed worth while. By its
own choice each membership could develop experimental
plantings and pool labor to establish nurseries for growing
the necessary planting stock. As they saw fit the individual
clubs could pool their common needs for buying and selling, or join in needed public works, such as road building.

The Reverend Mr. Farley smiled his agreement and suggested that the Chocolate Moses take over as organizer. Salvador declined; he explained that if the proposed clubs asked
him, he would do his best as a common member. To him
Moses was a commoner who served little men and a mighty
God.

"I believe I follow your meaning," the pastor-missionary
smiled.

Late in 1961, with some help from his two seminarians,
the Reverend Mr. T. Farley sponsored the first meeting of
the Asociación Para Desarrollo de la Zona Sur de Limon. As
a double magnet the Church of England men installed a
modest public reading room in an abandoned church and
served a simple but coaxing meal—both without cost to the
prospective membership.

By midmorning about three hundred interested persons
were on hand. Some had walked more than thirty miles; few

had walked less than five. The gathering took the form of an old-fashioned New England town meeting. Men, women, and children alike claimed the floor. The women strongly favored moves to better incomes by seeking additional crops. The men were most interested in discussing the need for roads and possibilities for building them. Salvador declined nomination for presidency of the *asociación*, but accepted an improvised post as "honored counselor," on condition that Pastor Farley share that honor with him.

The next association, founded in the remote jungle lands south of Puerto Limon, named itself the Bienvista Club. A third emerged during 1964, beyond the canton of Siquirres; the fourth materialized in 1966 on the almost unbelievably remote Peninsula of Nicoya.

By 1967 the Chocolate Moses was able to coordinate workable plans for a crop introduction program in which all four associations voted to participate. His first move was to join forces with a group of eight Mennonite missionaries who are stationed in Costa Rica as working leaders of a peace corps maintained by their church. Each of the Mennonites is a graduate of a distinguished college of agriculture; their vicar, Burnon Jantzi, has served on the agriculture faculty of Penn. State. The missionaries, with Herrera's energetic help, joined in setting up a modest but effective crop experiment station. The next move was to establish three small nurseries for developing planting materials. As preparations continued Salvador inveigled the active help of two other *Yanqui* experts in crop introduction, Russell Des Rosiers and Carl Koone, both of El Agencia Para Desarrollo Internacional. The actual crop introductions now in progress are being manned and womanned by volunteers from all of the self-help clubs, including the first chocolate cooperative.

As yet there is no rags-to-riches story to report. The task of effectively establishing new crops is gaining headway, but even its initial work term is at least ten years. Currently "sweet" peppers, Jamaica-type ginger, nutmeg, plantains, sweet potatoes, and pigs show the best promise as potential "family" crops. At least a dozen more are in try-out. The Chocolate Moses keeps his place as helper and counselor by invitation. All participants may buy their respective choices of planting materials at cost, which is extremely modest—somewhere near a tenth part of that prevailing in the United States. Each member retains the right to market his own harvests as he sees fit.

The ventures in food growing are supplemented by associated efforts at road building. Like crop introduction, this is a fundamental effort; effective farming demands the building of travelable roads. More than half of what is ceasing to be Squatter's Hell is still without minimal roads. At least for the time, the national government has no money for developing local or farm roads. Towns and cantons are able to provide limited help, but in Atlantica most of the road building must be accomplished privately and by pick and shovel and handax.

Road-building volunteers from each of the associations are opening more than a dozen new roads, mostly as "spokes" that use the towns as "hubs." Even so, most are "walking" roads. But the pick-wielders' masterpiece is a twenty-two-mile throughway from the lost village of Siquirres through and around flowery green mountainsides to the nearest rail terminal. Three towns, or cantons, and about three hundred association member volunteers "chopped it through" in twenty-one months. Recently I witnessed the opening of the first bus run over the new road, the first bus service for the long-lost world. Salvador Herrera was on hand to lead in prayer and cut the ribbon. But he was obliged to hurry down to the port to arrange a down payment on another slightly used truck and help install another cacao dryer.

Salvador Herrera reflects that Moses-ing had a most illustrious beginning, but lacks a predictable ending. As a humble but more than averagely effective participant he envisages more and better oncoming Moseses who will lead to more and better lands of promise without change of habitat.

RIGHT CROPS—WRONG CROPS

SALVADOR HERRERA makes no pretense of being an agronomist or nutritionist in any formal sense of the terms. His schooling, to use that term rather extravagantly, consisted of two grades in a thatch-roofed country school; at the time that was about the all-Honduras average.

Mostly on his own, or, as he says, "by way of going with God," Senor Herrera reads while he rests, and meditates and observes and listens while he works. He believes the living soil is the surest and most revealing of God's scriptures. Implicit in this tenet is the conviction that any mortal child of God who serves to bring people and the living land together is indeed serving God and man as a kind of Moses.

For God clearly intends, Salvador respectfully explains, that His children on Earth should till the land well and be properly sustained thereby.

Speaking and thinking as a child of God and a member of His age-old firm of sun, rain, and yielding lands, Salvador also believes that better use and development of people-sustaining crop lands is both the prerogative and duty of every true believer. In specific support of this faith, and from continuing and extremely practical experience, the

Chocolate Moses has grown certain that a first cause of inadequate farming and people-plaguing hunger is the ever
repetitious failure of most food producers to develop and
duly cherish a sufficient variety of food crops. In this very
basic belief *Señor* Herrera, who sometimes hears himself
addressed as *Don Señor* Moses, has many affirmers—many
more, indeed, than he even begins to know.

The fellow believers include greater and greater numbers
of scholars who are striving to find out responsibly, as just
one premier fact, how big the vegetable kingdom of the
earth really is. Salvador told me that he cannot even guess
how many more food crops are waiting by, undeveloped and
and all too little known.

I can at least appreciate his typically sincere admission.
Back in my college years (the early 1920s) the botany textbooks estimated with convenient vagueness that the earth's
census of seed-bearing vegetation was believed to include
somewhere near a quarter-million species. The subsequent
trend has been one of upward revision. Obviously, since
thousands of known plant species, including several food
crops, do not bear or have ceased bearing viable seeds, the
approximated 250,000 plant species was never meant to be
a "grand total."

From Cambridge University one of England's better
known plant scholars, E. H. B. Thornton, estimates what he
terms the "discoverable total" of plant species as 700,000,
adding that the currently known total of edible plants (i.e.,
those supplying digestible nutrients) is somewhere near
80,000. Dr. J. George Harrar, president of the Rockefeller
Foundation, estimates that about 3,000 vegetative species
have thus far been developed as crops, but only about 300
more are now in common use, with twelve species or genera
now supplying more than 90 percent of all edible harvests.

Mankind at large now takes at least half of his entire food

supply—as measurable in digestible calories—from only six crops. Rice still leads with about 21 percent of the people-sustaining total. Wheat, now gaining impressively in Asia, Africa, lower South America, Australia, and Mexico, crowds toward 20 percent of the grand total. Russia holds fast to first place in the steadily increasing list of wheat-growing countries, although percentage-wise, at least as this is written, India and Pakistan appear to be the fastest gainers.

Somewhere near two-thirds of the world's corn or maize crop is eaten by cattle, swine, poultry and other protein-yielding livestock. In the United States corn is still more or less synonymous with beef, pork, poultry, and dairy products. But for the world as a whole the magnificent giant grass that came forth from the highlands of Mexico or Guatemala, or perhaps both, provides at least 5 percent of the food intake of people. Potatoes, born of the Andean highlands of South America, hold fast their first place among all the vegetable crops and supply somewhere near 5.5 percent of the total human diet. Here again the Soviet Union leads the world in harvest and consumption of the magnificent tuber.

The ubiquitous Asian-born soya bean crowds into fifth place as the most-eaten harvest. The grain sorghums, certainly the fastest gaining of the edible grains—their combined harvests have gained somewhere near 1,200 percent during the past twelve years—are clearly headed for sixth place. Three other historic grains, barley, rye and the millets, now vie for seventh place among the most lamentably neglected of principal food crops. Cassava, the sweet potatoes, coconuts and the most eaten Musae—bananas and plantains—remain among the first twelve, and the oldest of the cultivated crops.

Meanwhile, the great and dogging paradox of food production lingers: as human population multiplies, the variety of most-eaten food harvests continues to diminish.

Ready confirmation is supplied in the United States, still by totals the world's leading food-producing country. The first comparatively competent census of the United States was compiled and published during 1930, although it was begun twenty years earlier. Though foreplanned as an industrial census, it was primarily an agrarian count. At the time above 80 percent of the U.S. public lived by farming, the greater number of them as subsistence farmers. The 1830 census mentioned a total of 139 different food crops that were then regarded as important. By 1870 the nation's crop list had dwindled by fifty-one principal entries, the census of that year enumerated eighty-eight principal food crops then grown in the United States.

As this is written, the U.S. Department of Agriculture's *Agricultural Statistics* details only thirty-seven principal food crops; of these, twenty-nine (in this instance including cattle, swine, and principal poultry) supply about 96 percent of the national food production. Thus, the surest records available show that somehow during the 140 years subsequent to 1830 close to 100 one-time food crops faded from principal view and use. Some died completely, while others, like the proverbial old soldiers, just faded away.

But here again there are qualifying and significant exceptions. One who follows international food news keeps noting instances of abandoned American food crops that other nations are ably and eagerly restoring to valid use. Quite possibly at your favorite restaurant in Rome, Paris, Berlin, Singapore, Moscow, or elsewhere abroad, you have had the pleasure of eating rampion salad. If you have, you were sampling one of the garden favorites of our Founding Fathers. Rampion went out during our grandfathers' times; it is now coming back in many lands under many names—

such as German rampion in Germany, French rampion in France, Russian rampion in the U.S.S.R., and, in Communist China, Freedom rampion.

China, Russia, Israel, and several European nations are ably and cogently introducing another old-line first American food crop—doubly misnamed Jerusalem artichoke: it is not an artichoke and in its beginning had nothing to do with Jerusalem. Rather *Helianthus tuberosus* is one of the sunflower genus that is indigenous to the U.S. West. Its distinguished food value is in its well-flavored, highly nutritious tuberous roots. Rated as a potato substitute, this American sunflower has the great advantage of thriving on lands that are too hot or dry for effective potato growing.

Or have you ever eaten tuckahoe? It was probably the first native food crop developed by English-speaking Americans (of the Jamestown or James City Colony). It lives on as a wild-growing wet-land tuberous plant that is heavy yielding (the tubers frequently weigh four or five pounds apiece), well flavored, and highly nutritious, and is a superb baking vegetable and flour source.

And there was, and still is, cowas, listed by earlier census takers as Indian parsnip. It was another great American root crop—a hardy, generous-bearing, nutrition-rich perennial that many Western Indians still know as "bread root." A vanishing rival is what the 1830 census called pandura; it survives principally as the wild-growing so-called "wild sweet potato." When used as a crop it was another superb people feeder, almost fabulous in yield; the highly nutritious roots weigh up to twenty pounds apiece.

There was also wapato, listed in early censuses as sagittaria. Certainly our forefathers and their Indian predecessors were the better fed for this superbly nourishing tuber. China's agronomists are restoring the crop as "tule." This bestirs the reminder that the designation "starch roots" is usually far short of accurate; many are teeming with mineral nutrients plus riboflavin, thiamin, niacin, ascorbic acid, carotin, and other nutrient elixirs. Many, too, are instances of "right" crops gone "wrong" by the process of unjustified abandonment.

In addition, there is a crucial list of food crops that although still in use are being permitted to lapse into abject unimportance. Included here are some of the truly valid grains. Man is still preponderantly a grain-fed animal. The Food and Agriculture Organization estimates that for the earth as a whole about two-thirds of all cultivated lands are currently planted to grains. Although the FAO keeps reminding us that the great nutritional fault of grains for human foods is their inadequacy of protein (its lack is the dogging establisher of malnutrition), mankind at large still takes about two-thirds of all his proteins from grains. The FAO's hair-raising estimate that, as of today 80 percent of mankind does not get enough protein for maximal health, stresses the absolute need for tireless improvement of the long-qualified food grains.

A century ago the almanacs told that the United States had a baker's dozen of grain crops. Certainly, of the known thousands of grasses with sizable seeds, thirteen developed grain crops can hardly be rated as excessive. But today, U.S. grain production is being ever increasingly centered on corn and wheat. The world at large is upbuilding its reliance on corn, rice, and wheat. And although these big three have great merits for nourishing people, they are simply not the best: their increasingly global gains are largely at the expense of three other grains that are generally superior people-feeders—oats, barley, and rye.

Here again, U.S. crop statistics tell the story pertinently. The oat, nutritionally one of the best balanced human food grains, and a highly valid livestock-and-poultry feed, which once vied with corn as the leading U.S. grain, is now very much on the skids. Our present harvest ratio is about twenty bushels of corn for three of oats.

From a hungry world's standpoint the permitted backsliding of rye is even more far-reaching and regrettable. Besides being a very good food and flour grain, rye is generally the hardiest of all the grains. It has the healthiest root system of any developed field crop, and it is expertly rated as the most efficient of all principal harvests. (According to the U.S. Department of Agriculture estimates, rye's losses to weather and insect and fungus enemies averages only 3 percent, by contrast to 8 percent for corn, 11 percent for wheat, and 13 percent for rice.) Yet U.S. rye harvests have dwindled to somewhere between 18 and 33 million bushels as compared with a prevailing 4 *billion* for corn and about 1.3 billion for wheat. In the United States barely a third of the prevailing rye acreage is harvested; the greater part is used merely as a cover crop or green manure.

The barley story is also one of regrettable fadeout. As one of the elite grains on which civilizations have been raised, grain barley is still the most generous-yielding of all the cereals. The United States, thanks mostly to valiant North Dakota, continues to lead the world in growing the grain. But the U.S. average yield is 33 bushels an acre, in contrast to hard-working Denmark, which now averages 75 bushels per acre and shows barley as one of the readier hopes for plowing under the world grain shortage.

Perhaps there is not sufficient cause for bewailing the passing of buckwheat, that engaging supplier of what many still regard as the best flavored of all the flours. But in the United States and scores of other countries there is ample reason for lamenting the people-hurting, hunger-helping fadeout of millet, a classic grain with the very special distinction of being the richest of all the list in protein content

—an average of 10 percent of edible bulk. This is at par with the protein score of good beef; it rivals that of eggs, crowds ahead of pork or mutton, far exceeds that of any other grain. Yet, most regrettably, the food-growing and food-needy world is now trading its inheritance of millet, not for a bowl of porridge—millet porridge would do any hungry person a lot of good—but without due cause for nothing at all.

Despite its centuries of use millet simply has not received the genetic attention or selective and improved upgrading of seeds that any successful crop requires. The moral, as I see it, is that, granting the food grower has a right to make his own choice of crops, whatever his place or resources he benefits mightily from access to a more liberal choice of better developed crops, including superior new strains of the already tried and proved.

More and more convincingly the rightness or wrongness of food crops is definable in terms of available choices—not two or three, six or twelve, or even twenty or thirty food plant species, but hundreds of these species and more hundreds of specific varieties, already tailored or validly adaptable to the precise needs of different places. Most obviously, neither the United States nor any of the other seventeen food-surplus nations can reasonably hope to stymie world hunger, or effectively mend the despair of the food-deficit nations by means of direct handouts from our own fields, gardens, orchards, ranges, or livestock pens. But just as obviously we can help ourselves and the world at large by restoring to more valid use and competence some of the good old crops and identifying and developing many more good new ones.

In rapidly increasing numbers people and nations are moving to remedy at least some of the crucial needs for a more adequate variety of crops. Noteworthy instances continue to rise like corn stalks in June sun. The so-called Republic of China claims first place in the number of food crops now available to its people, in all about 600. The U.S.S.R. officially reports more than 130 "important" food crops being grown within its vast land mass of 8.65 million square miles.

The tiny Republic of Israel (tiny in that its total land area is only a shade bigger than New Jersey)—with about 2.7 million people who are now more than self-sustaining foodwise, in a niche of erosion- and desert-punished 7,992 square miles that include the use-worn topographies of a Mediterranean coastal plain, a central hill country, a fragment of the Jordan Valley, and a much less generous cut of the Negev Desert—has now proved its place as one of the more effective adapters of food crops. Despite the erosion-plagued, water-short, cruelly abused soils on which successive races have hungered, Israel has introduced at least 50 food crops in half that number of years, a crop roster ranging from deep tropics stand-bys such as bananas and plantains to great temperate-zone grains such as rye and barley.

The payoff of crop diversification is in the pantry. The Jewish state began in the shadows of hunger. During the 1950s it more than doubled both domestic food production and range of crops, and gained virtual self-sufficiency. By 1967 the little republic had again doubled its food production and joined the ranks of food-exporting countries.

While the remarkable agricultural saga of the Israelis was beginning, one of the most noteworthy surveys of edible plants and potential food crops was under way on the subcontinent called Central America. The principals there included a six-member research team under direction of Robert S. Harris, director of the Massachusetts Institute of Technology's National Biochemistry and Nutrition Laboratories. Previously Dr. Harris and his M.I.T. food-survey team had made detailed studies of the native food plants of Mexico. These studies, like the subsequent Central American research, included both scientific identification of all edible vegetation and exacting nutritional tests of each of the harvests.

The four years of unrestricted studies in all topographies from Guatemala to Panama revealed a total of 244 highly nutritious wild-growing food plants, all in a land area about one-fifteenth part that of the United States. Forty-nine of these were already in fairly widespread use as taken-from-the-wild food sources. About forty were already established at least locally as garden or field crops. A comparable number are largely self-adapted food crops, such as the *camote* (a tropical sweet potato), the *cebolla* (native onion), the *puerro* (indigenous leek), the *rabano* (radish), the *jicama* (a white-skinned edible root without temperate-zone counterpart), the indigenous *yucca*, the carrotlike *zanahoria*, and *espinaca* (a succulent native spinach). Among the more unique of the native green vegetables are *tompala* and *Santa Maria*.

The survey showed wild-growing species of *pepinos* (cucumbers), various native tomatoes, and a particularly valuable list of indigenous beans and peas. The latter include *gamil* (a pigeon pea), *haba* (a lima bean), and the *habichuela* (kidney bean); also two valuable tree-borne beans, *paterna* and *guajiniquil*. The native *chile dulce* is ancestor of numerous sweet peppers. The indigenous squashes include the white-fleshed *pepian*, the yellow-fleshed *agote comun*, and the *chiberro*, or tropical pumpkin.

The list of native fruits is impressively long; it includes *aberia*, a bush cherry, *sarsil*, a kind of blueberry, the sweet tree berry *chachalaca*, the apple-like *icaco*, the quince-like *membrillo*, the illustrious West-Indies-native *mango*, which has gone wild in Central America; the *cirrula* or tropical plum; the *pejibaya*, a yellow-fleshed palm fruit; the *caimito*, or star apple; the *sapodilla* (chicle fruit); the *hijo carambola* and *dario*; the native citruses—*limones* (lemons), *mandarinas* (tangerines), *limas* (limes), and *toronjas* (wild oranges); and a magnificent variety of *pinas*, or indigenous pineapples, as well as dozens more. Among the more colorful of the native crops is the bean called *piloy*; the same pod often holds beans that range in colors from jet black or golden yellow to blood red.

The M.I.T. findings also establish some profoundly encouraging shapes for attainable food crops of the future. One of these is the brightening prospect of perennial crops with more than one edible part. Thirteen of the food plants yield both edible roots or tubers and edible fruit or seed. What might well be a pivotal food crop of the future (food crops, like eager tourists, have ways of migrating and settling in places quite distant from their points of origin) is a heretofore little-heeded perennial shrub commonly called *chayote* (*Secheum edule*). It usually grows wild, though it is now being adopted as a yardway or field border crop. Its particular claim to fame is its remarkable talent as a fourways food supplier. The pod comprises a nourishing, squashlike cooked vegetable. The tuberous roots, duly peeled and baked or roasted, are excellent eating. The young leaves excel as cooked greens, and the flower, also nourishing, provides a tasty flavor for soups or egg dishes.

Four-ways-edible plants may involve expecting too much. But double utility crops are unquestionably attainable in numbers, and the same holds for food crops with a much higher ratio of edible portions. By averages, less than 30 percent of a grainbearing plant is edible by people. In terms of plant weight, root crops such as cassava or taro and tuber crops such as common potatoes are around 66 percent edible. Establishing this percentage as a common average for food crops could be a particularly telling blow against hunger.

Dr. Harris and his colleagues make the point that there is unchallengeable cause for believing that every region of the habitable earth has its own special heritage of food plants, a great many of them developable as food crops.

The hope for a better-fed world is increasingly dependent on more diverse and better crops, and crop varieties better suited to places where they are most needed.

CHEATING THE TORTILLA

WHILE TAKING leave of the banana ship I strove to convince myself that thirty years really had passed since I first disembarked at that most historic of Central American seaports.

Thirty years earlier, leaving ship at Puerto Barrios as either a *bananero* or a *turista* was a carefree procedure. One sent ahead his lockers or valises by *muchacho* and in due course strolled through the receiving shed, preassured that his luggage waited unopened and approved by charitable inference.

It was an opulent entry into a very beautiful but preponderantly poor and perennially ill-fed country. I had not adequately grasped that fact at the time of my first entry. Indeed, my naïveté was then so encompassing that I voluntarily opened my army locker and my two folding suitcases to exhibit my total supply of shirts, dungarees, and underwear—excluding, of course, the BVD upper that was stuffed with Woolworth jewelry thoughtfully selected as gifts for the natives who might not be entirely friendly. At the time I was astonished by the chief inspector's display of boredom; he smiled only once, when he saw among my dirty shirts an oversize Kewpie doll, a duly cherished gift from Rose O'Neill, the engaging originator of Kewpie dolls, who had asked me to give this one to "a little Indian."

When the inspector asked what I had in mind doing with the doll and listened to my answer, he pointed beyond a succession of rusting railyards to a line of Indian women laden with headbaskets filled with edibles for peddling to the train passengers. The guard pointed in particular to a very pretty little girl, about six or seven years old; like her mother, she was garbed in ragged black.

I stalked across the cluttered railyard and placed the big Kewpie in the little girl's arms. She did not speak; instead, she clasped the doll tightly and smiled broadly, and in her great brown eyes I saw a wonderful light; it reminded me of morning sunlight filtered through a cathedral window. I also noted that the child was conspicuously malnourished; at the time, so I would presently observe, Guatemala as an ever colorful whole was much better supplied with dolls than with nourishing food.

The cause cried out for explanation, and none was wholly adequate. Even in the hot and besotted port village I was assured that the prime fault was *El Yanqui's*, a somewhat simplified synonym for United Fruit, frequently referred to as Mama Frutos. While transplanting banana bits (rhizomes) from Martinique (originally from Vietnam), Mama Frutos persisted in belaboring these tropical Americas with Detroit-style assembly-line techniques, Chicago-style cafeterias, Peoria-style washing machines, St. Louis-style bottling works, Boston-style accounting, and A&P-style chain-marketing procedures; all these along with a principal crop that simply did not fit in this Guatemala. Granted that Mama

Frutos had selected the wrong kinds of banana lands, and then encored by selecting the wrong kind of bananas (for Guatemala there is probably no right kind of banana). But Frutos Unidos had not adequately developed better fitting food crops, either.

Now, thirty years later, thanks in most decisive part to the Guatemalans themselves, bananas were being replaced with many excellent food crops. In the manner of a man who is no longer young, I kept reflecting on Guatemala as I had first and partly known it. The banana fronts, as of 1937, were particularly afflicted with inadequate farming and even less adequate eating. In principal part we *bananeros* were living out of cans (imported); rice, meal, and flour bags (imported); and brown bottles with white labels (inevitably imported). It was unholy belly filling, and most of us felt bad most of the time. About once yearly the manager maneuvered to purchase a native beef animal and parceled out the various cuts according to the relative importance of the recipients. The neck meat that eventually reached me was a bit tough; even so, it came as a gift from the gods. In any case, however much *El Gringo* groused, he never lacked for fellow sufferers, including the very young, the very old, and others far less able to survive what then seemed preordainedly bad eating.

A return to Guatemala after thirty years showed memorable improvements. There were noteworthy omens; the old port was jammed with merchant shipping; newly built highways reached literally to shipside; port officers were courteous but attentive to their duly assigned tasks. The Barrios waterfront was free of beggars. I could see no starving children. The ship had arrived too late in the day for me to take passage on the once-a-day train to Guatemala City. But there were plenty of buses, hard-used and battered but dependable. And on boarding, one notes an impressively changed scenery. Most of the once towering banana fields are vanished; corn fields, palm groves, cattle-grazed pastures, and bean fields, for the most part privately grown, are replacing them.

At a bus stop I chanced to meet a now aged citizen-farmer who used to survive by growing and selling bananas to United Fruit.

"This year, Señor, I market eight tons of palm oil, seven milk cows, two fine bulls and twenty-six home-fattened pigs," he recounted with matter-of-fact pride. He added that most of his cattle are crossed from native cows and pure-bred bulls, and that his corn and vegetables are of hybrid strains recently developed in Mexico for tropical propagation. The harvests of African oil palm, a lifetime crop that thrives on the abandoned banana lands, are being marketed in Guatemala to fill long-chronic shortages of cooking oils and margarines.

Still within what used to be banana country, the bus pulled into the Quirigua Village public market for a lunch stop. Once more we were surrounded by eager food vendors. Jim, my alert young travel companion, opened by investing five centavos in half of a slurpy homegrown pineapple. I countered by buying half of a superbly flavored mango for three centavos. I next took a "beef fritos"—a kind of open sandwich made of a hard tortilla topped with chopped roast beef and sprinkled with green peppers. The price was ten centavos. Jim went for the chicken plate—two thighs and drumsticks precooked in herb broth, then fried in red chili pepper. The completely homegrown platter included cabbage salad, sliced tomato, and green beans—all nutritious newcomers, at least to the lowlands and midlands.

For dessert I spent five centavos on still another new item of native produce: a midget watermelon. The flesh was bright red and intensely sweet down to the thin green rind. Jim invested in a bowl of homemade papaya-flavored ice cream. For drink we both took milk—deliciously flavored, home-produced *leche*, appetizingly cool. Jim's lunch came to forty-three centavos; mine, to twenty-eight. Thirty years earlier neither meal would have been procurable at any price.

In Guatemala City, which is now about as big as Boston and fully as well accredited as the metropolis of Central America as an earlier Boston was as the "hub" of New England, I continued to discover reassuring testimony of improving food production. This is most convincing, not in the local restaurants, which range from dreary and commonplace mediocrity to astutely selective excellence, but rather in the public markets and the miscellaneous food shops. The central public market where Indians rate "special days" twice weekly is particularly revealing. Here these first American farmers, bowed under boxes, baskets and backpacks of their own produces (or handiworks) keep on arriving afoot to display and sell what they grow or make. Guatemala City's Indian market is a somewhat oversize version of hundreds of others in smaller towns and villages. Its displays of foodstuffs are far more encouraging than they were a generation ago. On a first renewal of acquaintance I noted impressive improvement in the peas, beans, peppers, and other dried vegetables offered. The fresh produce, including salad greens, tomatoes, sweet corn, and various root vegetables, as well as native fruits—showed a like upgrading in quality, size, and as I presently discovered, flavor.

This show of progress in the very basic food production is closely interrelated with other memorable changes and more memorable restorations. Among these is the resuscitation of what school textbooks used to call "minority participation in investment enterprise."

The sense here is that Guatemala, once more a petite way-shower, has begun to welcome investors from abroad, but only as minority shareholders in corporate enterprises of which Guatemalans are the principal owners. On this basis the accent in encouraged investment is on primary root-level resources. Typical enterprises of the new at-home-and-abroad corporations include the processing and marketing of livestock feeds, the upgrading and export of Indian art and craft products, processing of various food products, building and supplying of waterworks and irrigation equipment, and so on down a lengthening list of "root resources."

Some of the directives are distinctly new, but the planning, one gathers, is long pre-Columbian. One of the more lucid explainers is Guatemala's distinguished journalist Alvero Contreras Valez. "We Guatemalans are a rooted people," Contreras explains. "Our Maya Indian roots are at least as old as the living philosophy of Aristotle; in working essence they are more pliable, perhaps, but hardly less resolved.

"We Guatemalans are of the very ancient race of misnamed Indian. We have survived only from frequent reawakenings to the age-old verities of our race and our fate. In these most necessary reawakenings we have suffered grievous lapses. Back in the early years of this century, when our government, then a thing self-raised by our landed aristocracy, permitted foreign corporations to completely take over great areas of our lands and our peoples, they were doing what the *gran dons* used to accuse the *brutos* Indian, or mestizo, of doing—cheating the tortilla.

"That means behaving like the imbecile or silly child who wraps his tortilla around his serving of meat, then squeezes it so that he may eat only the meat, without the bread part. Back in those years when you first knew Guatemala we were allowing the *Yanquis* to cheat the tortilla by eating the meat and leaving the bread.

"Meaning, of course, destroying the rightful balance of bread and meat. Now we and many of our Latin American neighbors are again awake to the prime truth of life that keeping balance is our only way to survive, *Señor*. It is our first hope for feeding people, including ourselves; for building and holding industries; for seeing what tomorrow turns out to be.

"I am an Indian, *Señor*, but I do not speak as a partisan when I repeat that keeping balance kept our Mayan forefathers a great nation for perhaps thirty centuries, much longer than any civilization of the white man has as yet endured.

"And I tell you again, this Indian-style balance that we of Guatemala are once more attaining, that which now nurtures our country, will in time feed and save your country and all others. We are proving this, *Señor*. And if you would like to seek a bigger proof, go have yourself a long, close look at Mexico. For there, within one set of boundaries, the whole food-producing world is well represented."

It was cogent advice. I had never doubted the cultural greatness of Mexico or its relevance as a way-shower or hallmark for other American nations, both smaller and larger. My lack of adequate firsthand acquaintance with the second power of North America had remained too typical for comfort. From train trips across parts of that country, and plane trips over it, plus some ground-level exploration of special portions, including the northern range and mountain lands of Sonora, Chihuahua, and far south parcels such as Chiapas, Oaxaca, and Campeche, I had gained some inadequate knowledge of it. More revealingly, I had learned about Mexico from Central Americans who almost invariably revere *El Méjico* as the biggest country they personally know or feel for.

As even the most casual viewer knows, Mexico is decisively Indian, mostly rural and relatively poor at least in mass buying power. Mexican climate delineates almost all ranges of the habitable earth. Only a fifth of Mexico's land mass is readily suitable for growing food crops. Another fifth may in time be developable as crop land, but the actual major area is of mountains, deserts (including some of the driest on earth), dry mesas and ranges, forests, chaparral, near-jungles, and other profoundly incompatible terrains.

Yet here in Mexico, where per capita incomes appear to have camped rather permanently beside those of India, below those of Japan, about half those prevailing in the U.S.S.R., and a third of those of the less-than-opulent average of the United Kingdom, a food-deficit nation has changed almost overnight to a food-surplus nation. And while turning the corner in terms of food, Mexico has been helping other nations turn the same people-saving corner. Since my own first venture into the American tropics, Mexico's food harvests had more than doubled.

Maize, or Indian corn, which originated in Mexico, continued to account for at least half of the country's total planted acreage. In 1937 Mexico's average corn yield was 485 pounds an acre; by 1966 it had more than doubled. The current harvest increase is about 5 percent a year, while average harvest value has climbed from about 200 pesos ($16) to about 1,000 pesos ($80) a ton.

During the 1960s the winsome neighbor across the Rio Grande gained world eminence in the field of corn genetics. The "germ plasm" bank and the businesslike International Center for Maize and Wheat Improvement were already in the throes of bringing together thousands of specimens of corn from Mexico and many hundreds of other countries. By 1967 Mexican plant geneticists had developed about fifty new basic types of corn, all selectively adapted to specific needs not only of the many and varying regions of Mexico but also to specific needs of Asia, Africa, Andean South America, and many other areas of the grain-hungry world. But the great forward thrust is in the maize production of Mexico, first homeland of what is now the greatest of all grain crops. At least for the present, no other nation takes so great a part of its total fare from the magnificent giant grass that we call corn (granting that *maize* is a more definitive name), and the glorious fact that Mexico now leads the world in improving her heritage of maize is a fortunate merger of poetic justice and higher practicality.

Recently, Mexican plant scientists have developed and made available to their countrymen and others splendid hardy strains of dryland corn with unprecedented resistance to drought and cold, other strains that thrive at altitudes up to ten thousand feet, and lowland varieties that flourish in near-jungle lands. The fifty new "basic types," all exhibiting the genetic traits of maximum resistance to vegetative diseases and adaptability to low organic contents of soils, are already being grown in about eighty countries.

Mexico's role as an improver of wheat is no less impressive. For at least a century the country had been obliged to import the foremost flour grain. Quite abruptly, during the 1960s Mexico not only became self-sufficient in wheat but joined the United States and Canada as principal exporters. West Pakistan and Israel are among countries that have become self-sufficient in wheat largely or entirely because of their reliance on Mexican-developed strains. In terms of average yields per acre, Mexico's expanding wheat crop is well ahead of the United States's and Canada's, and rivals the perennial champion yields of the United Kingdom, Germany, and France.

Brilliant and world-influencing as it is, Mexico's great victory as a grain-growing champion is only one phase of its emergence as a world-influencing food reservoir. Land ownership is being made available to the poor; the great haciendas of the "sterile rich" are still being effectively divided. During the past third-century, irrigation has been increased sixfold, from about 2.5 million acres to 12.5 million, to provide one of the highest per capita percentages of irrigated crop lands in the world. Use of commercial fertilizers is increasing at the virtually unprecedented rate of 25 percent yearly.

For all these and other good reasons, even while Mexico's population growth holds at a booming 3.5 percent a year, her agricultural growth rate is well ahead, with an annual gross increase of at least 5 percent in food production. The government administration of agriculture, which many students regard as the most enlightened in the present-day world, stresses the Chapingo Plan, which brings together and coordinates agricultural education, research, and extension services on a regional basis. And so the great Mexican story goes, a world story of magnificent, enlightening hope, and a new dimension of courage.

THE MUSING MOUSE

"SIXTY-FOUR," the helpful insurance man repeated, "is too old for any damn fool to be tropical tramping, and that goes for you. Any reasonably sane resident of these United States can stand at his own front door, or sit on his own front porch, and watch the world go by from there. Nowadays, whatever happens anywhere on earth or in nearer outer space gets to us and whatever goes here gets everywhere."

However obese and squashy, the thesis is far from vulnerable. But it cannot erase or effectively belittle the crucial and ever increasing importance of the tropics, the ultimate strongholds of vegetative lives between North and South Latitudes 23 degrees and 27 minutes. This age-old, globe-circling cradle of life has somehow remained the great and stubborn bulwark of hunger.

The paradox gains ever more formidable immediacy. The lands between or adjacent to the imaginary Tropics of Cancer and Capricorn are potentially the most productive on Earth, yet in terms of developed food harvests and the needs thereof they are also the hungriest. Four-fifths of the world's chronically malnourished or underfed people are now living in or adjacent to the tropics. More than three-quarters of the underdeveloped nations are tropical. So are the more formidable and less repressible centers of human increase. This latter fact, of course, is a forehead-creasing reminder that the tropics most clearly demonstrate that planet Earth, which required many millions of years to take on its first billion people, took less than one century to acquire its second billion, only one generation to acquire its third billion, and, despite pills and propaganda, now has a fourth billion coming into wombs.

The sensible hope for man's liberation from hunger is inevitably related to, if not literally rooted in, tropic earth, about which we are only now beginning to learn by smatterings. But we have the medium certainty that tropical lands as a vast whole are neither as fertile as enthusiasts might hope nor as leached out as pessimists have bemoaned.

It would seem that in terms of edible plants the tropics are the premier earthy strongholds of give and take.

We know for sure that practically every consequential field and garden crop which we now know and grow has come to us from the tropics; this holds even for the grasses, the largest race of flowering plants and one that includes all our principal grains. Belatedly but surely we are learning that from their adopted establishments in the temperate zones most of our now great crops can be successfully bred, pre-adapted, and otherwise vetted for successful readaptation to the tropics, too much of which are still afflicted with food shortage. Adaptation is likewise possible for great new breeds and crossbreeds of cattle and other useful livestock, preadapted to thriving on tropical grasses and jungle-edge browse, and for a vast new argosy of higher yielding food crops, particularly grains and vegetables.

Thus more and more of the already-gained increases in temperate-zone productivity are proving to be more and more effectively transferable to the tropics. Although it can no longer be blabbed about as the "world's best" or the most progressive, agriculture in the United States proves impressively the attainability of more abundant yields in other countries and other climate zones. Since 1920 the average yields of all field crops grown in the United States have risen overall by somewhat more than 70 percent, with many individual harvests showing gains anywhere from 200 to 1,300 percent. During the fifty years just passed, the productivity of the U.S. farm-man-hour has gained about 500 percent.

In 1910 the average U.S. potato yield was about 20 bushels an acre. As this is written, the average is 253 bushels, but the prevailing record yield (scored in California) is 1,180 bushels an acre. However temporary, record yields are noteworthy as earth writing for the future. Since 1940 U.S. average rice production has climbed from around 28 bushels to 60.6 bushels an acre. (In this instance, Australia now holds the world record at around 400 bushels an acre.) U.S. corn yields now average about 42.5 bushels an acre, in contrast to 26.6 bushels in 1920; the record, recently set in Mississippi, is now 304.8 bushels an acre. U.S. wheat yields are still disappointingly small. In the case of this Number 2 food grain, the most impressive average gains are being scored in the tropics or subtropics, particularly Mexico, India, and Pakistan, although the world-record harvests are currently being made in England—with yields of 125 bushels an acre.

Generally, regardless of latitude or longitude, continent or country, the powerfully and rapidly increasing productivity of agriculture is based on the improved correlation of people and land—as the textbooks say, "improved land management," and also on the improved control of plant diseases, plants and weeds, on the very rapid and ingenious improvement of farming machinery and implements, better use of fertilizers and soil improvers, and, most telling of all, the continued genetic improvement of food crops and food-supplying livestock. The great greening hope is in the transferability of all these and related productive advantages to the tropics—the aboriginal if thus far too little developed cradles of abundance. This hope is good and sufficient cause for continuing the diligent study of the tropics.

Recently I spent a long, warm morning strolling through newly developed pastures in inland Honduras, pastures that were successfully "carrying" beef cattle at the rate of one steer an acre—ten to sixteen times the prevailing averages of the U.S. West. Along the Ulua Valley of the same beautiful little country (Honduras typifies the "outmost anchors" of tropics agriculture) I saw hybrid corns (developed in Mexico) that, interplanted with bananas, outyield the better corn lands of Iowa. On the tropical lower fringes of Mexico's great Indian state Chiapas I recently viewed lowland wheat plantings that easily vie with the newly doubled Mexican plains averages of around thirty-three bushels an acre—far above the prevailing U.S. average and triple the Mexican averages during the 1930s. In Honduras and Panama I have lately seen test plantings of Philippines-developed rice that outyield the most fertile U.S. rice lands about two bushels to one. Tropics-adapted oat plantings in Ecuador and barley plantings in Colombia are easily doubling average yields in the United States.

Self-evidently, these crops are surpassing examples of new levels of food abundance known to be attainable in typical tropical areas, all currently listed as developing countries. In every instance the multiplication of yields is living proof of improving agronomy—better farmers making better use of lands and environment. This is a potent reminder that within the tropics at large some 750 million farmers, including tens of millions of superbly competent ones, are already well established, already contributing to the munificence of the globe-circling horn of plenty and the growth and multiplication thereof.

Certainly, no particular nation, race, color, or creed of tropics farmers can be rated as the best; certainly, no particular size of farm can be rated as first. The living truth holds that the all-necessary feat of beating down and eventually erasing hunger challenges all races and nations, and requires still more crops and all available kinds of crop-growing enterprises: big farms and little, family farms and corporation farms, and all kinds and sizes of gardens and orchards.

For all these are in line of the most elemental of human needs. And all are wearing down the most stubborn discrepancy in contemporary agriculture: the persisting inability to make adequate distribution of attained harvests. More emphatically than any other nation, the United States has demonstrated that world hunger cannot be remedied from the fields, gardens, groves, orchards, grazing lands, or fattening pens of any food-fortunate nation. The competent feeding of the hungry must be attained, if not within, then certainly near to homeland boundaries. Here again the demand factor is human; as populations increase, so must local or, at farthest, regional production of food.

But once more, obese generalities do not suffice. While agreeing that human census is prerequisite for competently estimating food needs, demographers, including those who believe mass birth control is attainable and those who do not so believe, are predisposed to point out that rates of childbearing are only one factor of human increase. Death rates and lifespans are also crucial factors. As recently as 1935 the world average death rate was about 25 for each 1,000 yearly; by 1965 it was down to about 16 for each 1,000, with one-time "sickly" places such as Ceylon, Singapore, and Taiwan now recording mortality as low as 7 for each 1,000. In startling contrast, and regardless of earlier assumptions that human birth rates of 45 for each 1,000 a year are maximum, censuses now being made in Africa, Asia and Latin America clearly prove that the attainable maximum can go well above 50 for each 1,000.

Even so, world food production is currently outgaining world population increases, formidable as these are. According to the U.N. Food and Agriculture Organization statistics (Agricultural Publication No. 1037, 1962), this visible gain of the figurative plow over the figurative stork made a first visible showing between 1948 and 1953. The running order changed distressingly as the 1960s began; by then, in at least 71 of the 115 countries human population was pushing ahead of food supplies. Various aggravants added to the imbalance. Far-reaching increases of earning power were being directed to larger food purchases by those able to afford them. Meanwhile, for the most part as the poor grew poorer they also grew hungrier; in more and more countries food demands played havoc with supplies. In 1965 the Food and Agriculture Organization repeated that nothing short of an increase of at least 26 percent—2.6 percent yearly—in world food production between 1965 and 1975 could prevent calamitous and farspread famines.

The 1960s also demonstrated still another inalienable truth regarding world food supplies. Inadequacies simply cannot be resolved by politicians' gismoes or contrivances. In terms of federal politics of the United States this pristine truth began to show structure as early as the 1890s, when the then new West, including the farther Great Plains, first burgeoned as a mighty new realm of grain farms. The ensuing unsalable, unstorable surpluses of grain, particularly wheat and corn, and the erratic but intense intervals of depressions engendered the concept of export gifts or "grants" of grain by act of Congress, for the supposedly joint benefit of agriculture in the United States and famine victims abroad. The first efforts, eloquently opposed by William Jennings Bryan, then a freshman Congressman from Nebraska, did not crop out.

However, the contrived "granting" of grain supplies by our federal government gained resurrection during and directly after the First World War. Following a frenetically unsuccessful Rooseveltian fantasy of federal storage of so-called "crop surpluses," the politicians' sponsorship of warehouse emptyings again gained giantism and a status of cerebral atrophy during the monumental tumult of World War II and the ensuing heyday of confusion. There was and is no real point to denying that the "emergency" give-aways of

grain and other government-acquired foodstuffs have bene-
fitted people in need. Unfortunately, there is little ground
for contending that the duress distribution was efficiently
effected, and no ground whatever for arguing that as a long-
time practice the gratis distribution abroad of government-
stored grain has helped U.S. agriculture per se.

The glibly named Agricultural Trade and Development
Act of 1954 professed the goal of safeguarding U.S. agriculture from intermittent market collapses, such as the 1920-21
disintegration of world wheat markets, but it failed to prove
that the politically contrived subsidizing and handing out of
particular crops necessarily solves their international marketing problems. However unsatisfactory as federal legislation,
the so-called "grain grants" of the Eisenhower administration
and their mimicking revivals as Public Law 480 of the subsequent Kennedy and Johnson administrations have confirmed
the tenet that the United States is inevitably concerned with
the problems and needs of the world's hungry people, and
may eventually become concerned with the needs of our
own tens of millions of hungry or chronically malnourished
citizens.

Certainly the controversial entry here is not the denial
or doubt of the desirability of public gifts of foodstuffs in
times and places of catastrophe, including war, insurrections, riots, floods, severe droughts, or other causes of
famines abroad or at home. It seems that the real area of
doubt deals with the moral and pragmatic correctness of the
assumption that politically maneuvered handouts of stored
food harvests in lieu of more compassionate and intelligent
efforts to help the food-deficit countries better their own
agriculture in their own ways is the correct course. The
world at large seems cogently aware that the political expedience of dumping surpluses abroad is short of being

exquisite benevolence. And one might question the wisdom of the food-abundant countries trying to guide or drive the hungrier nations with lures of "free" bread grains or potatoes or delicious and nourishing dehydrated beets.

Throughout its lingering years of expensive perpetuation, P.L. 480, the food-giveaway orgy (which the Kennedy administration relabeled "Food for Peace" and the Johnson administration renamed "Food for Freedom") has not made the United States extravagantly popular, nor has it impressively strengthened U.S. agriculture or its profoundly important place in world food trade. Examples are discomfitingly numerous. Wheat remains our largest food export, but as this is written about 60 percent of all U.S. wheat exports are by way of federal grants, more bluntly describable as political give-aways. The solid evidence persists that these handouts retard efficient production and distribution of most-wanted foodstuffs, whereas legitimate production and sale redound to the benefit of both producers and international consumers.

A brief smattering of statistics confirms the point. For the past twenty years U.S. wheat production has ranged from static to erratic. Between 1955 and 1959, U.S. wheat harvests kept to an average of about 1.095 billion bushels a year. In 1960 the count rose to about 1.3 billion bushels, then slipped back to the 1.09-billion bracket, spurted again in 1967, and vacillated during the subsequent year. Revealingly, the next three greatest wheat-exporting countries, all keeping with legitimate selling procedures, have gained far more consistently in yields, growers' profits, and steadfastness of export markets. Between 1955 and 1960 the annual Canadian wheat harvest averaged a little less than half a billion bushels. By 1963, valid exports, in great part to China and Soviet Union satellites, had contributed to raising the production to about 700 million bushels, and to figuratively saving the hides of a great many Canadian farmers.

Although its agriculture still suffers grave aftermaths of the Peron regime, Argentina by 1960 had resumed exporting wheat, principally to grain-short South American neighbors. Accordingly, the Argentinian wheat crop has grown from about 260 million bushels in the late 1950s to a fairly dependable 360 million bushels in the late 1960s. Australia, meanwhile, keeps proving itself the most consistent gainer in validly producing and selling wheat rather than giving it away. During the late 1950s the Australian crop was a comparatively paltry 170 million bushels a year. Legitimate sales to food-deficit countries have, thus far, more than doubled the Australian yields.

Briefly summarizing: by 1965 the United States was handing over, with various strings attached, about 547 million bushels of wheat yearly to other nations. Canada was legitimately exporting 435 million bushels by ethical process; likewise, Australia was exporting 237 million, Argentina 155 million. Despite credit shortages and unstable currencies, the food-deficit and -buying countries, for the most part whether "free" or "authoritarian," continue to prove by action their preference for conventional buying and selling, or, stated another way, for buying their own groceries and paying for them.

This musing, white-thatched reporter believes ever so sincerely that the valid incentives of farmers' enterprise and quest of profit are best for farmers, farms and food supply. The belief was not dimmed by attendance of a gathering of international grain merchants held at Winnipeg late in 1968. It has not been erased by the experienced testimony of individuals such as Hans Rommell, a foremost East European grain importer who explained, "When we need political advice from Washington, we shall ask for it, having first consulted our psychologists."

In a somewhat different tenor, Charles Shuman, president of the American Farm Bureau Federation, the largest organization of professional farmers in the United States, keeps urging the abandonment of all federal give-aways of farm products and all would-be "plans" to control U.S. farming. Shuman has supported his views by pointing out, again in the instance of wheat, that Washington efforts to "control" U.S. production have grievously penalized U.S. wheat farmers, passed over world leadership in wheat production to Soviet Russia, and seen U.S. wheat yields by acre tumble from second to fifteenth place among the principal wheat-growing countries.

The thesis of the Farm Bureau Federation includes the absolute belief that the effective working partnership of people and land stays the only real hope for feeding multiplying mankind. This view is strongly supported by the Food and Agriculture Organization of the United Nations and by respected ministries and departments of agriculture, including those of Canada, Mexico, Argentina, the Philippine Republic, Australia, India, Pakistan, Sweden, and Japan.

The compelling sense here is that agricultural food production keeps gaining in scope, reach, and preponderance.

For the world at large the industrial synthesization of foodstuffs has not attained mass consequence. Its immediate future is nowhere near as encouraging as it was more or less responsibly envisaged twenty-five years ago. To date, "tank farming" via bacteria, yeast, algae, or other calorie-building microorganisms, or effective recovery of ocean plankton, and food-making from specialized petroleum factors have not proved out. Unquestionably, the high-nutrient additives, including fish meal, synthetic vitamins, and soya or cottonseed meal, are proving beneficial as diet supplements but not as complete replacements or substitutes for the great people-feeding harvests. Respected appraisers such as Dr. Harrison Brown and his Caltech colleagues keep pointing out that immense and long-continuing increases of food supplies cannot be obtained decisively merely from expansion of farm irrigation of farm lands; there are drastic limitations of available fresh water and of effectively irrigable lands. The Atomic Energy Commission freely admits that the practical outlook for desalinating ocean water in amounts and at costs permitting extensive expansion of crop irrigation is not yet in assurable prospect. From the marine side the procurement of foods from the seas and oceans, while intermittently growing in tonnage, is not increasing proportionately to the human population increase; it is bobbing below its traditional level of about 1 percent of the total.

The necessarily worldwide crusade against hunger remains one of more people tilling more lands better, and at peace. On that basis the greatest of all crusades begins to succeed. But not on a basis of any one crop or any one group of crops, even the grains. For, great as the food grains are, and granting that about 1,600 pounds of raw grain can keep one adult human alive for a year, no exclusive grain diet thus far attained can be termed adequate. Furthermore, for the Earth as a whole, for every arable acre that is adequately suited to grain production at least sixteen are not so suited. Fortunately, the "non-grain" lands include vast areas developable as livestock ranges, or as strongholds for high-nutrients-yielding field-and-garden vegetables and orchard or grove crops.

In more and more instances and countries, the most impressive advances in food-growing agronomy are trending toward vegetables, tubers, fruits, and nuts. Emile Lederov of the Ukraine Republic's department of agriculture writes of the Soviet Union's successful drive to gain world leadership in potato production: "It is basic nutritional arithmetic that one hectare of medium potato plantings yields at least three times as many digestible calories as a hectare of superior wheat land, with much lower harvesting costs per ton of edible harvest." Lederov points out, too, that the use of artificial insemination and the continuing development of roughland pastures have already made the U.S.S.R. the world leader in sheep production and brought about very strong contention for world leadership in cattle growing.

Although the Soviet Union has legalized abortion, its member "republics" are seeking to raise food production to or above population needs instead of seeking to hold population to levels of food production already attained. In terms of these efforts there are both successes and failures to report, but there is also profound and far-reaching progress in food-crops improvement and increase, and some impressive attainments in fitting specific crops to difficult environments and exacting regional needs.

India, while effecting a most impressive, indeed, a magnificent victory in terms of improved grain crops, still faces the need for using government agencies and authority for holding down birth rates to correspond, at least in a general way, with already accomplished gains in food production.

Among the principal powers Japan, beginning with its Eugenic Protection Act of 1948, pioneered the first "national policy" effort in family planning by way of birth control. In 1956-57 India launched its own national effort at family planning. Subsequently, Pakistan, the Republic of China, Nepal, Thailand, Ceylon, Malaysia, Indonesia, Taiwan, Singapore, Hong Kong, South Korea, Iran, Turkey, Egypt, Tunisia, Morocco, the Philippines Republic, and in the Western Hemisphere Honduras, Jamaica, the Barbados, Chile, and Venezuela have accepted central-government responsibilities for helping their citizens attain some degree of birth control. Thus far the most impressive results have been attained in Japan, where births have declined from about 34 for each 1,000 in the latter 1940s to 14 for each 1,000 in 1966. This vies with Hungary for the world's lowest rate; still more impressive records are expectable during the 1970s.

There is no longer any real doubt that the era, or epoch, of the contraceptive is beginning to spread very widely. It can now be cited as being impressively effective among somewhere near half of all people now living. This is immensely important, of course, both as a defense against mass hunger and as a benevolent strategy for enabling food production to overtake aching hunger and/or imperiling famine. For the world at large, the progress of government-sponsored efforts in birth control is rather more effective than the ventures in government guidance of practical agriculture.

The reiteration here is of the interdependence, ever vital and ultimately invincible, of people and producing land. In this the United States remains an impressive proving ground. In terms of both basic and practical research, continuing advances in vegetative genetics and pathology, improved chemistry and use of fertilizers, superior farming and crop processing machinery and implementation, U.S. food production is still memorable, the more so because in all these areas of important gains, the benefits are being passed along to the world in general, including more and more of the avoidably hungry tropics.

The potentials for increasing food yields with improved fertilizers reach toward the fabulous. Already, current average harvests of important food crops are being doubled, tripled, quadrupled, and so on upward by means of continuously improving plant food compounds. Improved hand tools and small farm implements, in many instances manufactured in the United States, are benefitting small farm operations in Latin American and other tropical countries. This writer has been most favorably impressed by the "special uses" hoes and lightweight manually operated spray pumps now being manufactured in Iowa for the use of small-plot farmers in the Americas to the south, particularly Mexico, Central America, and Brazil.

The continued improvement of food-processing machinery, another area of eminence for U.S. inventive and manufacturing talent, is also proving of profound importance to more and better people-feeding. The background of need here is that the hungrier hundreds of millions of people do not have what we know as modern kitchens, including refrigeration facilities. In great part the hungrier people still cook their food in boiling pots, or on primitive grills, or in crude ovens, fueled with wood or any other locally available flammables—from dry grass to dry dung. In most of the food-deficit world mechanical refrigeration remains extremely scarce or wholly unattainable. For consumers who are not financially able to buy refrigerators or lack access to power or gas lines, the developing "dry-freezing" processes are of very special importance, since many kinds of meats, seafoods, and vegetables, after being subjected to treatment by simultaneous drying and freezing, can then be stored for long periods at room temperature. Other new processes that feature bulk freezing by means of liquid nitrogen and extremely low temperatures are making food freezing more economical than it was only a few years ago.

There is very impressive progress, too, in the use of high-protein, amino-acids-rich additives that enrich the nutrient content of bulk foods such as the less costly grains. The enrichers, which include fish meal, special vitamin preparations, and high-protein vegetable harvests such as soya and other bean flours and cottonseed meal, are helping notably in overcoming deficient diets at minimal costs.

The progress in improved dehydration techniques is no less encouraging. One excellent example here is the recent development of well-flavored, water-restorable dried whole milk as a replacer of the usual dried skimmed milk. Others include well-flavored powdered meats and dried purees, such as soup or gravy concentrates.

And there is also the new generation of so-called meat "analogs." These are not synthetics in the usual sense of that ominous term; rather, they are transformed foods, made of selected vegetable isolates and processed to look, taste, and chew like beef, pork, or other favored meats. The synthetics' proteins and other nutrients can be superior to that of prized meats. The analogs are not yet developed to extensive use as "mass" foods, but they portend the coming of meat equivalents for great numbers of people who cannot now afford red meats and cannot as yet be listed as meat eaters. The still materializing new epoch of food-processing is ingenious, valiant, profit-motivated, and people-benefitting.

And so go the gains. Exceptions admitted and paradoxes be damned, agricultural food production keeps on advancing as yet more people make the lands of earth more productive. And in terms of total resources, though not necessarily of particular needs or desires, there is no overall shortage of land. The exceptionally scholarly U.S. Soil Conservation Service stresses that at the present time no more than 56 percent of the obtaining total of provedly arable lands of earth is currently being farmed. As yet hardly more than 8 or 9 percent of the earth's habitable land masses is productively in crops. To this one may add the more readily evident fact that people are only now beginning to learn how to use land productively.

The supporting evidence and exhibits for advancing food production are far too numerous to be accommodated by the type frames of any one book. Even so, there are epochal instances that cry out for mention. Included is the literally man-effected creation of new food crops—not only improved strains, clones, or hybrids of established crops, but a new, self-propagative species.

So far as anyone knows for sure, the first crop species yet created by man is the new and developing grain crop "triticale" (from *triticum*, the genus name for wheat, and *secale*, for rye). As indicated, this first man-made grain (the only new grain to have materialized in at least 10,000 years) is no mere hybrid. Although it began as a tweezers-maneuvered cross between rather distant grass cousins, it now emerges as a distinctive, self-perpetuating species with its own enduring and viable pattern of chromosomes.

In 1968 triticale was in its sixth year and eleventh generation as a bearing and widely adaptable field crop. It has successfully leaped over the hundreds of centuries and bypassed the one-in-a-million lucky breaks that go into the natural evolution of crops. It specifically symbolizes a time—in the comparatively near future—when man can and will model and create valid food crops perhaps even more effectively than he now models autos or comptometers, and vastly more beneficially.

Plant scholars are generally agreed that this brand-new (if perhaps badly named) international grain crop is the first grain already as far along in development as our bread wheats were a mere century ago. Since 1960 more than six hundred strains have been developed, some thirty of them of outstanding promise and at least six in or at the verge of commercial seed production. Attending geneticists are agreed, too, that still more effective hybrids can be developed within the new species and that the new annual can be changed to a perennial if such is desirable.

Like corn (maize), this newly devised grain is a valid food crop for people; its protein-amino contents are well above those of most other cereal crops. Triticale is also a superior feed for livestock. Its proved yields are substantially greater than those of wheat, rye, millets, or barley. It has vigor comparable to that of rye (long revered as the healthiest of all field crops), and adaptability to rough lands and to hugely varied latitudes, from equatorial to subarctic, and altitudes ranging from sea level to 12,000 feet or higher.

Most appropriately, triticale begins as a world crop. Currently its proving centers range from Colombia (South America) to northern Sweden; its principal stations for developing breeding materials are at Canada's University of Manitoba at Winnipeg and Mexico's no less competent Centro Internacional de Mejoramiento de Maize y Trigo (International Maize and Wheat Improvement Center) at Chapingo.

The chronicle of the great new grain began in England with a successful wheat-rye cross first reported from Oxfordshire in 1875. The first hybrid was apparently not sufficiently successful for immediate acceptance as a commercial grain. Next, in 1932, a Swedish plant geneticist, Arne Muntzing, undertook to develop the hybrid as a commercial crop. He managed to "stabilize" a hardy winter-resistant grain with fair milling qualities; the unimpressive yields were a factor of discouragement.

During 1949 a Spanish plant breeder, Sánchez-Monge, undertook to revive the promising but still erratic grain in his own homeland. The philosophical Spaniard succeeded in developing a vigorous hybrid, though not a species; the plants he selected remained unable to bear or even to "set" consistently virile seed.

Presently, researchers in central and western Canada took up the quest, but the first determined followers were associates of the University of Lund in Sweden. With a grant of $40,000 from the Rockefeller Foundation a team of Swedish geneticists next set out to improve the hybrid and make it an effective crop, though not necessarily a species. Less noticed but no less able competitors were a Hungarian plant physiologist, Dr. P. V. Kiss, and a brilliant Spaniard, Dr. Enrique Sánchez-Monge, now of the Instituto de Investigaciones Agronomicas of Madrid.

By 1954 grain-interested Canadians began joining what was still the very-long-odds gamble. Their number included the Bronfman Family Foundation, endowed by the heirs of Samuel Bronfman, founder of the Distillers Corporation of Canada (Seagram's). The Bronfman heirs opened in 1954 by endowing the Rosner Research Chair in Agronomy at the University of Manitoba and made funds available for continued research in further developing the still recalcitrant grain hybrid. Two Canadian plant scientists, Dr. B. C. Jenkins and the late Dr. John N. Welsh, both experienced grain growers, joined in the complex work of encouraging the erratic hybrid to change to a stable species. While the University of Manitoba researchers began collecting other grasses suited to possible interbreeding with the earlier triticale hybrid, the Canadian Research Council, the Manitoba Department of Agriculture, and the Manitoba Pool Elevators joined in the expanded attempt to qualify triticale as a crop species. The Rockefeller Foundation aided the undertaking.

By midyear 1954 the University of Manitoba (near Winnipeg) had "taken on" triticale as its special devotion and adventure. Throughout the first five years, the work was necessarily limited to collecting relevant hybrids from all available sources, including Sweden, Spain, West Germany, Rhodesia, and, to the delighted surprise of the Canadian researchers, the United States. Actually, the first donation of "raw" hybrids consisted of eight odd-looking oblong seeds developed and contributed by Dr. J. G. O'Mara, one of the many able plant breeders at Iowa State University.

The initial hybridization labors continued through 1962 and marked the development of first hardy intercrosses that gave promise of the coming of a true species. The special hero of this phase was John N. Welsh, who had earlier won renown as the Canadian Ministry of Agriculture's exceptionally able improver of oats. As the now renowned "Welsh crosses" began to materialize, the veteran geneticist died of a brain tumor. He was succeeded by another already eminent Canadian geneticist, the big, blond, and eagerly diligent Dr. Edward N. Later, previously of the University of Saskatchwan, and Rosner Research professor at the University of Manitoba. Other able geneticists, including Dr. R. C. McGinnis, head of the Plant Science Department at Manitoba, Dr. L. E. Evans, internationally honored as a creative geneticist, and a four-woman team of laboratory technicians presently joined. Leonard Shebeski, dean of agriculture at Manitoba and the farm-raised son of Polish-Canadian grain farmers, filled the role of supervising encourager. His boyhood farmer friend Allen V. Arnott, one of Manitoba's most successful grain farmers, oversaw field planting ranging from Obregon, in Mexico's state of Sonora, and Del Rio, Arizona, to forty testing farms in central and western Canada.

By 1962 triticale (which Canadians pronounce *trit-ee-kay-lee*) had gained establishment as a true species. Preliminary tests in rural Manitoba had proved its value as a whiskey grain, a brewer's or malting grain, and a particularly promising livestock feed. The attained yields were comparable to those of improved bread wheats and barleys; both the protein and amino acids contents had proved most promising. But the field plantings were still too tall for efficient harvest and the weight of the oversize grain heads made the new species an easy victim of high winds and heavy rains.

The procurement of seed remained a serious problem and impediment. In instance after instance, hundreds or even thousands of hours of skilled labor were required for establishing a cross or "line." As the building of a species progressed, hundreds of genetic lines had to be developed, and the successive progenies required field testing. Of the first 525 generic lines developed at the University of Manitoba, thirty equalled or excelled the now standard varieties of wheat. However, most of the triticale lines were excessively tall and too late-maturing to suit the rigorous Canadian climate.

Because the more promising lines were the results of "wide" crosses—of strongly contrasting parental hybrids— the earlier vegetative fledglings were not able to produce viable seed. In order to sustain the seed development it became necessary to excise the embryo hybrids from the tissue of their mother plants about two weeks after fertilization and to feed the "borning" plant with hypodermics of a culture medium such as the chemical colchicine. (Perhaps ironically, this compound was first developed as a gout remedy.)

With complex and formidable labor the Manitoban researchers succeeded in confirming the required sets of chromosomes and, in time, seed-perfecting breeding lines of the first man-devised crop.

By the winter of 1965 the experimenters at Winnipeg had produced a selection of plants that conformed closely to the height, growth rates, and seeding capacities of the bread wheats now grown in their area. During the same winter, with additional help from the Rockefeller Foundation and the Mexican Ministry of Agriculture, the determined Manitobans effected successful lines of "winter" triticale for planting in the area of Obregon and on selected sites in lower Arizona. During the summer of 1966 they successfully moved the progenies of the Mexico- and Arizona-grown seed back to Manitoba, thereby proving triticale an international crop.

By May of 1965 the Manitoba researchers had a total of 80 pounds of triticale seed for Canadian planting. By the autumn Al Arnott and his farmer colleagues had grown about 2,400 pounds of viable seed. Winter plantings in Mexico and southern Arizona increased the field-worthy planting stock to 50,000 pounds. When another May in Manitoba brought its first showing of brave young leaves Arnott and his neighborly grain farmers had their fields ready and their tractors warmed and waiting the arrival of the truckloads of seed from "the far South." Within hours they had the newest harvest planted; in Manitoba, every hour and day of growing weather is precious. About 110 days after planting, the subsequent seed harvest totalled about 1.5 million pounds—upped from 80 pounds in less than twenty months! This may well have been the most rapid seed multiplication yet attained. Certainly there was symbolism in the fruitful multiplication. And the fact that the new crop species had immediately adapted itself from the comparatively short days of the subtropics to the long days prevailing in the Canadian planting sites was proof of amazing natural expedience.

By then, undeniably triticale was on its way. During the summer of 1967 the trial plantings covered 3,700 acres in western Canada, with additional test plots in the U.S. West, from the Dakotas to Arizona. In Canada the weather of 1967 varied erratically from extreme drought to excessive wetness, from stubborn cold to unseasonal heat. But the triticale thrived, with test yields repeatedly exceeding those of the prize Manitou wheat and the prolific Conquest barley—both of which were used as "gauge" crops.

Following another successful "run" of winter plantings in Mexico and the U.S. far Southwest, and field trials in a dozen other countries—from Colombia and Ecuador to India and Pakistan and upper Scandinavia—1968 came forth as the year of final confirmation. From the fertile, grain-prone black lands of lower Manitoba, Len Shebeski and his crop-creating colleagues at the University of Manitoba chose August 20 as "International Exhibition Day" for triticale.

Reader's Digest assigned this reporter the exciting but less than easy mission of covering the unprecedented event and the Rockefeller Foundation asked me to take on the official mission of observer for the Foundation.

Aboard the plane for Winnipeg, I reflected that exactly forty-five years and five months earlier I had set out on my first Ozarks-tramping journey, in quest of learning of lands and people. As the jet plane lowered for Winnipeg my reflections changed to a silent prayer of thanks—to God, and readers, and long-suffering editors, for having borne with me so long and so graciously.

It turned out to be a climaxing reportorial adventure. Grain geneticists, plant scientists, grain merchants, millers, brokers, and grain-interested public servants from all provinces of Canada and much of the world beyond had come as viewing advocates of the first major commercial harvest of the first man-made crop.

About 3,500 acres of the heavy-topped, green-golden man-devised grain were ripening. I joined in tramping the

muddy fields and in viewing and touching the heavily til-
lered grainheads. Intermittently, I watched Dean Shebeski's
irrepressible pantomine of elation while listening to Al
Arnott's engaging French-Irish-Canadian wit. In due course,
the soft-spoken, poet-featured Canadian Minister of Agriculture soliloquized, "This is grain history come alive . . .
the most historic day in agriculture . . . for Canada, for
everywhere else."

Slight, tense Freisden Vladmiran, of the Soviet Union
Academy of Agriculture Science, favored with the most
angelic smile I have ever seen. Tall, stately Archie Gray, a
veteran grain farmer from Stonewall, Manitoba, steered me
through an interval of jet-black mire to view his own testing field of eight acres of triticale and eight of barley. A
week earlier a violently outrageous wind and rain storm had
laid flat all the heading grain. The barley still sprawled in
mud, but the triticale was standing straight—"straight as a
crack regiment set for inspection," Archie noted, then
added: "It's a living miracle I never saw before. Some kind
of an elixir in the stems. Nobody knows just what or how it
works. So I call this a magic harvest—that comes of the
mortal knack of helping nature help herself."

I could only agree. For here was and here will recur the
living, people-sustaining proof that man can indeed create
more provident food crops than ever before grew from
earth, and so build for abundance, for nutritive excellence,
and for superlative flavors as yet unknown, as yet not clearly
envisaged.

This first man-made crop could be the first worldwide victory in the fight against hunger.

INDEX